Books by Gladys Hasty Carroll

AS THE EARTH TURNS

A FEW FOOLISH ONES

NEIGHBOR TO THE SKY

WEST OF THE HILL

WHILE THE ANGELS SING

CHRISTMAS WITHOUT JOHNNY

ONE WHITE STAR

SING OUT THE GLORY

COME WITH ME HOME

THE ROAD GROWS STRANGE

THE LIGHT HERE KINDLED

COLLECTED SHORT STORIES

HEAD OF THE LINE

CHRISTMAS THROUGH THE YEARS

NONFICTION

DUNNYBROOK

ONLY FIFTY YEARS AGO

TO REMEMBER FOREVER

Christmas Through the Years

Christmas Through the Years

by

Gladys Hasty Carroll

LITTLE, BROWN AND COMPANY   *Boston • Toronto*

Grateful acknowledgment is made to The Macmillan Company for permis-
sion to reprint selections from *As The Earth Turns* by Gladys Hasty Carroll,
Copyright, 1933, by The Macmillan Company; and from *West of the Hill*
by Gladys Hasty Carroll, Copyright, 1946, 1949, by Gladys Hasty Carroll.
The poem on page 000 is reprinted from *Collected Poems* by Elinor
Wylie, by permission of Alfred A. Knopf, Inc. Copyright 1921, 1932, by
Alfred A. Knopf, Inc.

Published simultaneously in Canada
by Little, Brown & Company (Canada) Limited

PRINTED IN THE UNITED STATES OF AMERICA

To
my children
and
grandchildren

Christmas is coming, the geese are getting fat,
Please to put a penny in an old man's hat.

— OLD FOLK RHYME

Contents

Christmas Through the Years

The Higher the Tower

I have often written of Christmas, and perhaps I have usually stressed that it is cumulative. So it should be, and for many of us it is.

The twelve-year-old approaches the holiday season clothed — however unconsciously — in that first Christmas which stamped itself upon his mind and wove itself into his life — the year he was two or three — and of the Christmas a long-eared puppy blinked at him from the top of a big stocking, another Christmas when he gave his mother the red box he made himself and which now holds her recipes on the kitchen counter. The girl of twenty

comes to Christmas sensing not only the delight of holding her first big doll in her arms, finding a Persian kitten
on the foot of her bed, knitting a pair of socks for her
father, but also of carrying Christmas dinner and a basket
of books and toys to children whose mother was in the
hospital, of going with young friends to a midnight service, of receiving a bracelet marked with her name and the
initials of a boy she may not have seen now for a long
time. Middle-aged parents build each Christmas on the
foundation of their own childhood Christmases, all their
children's Christmases, and even of their parents' childhood Christmases given to them long ago in stories perhaps forgotten in the rush of busy years, but coming back
now in this quieter time of life.

The longer one lives the higher the tower from which
the Christmas bells ring and the angels sing and the Star
of Bethlehem shines, and so the more splendid is the caril-
lon, the fuller and sweeter are the heavenly voices, and the
more brilliant is the Light.

Yet we are deaf to the glorious sound and blind to the
brilliance to the extent that we have lost the capacity for
wonder with which every one of us was born endowed.

We are not deceiving children when we tell them that
Santa Claus, a round, jolly little creature, half-goblin,
half-fairy, fills their stockings at the fireplace. We are only
going a little way with their knowledge — which cannot
be imparted because they have no words to express it —
of the marvels of Christmas Eve.

There is no more and no less magic in the modern little
silver table "tree" lit with glowing blue bulbs than there
was in the great fir balsam with red candles pinned to its
branches and strung with chains of popcorn and cranberries. There was no more and no less magic in riding over
the river and through the snow to Grandmother's house
in a one-horse open sleigh with a buffalo robe pulled up to
the chin than there is in flying to Grandmother's house
over mountains and cities on a bird with a wingspread of

hundreds of feet. There is not and has never been more or less magic in diamonds than in bits of bright glass, in cloth dolls than in plastic, in fine bindings than in paper, in runners than in wheels, in pure silk than in calico, in an isolated farmhouse than in a skyscraper, in a shop window than in a pine forest, in a cathedral than in a barn, in a symphony than in silence, in vibrant color than in glowing black, in solitude than in a crowd, in what is soft or sleek to the touch than in what is crisp or rough, in plum pudding than in Persian melon, in all the perfumes of Araby than in twigs from an apple tree crackling in a cookstove.

Magic is not in the object, nor even in the senses it arouses. Magic is within the human heart, if it is open, in the eyes, if they are lifted up, in the ears, if they are intensely alert; and it is drawn from the Source and the Cause of all wonder which too often seems so far away as to be all but inaccessible, but which at Christmas flows so close to us all that if we will but receive it, whoever we are, wherever we are, we are flooded with ecstacy.

CHAPTER I

Christmas 1898

Brad is a young Maine farmer and fish peddler. He found Molly friendless and frightened on the shore, brought her home and married her. While awaiting the birth of their first child, they have adopted a small boy as friendless and frightened as Molly had been; and all that they have they are sharing with him. This is the first Christmas Molly and Robbie have ever known.

Winter shut down early in December and Molly did not step beyond the door rock again until the spring. Brad hung out her clothes for her and brought them in, stiff-frozen, to dry behind the stove. It snowed nearly every day, and the snow was heavy. Rene and Brad worried. But Molly did not worry.

She said, "It will be gone again before ever my time comes."

Besides, she had Robbie with her, as well as Brad.

The pig had been killed and the hams and bacon smoked, the sides put down in brine. They had all the fresh pork they wanted that month, with fish every Friday, and baked beans and steamed brown bread Saturday nights and over Sunday. The cellar bin was full of potatoes, and Brad had built shelves to hold his cabbages, turnips, parsnips, beets, carrots, and apples. There was corn up chamber for popping and parching and for the hens; dried apples, too, in bags, and hickory and hazel nuts. As soon as the pig was killed, Molly had more milk than she would have known what to do with without Robbie to drink it, though she let it sour and made it into cheese twice a week. By the time the fresh pork was gone, the hens began to pick up on their laying, so that she had eggs and to spare, and Brad sold them at a high price on his fish route. For Thanksgiving they dressed out ten big roosters to sell. Before Christmas Brad took some of the salted pollock to the stores, and the storekeepers kept clamoring for more every week at fifteen cents the pound.

Was it any wonder Robbie's cheeks filled out — and Brad's and Molly's, too? Any wonder Robbie began to look his rightful age, and brought the wood, and learned to milk the cow, and went sliding down the hill on a barrel stave to play with Dan and Albra after school? And read aloud to Brad and Molly in the evenings from Jediah's books, and sang the hymns and old songs as loud as either of them, in his high, strong soprano, and ate two apples and a popcorn ball and went to bed and slept like a healthy woodchuck?

Oh, sometimes he would still cry out, or begin to grind his teeth, but when Brad spoke to him, low, in the night, or

Molly touched him, he would rouse up and turn over, and they never heard another sound of him 'til morning. Then a good many times he was the first one up, and built the fire, and called his kitten in from the barn. He had a little light-yellow cat with green eyes, that he called Creamy. He knew, now, about cream; how velvety it was, and warm-colored, and sweet.

The last Thursday night before Christmas, Brad asked Robbie at supper if he had been thinking of anything he might like for a present.

"A present?" Robbie asked, surprised.

"Round Christmas time," Brad said, "folks 'most always get some kind of a present. Not always. But most us'ally. Some little thing or other."

Robbie sat thinking.

"I've got 'bout everything," he said at last. "My cat. My knife. My suit of clothes. My handkerchiefs. My sled. All I can eat."

He looked from one to the other.

"Brad didn't know but you might like a pretty book," Molly suggested.

"We've got all Brad's father's books."

"They don't have many pictures."

"They don't need pictures. I like to make up the pictures in my mind."

Molly said, "I told you, Brad. He's got an old head."

"Well, by zounds!" Brad exclaimed. "Be we so 'tarnal rich now we can't think of a thing more to wish for?"

Molly laughed comfortably but Robbie did not laugh.

He put down his knife and twisted a little in his chair.

"What is it, Robbie?"

"Well . . . I could wish for something. . . . But I don't feel as if I orta."

"Oh, go ahead, boy," Brad urged. "Wishin' won't cost me a cent."

"Well . . . there is another kind of books . . .

school books. 'Rithmetic. G'ography. Grammar . . . I
— I saw Danny's."

Molly bent toward him across the table. The light of
the lamp was pink on her eager face.

"Robbie — would you go to school?"

He jumped up and stood behind his chair, gripping the
knobs of the back in each hand.

"Molly — Brad — could I? Could I go to school? I
didn't know as I — you never said —"

Brad was so pleased and proud he could not speak
without shouting.

"Go to school? Why in thunderation couldn't you go to
school, if you want to?"

But Molly said, "Robbie. Come here." She put her
arms around him. "We just been waiting for you to say
the word, dear. We didn't know as you was just ready. I
told you how I felt when I first came here. I didn't feel
then as if I could bear to be with strangers, till after a
while. But, like I said, we've only been waiting. We want
you to go to school more than anything, right now.
There's a lard pail I never used. It's got a blue band
around it. It will hold your dinner. We want you to go to
be with other young ones and learn all we ever learnt and
more, and come home and learn it to us . . . me, especially, Robbie. I never got to school but very little. . . .
Why, this is the best Christmas present Brad and I could
have. And you can start when the new term opens. Our
schoolboy!"

He got his books on Christmas Eve.

He got other things beside: a slate and pencils, a big
bow and three arrows Brad had whittled out, a short-coat
Molly had made from new gray cloth, thick as a board; a
red knit cap and mittens from Rene, a ball from Min, a
hatchet from Gran, two oranges and a handful of licorice
sticks.

Brad and Molly got presents too. Robbie had made a

crocheted muffler for him, with Molly's and Min's help, and a leather-covered needle book for her, with Brad's help. Molly had saved the first pair of shirts she had ever made, to give to Brad that night, and Brad brought out a half-bolt of peacock blue linsey-woolsey, unrolling it as a peddler might and letting it fall in a swirl until it reached the floor.

He said, "Might be enough over, after a dress pattern, I thought, to make a small cape-thing besides, if you should want to."

"Oh, Brad . . ."

In the parcel Min had brought up from Stacys' there were long, black, rib-knit stockings, gray highboot socks, a red tablecloth with silvery ostrich feathers woven into it, and a big plum pudding.

"We'll take the table into the front room tomorrow," Molly planned. "I'll put the new cloth on it. We'll have a rousing big fire there, to eat our dinner by."

"And we will eat," Brad said, "of this plum pudding."

"After," Molly laughed, "we've eat of that nice piece of beef you got from Gran, and potatoes and carrots fried raw in the pan the way you learnt to do it at the mill, Braddy; and big sour-milk biscuits and barb'ry sauce."

They looked at Robbie, sitting there round-eyed.

"Let's sing," Brad suggested. "All the Christmas hymns and carols. We know them by heart, Molly. I'll turn down the light."

He took the schoolbooks from the boy's knees and put them on the shelf. When the room was dim, he drew their three chairs before the oven door and sat in the middle, one arm across the back of Molly's, the other across the back of the boy's, threw up his head, and began:

> *Silent night, holy night;*
> *All is calm; all is bright,*
> *Round yon heavenly mother and child —*

CHAPTER II

hristmas 1910

Marcy and Hal are the children of Verd and Frances Hasty. From her childhood Frances has always been called Frankie or Frank. This is a true account of one Christmas in the Hasty family. The head of the Hasty house is George, Verd's father, whose favorite sister Annie lives in Lawrence, Massachusetts. Vinnie is his unmarried daughter, Hattie his married daughter. Frankie's family are the Brookses — her mother Louise, her sister Lula, her Aunt Em and her Uncle Than, her cousin Grace.

December is Christmas.

The first rising of the December sun brings with it a gleam of wonder, narrow, distant, but clearly discernible, glowing like mother-of-pearl. The farmer is aware of it as soon as he opens his door to go toward the barn, the housewife when she comes shivering into the kitchen and glances out the east window, the child at the lifting of his eyelids from sleep.

With each setting of the sun, and each rising and setting of the moon and stars in the dark sky, the wonder grows. It is not so much in color as in absence of color, less in sound than in absence of sound, not at all in fragrance but in absence of fragrance; that is, of earthly color, sound, and fragrance. Each day there seems less of all that has been familiar in the earlier months of the year, and more that is new though not strange. Gradually the world becomes quite another place, suffused by gentle radiance, cupped in innocence and infinite wisdom, carried aloft by unseen winds which bear it closer and closer to the Source of all wonder.

Why are human beings not frightened by the transformation? Why are they not reluctant to be transported? We do not speak now of those who are in such dark places that they do not see or feel what is happening, but of the farmer, the housewife, the child, and all who are keenly aware of it from the beginning, from that first pearly gleam at the first rising of the December sun. Why do they go so eagerly, though on tiptoe, to meet it, turn up their faces to it, open their arms to it, wait to be caught up in it as in their natural home, as by their dearest beloved? There is something written here to strengthen man's self-respect, if he can read the script.

God so loved the world that He gave His only begotten Son . . .

Would He have given Him to the world had He not *known* that there were those already there and many more to come who longed for Him, could recognize Him, would cherish Him and follow Him?

This year there was the morning when Frankie, Hal, and Marcy climbed into Verd's pung at daybreak, and rode with him to the Junction to take the train to Portsmouth. The snow was so cold that the runners squeaked as they moved and Bess's flying hooves threw out icy snowballs. Frankie had put hot beach rocks on the floor and brought hot potatoes to hold in their laps, but the air was so cold that it stung Marcy's nose until she hid it in her father's sleeve; but she could not bear to hide her eyes, for there was the moon, a silver crescent, swinging ahead of them in the pale sky. The bells on the shafts rang out sharply against the frost, and the white foam on the fence rails was turning pink.

The Junction is so called because not long ago it was a railroad center where the Eastern and Western Divisions of the Boston and Maine came together, there were great sheds to house the fuel for the wood-burning engines, there was a restaurant known far and wide for its Berwick sponge cake, and Mose Bennett kept a store and a post office. But now the Eastern and Western Divisions meet farther down the line toward Portland, the engines burn coal, the sheds and the restaurant have been razed, the mailman brings winter letters in his sleigh to the farms, the store is closed, Mose Bennett is dead, and Mose's son works at the shoeshop in the village. He walks to the shop and carries a lantern in winter when it is dark in the woods at both ends of his work day.

Marcy saw the glint of light at the tree line as Bess whirled into the station yard.

"What's that?" she asked. "That light in the woods?"

"That's Charlie Bennett going to work. He always goes down the Old Track," her father answered. "I'd give him a ride but he says Bess goes too fast for him. Says he don't like to run sitting down. Says the only time he rode with me he could have set a hen on his coattails and never lost an egg."

Hal laughed in the back seat of the pung. Hal does not often laugh aloud.

Verd said to Frankie, "You'll need some money. I think I can get some across the road. Jim's owed me for painting his buggy for some time, but I guess he'll want to pay up before Christmas." He pulled out his watch. "Ten minutes till train's due. You go in where it's warm."

In the little station a fire crackled in the chunk stove, reddening the cover. The narrow boards of the floor had been oiled. The wood settees had been varnished. The only sound was the clicking of the telegraph. They sat listening to it.

"If Papa can't get the money, can you buy our tickets?" Marcy whispered.

"No, but he will get it. Your father will tell Jim we are waiting for it to go to Portsmouth with. Jim is honest. He will pay what he owes."

"What if the train comes before Papa does?"

"It won't."

Verd came in and gave Frankie money. He gave Marcy a dollar and she put it in the crocheted pocket buttoned to the belt of her coat. He asked Hal if he needed money and Hal said no, he had his own. Verd's collar was turned up and the earmuffs of his fur cap were turned down. His face was red from the cold. He was smiling and his teeth looked very white.

"Not a cloud in the sky," he said. "Good day for your trip. I'll get your tickets."

He went to the high gate in the wall. Through the gate they could see the station agent blow out his lamp, spin around on his chair, take off his green eyeshade, and come to meet Verd.

"Morning, Herb."

"Morning, Verd."

"Three to Portsmouth. One's under twelve."

"Round trip?"

"No. They're coming back by way of Dover on the electrics."

Drawers opened and closed. Money was pushed under the gate. Tickets and money came back.

"Train 'bout on time, Herb?"

"Ought to be coming round the bend any minute now."

"Better head my horse towards the village then. She's skittish."

"Always said you ought to made a racer out of her."

The words were like bright round beads strung on the chain of the clicking telegraph in the silent room with the oiled floor and the varnished settees.

Verd came back and gave Frankie the tickets. He stood putting on his mittens, smiling down at the three.

"What do you think — going to wait where it's warm or go out on the platform and watch her come in?"

They went out with him. He touched Marcy's chin, clapped Hal on the shoulder, looked at Frankie in her black caracul coat and muff, with a bit of her garnet cashmere dress showing where the skirt of the coat parted in the wind, her black velvet hat held on by garnet-headed pins thrust through her dark hair and by a long scarf of golden gauze.

"Well," he said, "you've got a great day for it. I'll meet the five o'clock car in the Square."

He sprang into the pung, pulled up after him the iron weight to which Bess was tied, and a minute later had jingled away among the dark willows of Old Swamps.

The three were alone with the sun coming up and setting the pure white world aglisten. The square little station behind them was such a house as the Three Bears or the Seven Dwarfs might have gone out from in the forest. Between it and the frozen river ran two black lines equidistant from each other as far as the eye could see in both

directions. Nothing moved and there was no sound. But in
the black lines there was a pulsing as in the wrist even
when no finger touches it.

And soon there was sound, a puffing, a rumble, a high,
long, sweet whistle, *"Too-o-o-o, too-o-o-o, too-too."*
Around the bend of the river, out of the dark trees into
the glistening world, along the black lines came the lacy
black triangle of the cowcatcher, the rolling black iron
wheels, the smokestack tossing dark balloons with flecks
of fire in them against the blue sky, the brass bell rocking
and clanging.

Marcy reached for her mother's hand.

She came straight toward them, nearer and nearer, and
the wind she made pushed Marcy backward at the same
time that the great wheels wove a spell which drew Marcy
toward them. The noise of bell and iron on iron and
screeching brake was deafening.

Then she stopped, and everything was still again. From
an open window below the smokestack an old man with a
beard, wearing a bright blue cap and a coat with brass
buttons, smiled down at Marcy.

"Well, well, little lady! Where shall I take you this
bright morning? To the North Pole?"

"All aboard!" a younger man in darker blue with brass
buttons was calling as he swung down high steps. "All-l
aboard here —"

Frankie hurried Marcy along the icy platform, past a
little red car heaped with black coal where still another
man in a blue coat was shoveling but stopped shoveling to
wave at them. The young man reached out for Marcy,
picked her up and stood her on the top step saying, "All
the princesses ride in my coach," and turned to put his
hand under Frankie's elbow.

"Take seats at this end near the stove," he said.
"Upper end is still cold. Set on a spur track all night, and
ten below when we left Portland."

Their seats were of gold with red velvet cushions, and

faced each other as the seats in royal coaches always do. A lady in furs and a gentleman in a brown derby hat sat nearby. Perhaps they were a queen and a king. Several men sat alone, some of them reading newspapers. Perhaps they were footmen. There was no other child but Marcy.

The train began to move.

"I didn't have time to answer the nice old man," Marcy whispered. "He doesn't know where we want to go."

"He is the engineer. The man who was shoveling coal is the fireman. The one who lifted you in is the conductor. The conductor is coming now to take our tickets. The tickets say where we want to go."

But Marcy did not think tickets could speak as plainly as she could. She summoned her courage, and when the conductor came she said aloud:

"Please, sir, tell the engineer we want to go to Portsmouth. If it — isn't out of his way."

"I will tell the fireman," said the conductor, bowing. "He will tell the engineer. At once. Yes, ma'am."

They were flying now through the glistening fields.

The conductor opened the glass door at the end of the coach and stepped out on the platform. The fireman looked out of a little window beyond the coal, and then turned and spoke to someone behind him. When he turned back he tossed a small package across the coal. The conductor caught it and brought it to Marcy.

"He says he will be glad to take you to Portsmouth on our way to the North Pole. And he sent you this which he brought back from his last trip up there."

It was a small gold box with white paper lace inside. Under the lace there were four cookies shaped like snowflakes. Each cookie was two cookies with cream candy between. One was chocolate with white cream. One was white with pink cream. One was crusted with sugar crystals. One had yellow frosting. There was a shiny white card lettered in gold, "Compliments of the Sunshine Biscuit Co."

"Are you going to eat them, Marcy?" Hal asked.

Her heart stopped beating. If one was eaten, it would be gone forever. There would be an empty place in the gold box which had come to her from the bearded old man with the twinkling eyes, the North Pole, and the Sunshine Biscuit Company. . . . But there had been no present for Hal. Nobody had even spoken to him.

She took off the cover and turned back the lace.

"You first," Hal said. "It's yours."

A lump began rising in Marcy's throat. She knew she could not swallow.

"She loves so to keep things, Hal," Frankie said. "You can't be hungry yet. You had a good breakfast. We'll get something to eat in Portsmouth. Or Dover."

"Oh, keep it, Marcy, if you want to, till it turns to dust. Let's watch for the Webber place and the Bannister place. Aunt Hattie might be out feeding the hens. Aunt Vinnie might be hanging out clothes."

Rushing through the glistening new world, past little fences around little white houses and little red barns, now and then they saw little figures moving about or riding in little sleighs behind little horses. Perhaps one of the little houses was Hattie's, or one of the little figures Vinnie.

"We're coming into Kittery Depot," said the conductor. "When we stop, young feller, you want to come up front and ride into Portsmouth in the cab?"

"With the engineer?" Hal exclaimed. "You bet! Gee!"

As soon as the train stopped, Hal went up the aisle with his mackinaw unbuttoned to show his blue shirt and with his knitted cap pulled low over his eyes as if it were visored. The glass door closed behind him. Marcy watched him balance on the side of the coal car as on a tightrope and disappear into the cab. The smoke came out of the stack blacker than ever.

"Will the engineer let Hal drive the train?" asked Marcy.

"Maybe," said Frankie dreamily. Of course he wouldn't. But would he — today?

Marcy thought Hal drove the train very well. It stayed right on the tracks. She took the cover off the gold box and touched the crystal-crusted cookie with the tip of one finger. It felt sharp.

"See the harbor, Marcy," said Frankie. "There's the Navy Yard where Uncle George works."

They were on a high bridge over the Piscataqua River, the blue sky and blue water on both sides of them. Dories, fishing boats, cargo boats and a ferry sat on the water like brown and white ducks and ducklings, those at the shoreline frozen in. The low yellow buildings of the Navy Yard covered the island at the mouth of the river and beyond them a tall ship like a white eagle with wings spread was moving out into the open sea. Ahead of the engine were the red brick walls and the black chimney pots of the city of Portsmouth.

The train came to a stop. The people who had been together on it separated and went out into the narrow streets, up the hill to cobblestoned Market Square and the stores which surrounded it. Hal had ridden with the engineer. Marcy had her cookies from the North Pole. Frankie had money in her beaded bag.

Every door had a green wreath tied with a bow of red ribbon. In a few windows there were Christmas trees hung with many colored balls and silver cones and tiny golden trumpets. One window had nothing in it but a great framed picture of Washington's Christmas at Valley Forge. Hal looked at that for a long time, and kept going back to look at it. All the other windows were filled with wonderful things to look at. Wherever they went inside there were more wonderful things still, and when Frankie bought a pillowtop for Vinnie, with skeins of floss to embroider the pattern printed on it, the money she gave the saleslady was put into a little wooden box which was snapped onto a track and went zinging up to the ceiling and down the whole length of the store to a balcony where a girl with red hair took out the bill and put in some coins and sent the box zinging back to the saleslady and Frankie.

They were outside and it was very cold. The horses hitched to the granite posts were blanketed, and the chimes were playing in the church tower.

Sometime while the sun was high they rode on a ferryboat across the river to where an electric car, painted yellow, came into Kittery on its trolley wire much as the little wooden box had traveled to the balcony and back. Frankie and Hal and Marcy got into it and went zinging through snowy woods and fields to Dover. Here, too, were the wreaths, the little trees with bright balls, the wonderful things in windows and on counters, the blanketed horses, and the chimes. It must be that they were not far from anywhere. Ride in any direction and you would come to them.

Somewhere they sat at a table covered with a white cloth and ate steaming oyster stew. Somewhere Marcy was alone with Hal and bought a great blue vase for her mother; it was blue but it was green and purple and garnet, too, changing magically from one color to another. Somewhere she was with her mother and bought socks for her father, grandfather, and Hal, a set of three bluebird pins for her Aunt Vinnie and a new moon pin for her Aunt Lula, small vases for her grandmother, her Aunt Hattie and her teacher. She had just enough money left from her dollar to buy what she had wanted most to buy, except the blue vase: a coral bracelet for Bernice.

Somewhere they found an ice cream parlor and sat in chairs with heart-shaped backs to have ice cream sodas. Marcy's was pink; strawberry. Frankie's was brown; sarsaparilla. Hal's was almost black; chocolate. The presents they had bought were heaped around their feet, and the chimes were playing, and all the people were talking and smiling. They didn't smile only at people they knew. They smiled at everybody, especially at children. They smiled at Marcy and Marcy smiled back.

She thought, "I love you. I want to take you home with me."

When they got off the electric car in the village square it was growing dark and the conductor held his red lantern to light them down the steps.

"Here you are," he said to Verd. "Got 'em all back to you safe and sound. Leave it to the old P. D. and Y."

"Much obliged," Verd said, "but I probably won't chance it again for another year."

They both laughed.

"Wish you merry Christmas, Mr. Conductor," said Marcy boldly.

"Well, God love ye, wish you the same."

The electric zinged on toward Salmon Falls. Verd put the packages under the pung seat, they all climbed in, and Bess set off full tilt toward home. The farther they went the darker it grew, and the brighter the lamplight was in the windows of each house they passed.

"Must have seen and heard and done a lot today," Verd said. "What did you think was the best of it all?"

"Oh, the sunshine on the river and the boats in the harbor," Frankie answered. "And the music. The chimes."

"The engine," said Hal. "I rode in it with the engineer. And a picture they had in a Portsmouth window. Christmas at Valley Forge."

"What do you say, Marcy?"

She thought of the royal coach, the golden box of cookies, the wreaths, the Christmas trees, the zinging wooden box, the zinging electrics, the oyster stew, the strawberry soda, the dolls and toys, the vases and pins and bracelets.

But she said, "The people. All the smiling people with love in their eyes."

There were the days the mailman left postcards and

packages stamped "Boston" and "Lawrence" and "Eliot."
Frankie put the packages in the sitting-room cupboard
but the postcards were passed from hand to hand many
times before being tucked into the album. There were
glazed cards and frosted cards, pictures of Santa with
his pack, a mother cat with a holly-trimmed basket of
kittens, the Wise Men following the Star, and the Baby in
the manger. One of Frankie's was from a woman she had
gone to school with when they were little girls. They had
not seen each other for years but they write when they
can. The card had a picture of two little girls running
through the snow, and a verse:

> *No gift to send,*
> *Only love to share*
> *With my old friend —*
> *A friendship rare.*

There were the evenings Frankie sewed, and helped
Marcy with her pincushions, needlebooks, and book-
marks, while George, Verd, and Hal packed a barrel for
Annie, filling it with the vegetables she so enjoyed, pro-
tected with hay from the cold, a big piece of salt pork, a
slab of home-cured bacon, and a slice of deer steak. Always before bedtime Verd brought up a basin of Strawberry Baldwins from the cellar, peeled them, and passed
around quarters on the point of his jackknife.

There was the Sunday afternoon when Grace and Bernice came, and Frankie asked Verd to build a fire in the
sitting-room stove so that the children could play in that
room while she and Grace talked in the kitchen.

As soon as the women were alone, Grace took Larkin
catalogues, record books, and order pads from her bag,
and Frankie brought hers, along with ink bottle and pens.
When these were spread out, they covered the table, and
the women began eagerly to check each other's figures.
Grace's total was higher than Frankie's because she had
had a horse to take her over many roads where people

lived who gave her orders, but Grace had two sons to earn premiums for, while Frankie had only one. And Frankie had been helped by orders Vinnie, Hattie, and Annie had given her. They rejoiced together that not only had each sold enough to get the Big Doll, but Frankie could get a set of drafting tools for Hal, and Grace could get a catcher's mitt and mask for Clyde, a new wheel and a bell for Leslie's bicycle.

They wrote the orders for the boys' gifts quickly, but selection among the dolls was a happy task they lingered over, reading the descriptions aloud in low voices, studying the pictures of perfect little wax faces, dimpled hands, shod feet, and pastel silk dresses.

"Look at the length of this one's eyelashes."

"Oh, Grace, what would we have thought to have a doll like that when we were their age?"

"There, dear, what we didn't know of didn't hurt us. We thought my Adelaide was the handsomest thing we ever —"

"Sh-h-h!"

Frankie had heard Marcy's voice raised in the next room.

"You know what? We don't *have* to write letters to him! We could *talk* to him right here because right behind that tin that the stove funnel goes through there's a fireplace. I always used to wish they didn't have to set up the stove before Christmas, and I never thought until now — the fireplace is *there* just the same and I guess he can hear through a little old piece of tin!"

" 'Course he can," Bernice agreed. "You talk to him first."

"All right. We'll have to talk *loud*. Because of the tin. Besides, he's so old he may be getting a little mite deaf."

"Listen, Grace. They're going to tell Santa Claus what they want."

Frankie was smiling, both in amusement and in pride. Marcy had not been long in school when older children had told her there was no Santa Claus. It pleased Frankie that Marcy was not passing on any such disillusionment to Bernice, who had not yet been to school. It also amused her that Marcy was making sure her histrionic effort would not be wasted.

"Hello, up there, Santa Claus!" shouted Marcy. "I have been as good as usual, and I hope you will bring me a new doll. If possible I would like to have a bed for her and Margery to sleep in. Hal would like a compass to use when he takes geometry. I hope you know what kind of compass he means. It is not the kind you carry in your pocket to help you find your way when you are lost. We would also like oranges and sheep's-foot nuts. I hope this isn't asking too much. Thank you, Santa Claus, and Merry Christmas! . . . Now it's your turn, Bernice. Get right in close, back of the stove, and talk *loud!*"

"Hello, Santa Claus," piped Bernice. "I think I have been good. Please bring me a new doll, and — and picture books, and a new album to put my postcards in, and Christmas candy. Clyde wants a new mitt and Leslie broke the front wheel of his bicycle. If you can only bring one thing for me, what I want the most is a new doll with — with brown hair. Thank you, Santa Claus."

"Did you hear her, Santa Claus?" bawled Marcy. "She said *a doll with brown hair*. I'd rather have a doll with yellow hair like hers. She wants brown hair and I want yellow hair, Santa!"

"Well, I guess that settles the hair," Frankie murmured.

Grace's face was all lighted up. She put a hand over Frankie's.

"Oh, am I thankful, dear!" she whispered. "I held my breath. You see, Will's niece told Bernice when they came on a visit last summer that there isn't any Santa Claus. Bernice felt awful bad at the time, but she hasn't said anything about it since. I was so afraid she'd tell Marcy."

There was the Saturday after a three-day storm when

George and Hal drove to the beach for a cartload of sea-weed to be used as fertilizer in the potato hills next spring, and Hal brought back a pailful of shells of many shapes and sizes which he and his mother and Marcy decorated with red and gold paint Verd brought home from the shop. Hal chipped a small hole in each shell and Frankie threaded them with red twine for hanging on the tree, which had not yet been brought from the woods. As they worked, Hal tried to tell them about the sight and the sound of December surf.

"It's nothing like the summer ocean. I don't know words that would describe it. I wish I'd taken your camera."

"I guess a camera couldn't see all of it. Maybe a painting — but we'd still have to imagine the sound. Or music, some great piece of music — but then we'd have to imagine the color. And the cold. You know, the poorest people are the people who don't have imagination. Even if you don't have all you want to eat, or felt boots, or a tight roof over your head — if you just have imagination —"

That night after Marcy went to bed she practiced imagining. She imagined that her bed was a sled on which she lay while her father pulled it along the cobblestone street of a city like Portsmouth. It was snowing. She could feel the little prickles of snowflakes on her face. She looked about her at the ribboned wreaths on the doors, at the dolls in the windows, at the ships in the harbor, the engines puffing smoke, and the zinging electrics. It grew dark and very cold. She snuggled deeper into the comforters. At last they stopped under a tall gaslight and her mother began to sing. Her mother's strong clear, sweet voice ran up the lamppost, spread out from the top in bright rays of light, and unfurled over the city like a shining banner . . . *"O little town of Bethlehem . . . Silent night, holy night"* . . .

Her father had taken off his hat, stood bareheaded in the sifting snow. The wreathed doors opened and smiling people came running out. Smiling people came off the ships and out of the trains and down the steps of the electrics, and made a smiling circle around them. At the end of the singing they tossed gold pieces into Verd's hat until it spilled over and the bright coins sprinkled, tinkling, on the ice.

"Now we shall have wood for a fire and matches to light it," said Verd. "We shall have good bread to eat, and maybe oranges for Christmas."

"Why?" Marcy asked sleepily. "Why do they give us these things?"

"Because they love us," Frankie answered. "Because this is a holy time. Because they are good and kind . . ."

"And because," Verd added, "of the way your mother sings."

There was the night of the Christmas Party at school. For the first time in her life Marcy left home after supper, sitting between Verd and Frankie in the cutter, buried to her chin in the buffalo robe. She saw the streak of light from the lantern hung on the corner of the dashboard. She saw the dark, and she saw the stars. She heard the sleighbells. She felt the curves of the road, the planks of White's Marsh bridge, the pitch of Nason's hill. Then she came up out of the robe and saw beyond the horse's head the lighted windows of the schoolhouse, a dozen horses and sleighs hitched to the schoolyard fence.

The schoolhouse door was closed. When they opened it and stepped inside, the little room was full of people and lantern light and the smell of spruce and kerosene. It buzzed with voices. It rocked with footsteps. And the great tree, hung all over with books and toys and packages and red cheesecloth bags, was like a happy mother beaming on a great brood of noisy children bringing more and more packages to put in her hands, lay at her feet, and pin in her hair.

Teacher in a red velvet dress, at a desk streaming evergreen, tapped her bell.

"Santa Claus is coming soon," she promised. "All take seats, please. The pupils in front. Parents in back. We have prepared a program we hope you will enjoy."

"Marcy." It was Bernice. "Marcy — can I sit with you?"

Marcy moved over. The seat was very narrow. They clung together to stay on it, and because they were so glad they were both there.

"The December Song," announced Teacher. "By our youngest pupil, Marcia Hasty."

It was terrifying to be first, to leave Bernice and stand alone on the platform beside the tree, to see all the dark heads bobbing against the lantern light, to open her mouth and let out the first note. It might so easily be the wrong note. It so often was the wrong note.

"Jesus, help me," Marcy prayed.

> *Oh, December, how we love you, and the many*
> *joys you bring*
> *'Tis the time of dear old Santa, when the merry,*
> *merry sleighbells ring,*
> *Jingle, jingle through the frosty air, folks are*
> *traveling here and there,*
> *Laughing, singing, happiness to spare, jingle,*
> *jingle, jingle everywhere.*
> *Tiny stockings hanging in a row; children*
> *sleeping, lights are burning low,*
> *Santa comes with many gifts and toys for all*
> *good little girls and boys.*

Marcy's eyes sought her mother's face. Frankie nodded and smiled. Most of the notes must have been almost right.

She ran back to her seat. Bernice's arm was waiting. They hugged each other fiercely

It was wonderful to have been first.

"I put a present on the tree for you," whispered Bernice.

"I put one on for you, too," Marcy whispered back.

The other pupils recited and sang and did a little play with three big boys dressed as the Wise Men and a big girl as Mary holding a big doll. The grown-ups listened. The children watched the tree and the soft shadows, smelled the spruce, and thought about Jesus. This was Bethlehem and they knew He was about to be born.

The last number on the program was the singing of "Jingle Bells," and Teacher asked everyone to join in. Marcy could hear her mother's voice above all the rest, strong and gay and sweet. . . . *"Bells on bobtail ring, making spirits bright, What fun it is to ride and sing a sleighing song tonight!"*

Jingle-jingle-jingle . . . Ho-ho-ho . . . Whoa, Donder . . . Whoa, Blitzen . . .

"Well, well, *well*! Here you are, then! Merry Christmas, young folks, old folks, and folks in the middle! By zounds, what a handsome tree! Who do you suppose these presents are for? Just a minute till I wipe off my glasses —"

Red suit, red stocking-leg cap, white beard, twinkling eyes, fat stomach, high black boots. . . It was Hal. It was not Hal. It was Christmas very close now. Not close enough to touch. But very close.

The warm, booming voice was reading names. The gloved hands below the white fur cuffs were passing out gifts.

"Albra! Albra! Where is Albra? . . . Here's a pretty book for you, Lucy . . . Mar — Marcy — *Hasty*! Ho, ho, ho, so you're Marcy Hasty, are you?"

"Yes, I am," answered Marcy pertly. "I should think you'd know me, Santa Claus!"

"Ho, ho, yes, indeed. I know all you children. But once in a while I forget a name for a minute. Old man, remember."

Marcy's gift was a picture of a little girl in a sunbonnet. It had a scalloped gold frame and a gold chain to hang by.

On the cardboard back was written, "Marcy Hasty. Merry Christmas from Teacher."

"You'll get a present from her as soon as you come to school," Marcy told Bernice. "She always puts something for every one of us on the tree. But I never thought I'd get a picture. I never had a picture of my own before."

There was a red cheesecloth bag with a popcorn ball in it, and peanuts and peppermint sticks, for every person in the room; and some left over to be sent to small children who had not come.

"Bernice! Bernice Dorr! Now where's that little Bernice?"

"You get it, Marcy," Bernice whispered, sliding low in her seat.

"I'll take it for her, Santa! Here. I got it for you the day I rode on the train."

"Where's mine for you?"

"He just hasn't come to it yet."

"I'm going to wait till you get yours."

That was how it happened that at the very end, when Santa had gone and boys were pawing through the branches piled around the trunk of the tree to be sure nothing more was hidden there, and mothers were coming with coats and leggings, and some of the lanterns were beginning to sputter because the oil was low, Bernice and Marcy pulled the red ribbons from two little white boxes and took off the covers. A card in one said, in printed letters, "Merry Christmas to Bernice from Marcy." A card in the other said in Grace's handwriting, "To Marcy with love, from Bernice." And under each card was a coral bracelet.

Now Christmas was rising to a crescendo.

There was the day Mr. Bannister brought Vinnie home, and had to leave right away because he was going to travel on a train all that night and all the next day and all the next night to be a Christmas present to his sister in Florida.

When he had gone, and Vinnie had taken off her hat and cape and sat down in her rocking chair by the back window, it was as if she had never been away. The fire crackled and the teakettle sang and when Hal brought in the mail the usual black type and blacker headlines of the weekly *Independent* were surrounded by dark-green leaves and bright-red berries, and the rays from the Star in the corner swept the whole page.

That night they made long strings of popcorn and cran-berries.

The next day — the morning of the day before Christ-mas — Vinnie said as soon as Frankie came downstairs:

"Now Verd and I have planned it all out. He and Hal are going up on the mountain this afternoon to get a tree he's taken a notion to up there. So why don't you and Marcy ride along with them to Clarence's and take your presents to your mother and Lula? I'll cut some nice slices off that ham I brought, so if your mother's baked some bread you can have some good sandwiches for your din-ner, all of you. Verd says he'll come back for you before dark. They'll bring the tree down first, and Hal and I fig-ure to have it decorated before you get home."

Marcy rode down the lane and down the hill and over Warren's bridge between Verd and Frankie on the seat of the woodsled, with Old Bell swishing her tail before them. Hal stood in the back. Everything was blue above and white below except for the red barns and the dark trees.

At Emerys', Frankie's Aunt Em was taking a handful of bright cards from the mailbox.

She pushed back her shawl from her cheek, and smiled, and said, "Well, now, where you folks off to?"

"Up to Lula's to spend the day," Frankie called back. "That is, Marcy and I are. Verd and Hal are going after the Christmas tree. What are you going to do tomorrow, Aunt Em?"

"Do! I guess there'll be enough to do! All of them that aren't here are coming for dinner and the tree in the afternoon, way they always do. Grace and her young ones, and Maude and hers. Georgie's got our tree set up, and Cathie'll be baking all day."

"Oh, what a good time you'll have!"

"Wait a minute," Aunt Em called after them. "I've got a card here from Nell. Let's see what she says. Oh — says Than thinks to drive down this afternoon. Tell Louise he may be up there before he goes home."

"I'll tell her," Frankie answered. "I hope he will. I'd love to see him."

Than Brooks is as near to a brother as she ever had, though he is her uncle. She grew up with her grandparents, and he is only thirteen years older than she. Hal is eight years older than Marcy.

They rode on the blue sleds into the dark and white woods. Above their heads there was a ribbon of blue to match the sleds. When they came to fields again, they were Clarence's fields, and Clarence's little white house with green blinds and a red, smoking chimney was waiting for them at the top of the bank wall.

Lula opened the door and ran to the steps in the bank wall to meet them; bareheaded, bare-armed, her hair — the color of the honey of Clarence's bees — pinned low on her slender neck, her eyes — blue as turquoises — laughing.

"I had a *feeling* you'd come! I told Mama —"

"Oh, Lula, you naughty girl! Get back inside before you get your death of cold."

"Know what I'm making? A tapioca pudding with bananas and oranges!" She drew Marcy into the circle of her arm, waving to the men with the other hand. "You like tapioca pudding, Marcy? And Grammy's bread — if nobody makes you eat the crusts?"

They all went into the house, and Louise came out of the pantry, which was painted spruce-gum pink and had shelves filled with blue and white plates and platters and cups and saucers all alike. She was wiping floury hands on her apron, and her scalp showed pink through her fine, silvery hair, and her eyes crinkled at the corners.

"Well, my land sakes alive," she said gently, "what a surprise, Frank! But Lula did say this morning she had a feeling —"

They had a box of new wax crayons for Marcy and they found some old magazines with pictures of ladies and children in fancy old-fashioned clothes. While she colored by the window they cooked and talked and gave each other aprons and handkerchiefs with tatted edging and little bags of sachet to tuck under bed pillows and crocheted flowers sewn to safety pins to hold their collars together.

They ate their ham sandwiches and pudding and drank their tea — there was cambric tea for Marcy — and Marcy gave her grandmother the little vase which changed from rose color to gold and back again, and Lula the new moon pin. She had painted a Bible and a gold cross on a bit of purple satin ribbon for a bookmark for her grandmother, too.

Lula put the pin over the top button of her blue wrapper and said, "There, Marcy, now I'm all dressed up."

Louise laid the bookmark carefully in her Bible and said, "When the cinnamon roses bloom next summer I'll have something better than a milk pitcher to put them in, won't I?"

"Are you going to sing?" asked Marcy. They always did.

"Sing? We'll sing our hearts out," cried Lula. "I'll get the books. They're on the stairs."

They were singing "We Three Kings of Orient Are" when the door opened and Em's strong soprano and Than's deep bass swept in and joined them. Lula jumped up, hugged them both, took their wraps, and they went around the table and kissed everybody, but nobody stopped singing.

Than swung Marcy out of her chair, dropped into it

himself, pulled her onto his knee, and threw an arm around Frankie, leaning over to see the words of the second verse on her book.

They sang "Joy to the World," and "O Come, All Ye Faithful," and "Deck the Halls," and "We Wish You a Merry Christmas," and "The First Noel," and "It Came Upon the Midnight Clear," and "Hark, the Herald Angels Sing" — all the verses of every one and some of them over and over.

"Well, Louise, I've got to go," Than said suddenly. He kissed Marcy, set her on her feet, and rose. "It's many a mile to old North Berwick, and I've got twelve cows to milk before supper."

"Have a taste of my pudding before you go, Uncle Than," Lula said.

She dipped some into a saucer.

"Oh, give Em the taste," he said. "I'll take the dish."

He picked up the bowl and a spoon and stood in the middle of the kitchen, eating, rolling his eyes, licking his lips, a big, happy, brown-faced, hawk-nosed giant. Than Brooks is six feet, four inches tall.

"My stars and garters, Lula, that's the best pudding I ever ate!"

Clarence came in from the woods with a little fir balsam. Verd was right behind him. They took off their mittens and shook hands with Than and Em, stood talking with Than while the women put on their wraps.

"Oh, Em, I'm so glad you came with him. I wish you could get up here oftener."

"Well, any chance I get I take. When he said he was coming up, I said, 'Well, I'm going to drop everything and go with you. Best present I could have.' "

"Oh, it does us all a world of good to get together and sing."

"Now you have a nice day tomorrow."

"I'll be thinking of you — and old times —"

"Give our love to Nell."

Louise and Lula stood in the doorway as the others climbed into the two sleighs. The sun was just dropping behind the trees.

As Than pulled on the reins to start his horse, he said in his deep, carrying voice:

"Well, here 'tis again. Christmas Eve!"

And there it was. The snow all turned to pearl, the dark trees strung with pearls, the sky beginning to glow with such a radiance as never was on land or sea. And the stillness everywhere; the live, vibrant stillness of just before a great orchestra begins to play, or angels to sing.

Later in the evening Marcy stood alone looking at the Christmas tree in the parlor, where a fire burned in the little round stove. The tree was looped around from top to bottom with the popcorn and cranberry strings. Hattie had sent three little red balls, like shiny apples encased in golden mesh, and Vinnie had brought two silver cones and four little golden trumpets. They all hung here now, among the seashells, and the lamplight picked them out, every one. But best of all was the gold star Vinnie had brought and Hal had fastened to the very point of the tree, almost touching the white ceiling.

"Is it almost too beautiful to believe?" they had asked her when she first saw it.

Marcy had thought about that, and then shaken her head.

"The more beautiful it is, the easier I can believe it."

Now her father came up behind her and put his hand on her shoulder.

"Want to see what I got for your mother, Marcy?"

"Oh, yes."

He took a little bottle of perfume from his pocket. He held it to the lamp and she could see the pale yellow perfume inside. She thought it was pretty but she thought it was very small.

"It's the kind she likes," he said. "I had to go to Dover

to get it. I got her something else, too. But mind you don't tell her."

"Oh, I won't."

He took the lamp to light a dark place under the stairs. There was a wooden box with a domed cover and beside the box there was a horn.

"It's a graphophone," he said, low. "Like the one they have at Dorrs' that she likes to go to listen to. Only theirs is an Edison and this is a Columbia. There are twelve cylinders for it. Six of them are hymns."

"Oh, Papa! Now she can have music even — even when she's hoarse and can't sing."

"Yes. Now she can have music all the time."

Music all the time . . .

As Frankie kissed Marcy good-night and was turning out the light in the alcove at the head of the stairs, Marcy asked drowsily, "Do you go out to see the cattle kneel down in the stalls at midnight?"

"No, Marcy."

"Why? Have you gone to sleep by then?"

"No. I'm in my room, kneeling too."

"I think — that's nice. That's what I'll do, too — when I'm old enough to be awake."

"Yes, dear."

Frankie went down to the parlor where Hal had brought in his Flexible Flyer which he had painted blue and gold for Marcy. Verd was just bringing in the bed he had made and stained red for the golden-haired doll. It had a spring of chicken wire and a frame to hold curtains at the head. Frankie began making up the bed with small sheets and pillow, a small tufted comforter, and white Marseilles spread and curtains.

In the kitchen George was saying, as he lay on the couch and Vinnie rocked quietly by the back window looking out at the stars:

"Good to have you home again, Vinnie."

"I'll be back to stay awhile, by February."

"How's that?"

"Mr. Bannister is going to be married." She laughed softly. "On Valentine's Day!"

After a minute he cleared his throat and said, "Some thought you might be going to marry him."

She laughed a little again.

"There was never such a thought in *my* mind . . . No, I want to be here when the ice goes out."

Later he sat up and felt for his slippers, looking over at her.

"Must say, you've give me all the Christmas present I need."

"Likely you'll get other ones. I made you a pair of shirts."

"Wool ones?"

"Yes."

"They'll come in handy."

Hal had gone up to bed, but he could not sleep. Lying on his side he could see the sky all bright with stars, and one brighter than any of the rest.

Frankie blew out the parlor light, and went upstairs carrying a hand lamp. Verd followed her. Their shadows moved with them along the wall.

In their chamber she turned down the bed. Even this room was warm tonight, for he had kept a fire in it all the evening. He put a last chunk into the stove and closed the drafts. She stood at the bureau unpinning her hair. It fell in heavy, purplish-black masses to her waist. He came up beside her.

"Merry Christmas," he said, and gave her the little bottle.

She held it for an instant in both hands and then put it against her cheek. Her eyes were like June pansies.

"Oh, Verd!" she said. "The kind I love best!"

The last light went out and the little white house, at other times moored so securely to its granite foundation, seemed to set off like a sleigh along a smooth, dark road leading straight to the Milky Way, with the red barn following closely.

The kitchen clock struck midnight, and Bell, Bess, and all the cattle were kneeling down.

Now it is the last night of the Old Year and we lie in the dark below a sloping ceiling, or sit before the open oven door by the light of a lamp with wick turned low, waiting for the midnight stroke which will usher in a new year. One after another the old years go; one after another the new years come. We have no way of knowing what changes each will bring, but we go forward with faith that God will never ask of us more than we are capable of, and that what we earn, what we deserve, we shall receive in the coming year and all the years ahead.

CHAPTER III

Christmas 1915

Miriam had a bad cold. She lay on a cot in the sitting room, close beside the stove, with blankets hung across the lower half of the windows to keep off the draft. Her face looked pink against the pillow, and she was using strips of cloth for handkerchiefs because she needed so many; she had even begun to cough. It was plain she could not go to the Christmas Eve social at the church. The only question was, who should stay with her?

"I never ought to have said I'd tend to the kitchen for them up there," Mrs. Bradley fretted. "I might have known one of you young ones would come down with something if I did. If there was anybody to take my place it wouldn't make so much difference, but they're awful shorthanded, with all the sickness there is around."

"Couldn't Papa —"

"There! Your father!" Mrs. Bradley disposed of him. "You ought to know how much idea he has of looking after the sick. I should expect to come home and find her up in her bare feet, getting a drink, and him asleep in his chair."

"I wouldn't, either, get up," sniffed Miriam.

She hid her face and cried as quietly as she could, but it was no small tragedy to be nine years old and not to go to the Christmas Eve social. The church had not been used since October, until then, and afterwards the little white clapboarded house would stand desolate at its fork in the road until spring. And Miriam was to have spoken a piece of fourteen stanzas — she knew it perfectly — as well as to have helped Santa Claus strip the tree of presents.

"There, now, Miriam," her mother said. "You'll make your head ache. You won't be left alone, don't you worry. A little girl like you! . . . No, Mother'll stay with you, and we'll cut out paper dolls. Or maybe I'll find some catalogues up in the shed chamber and you can color the pictures. We'll have a fine time."

Miriam felt better. She and her mother always had fine times together. She swallowed the last of her tears, and smiled, and took her medicine, and promised to try to go to sleep now like a good girl. After the others had gone, she would recite the fourteen stanzas to her mother, and her mother would think it was wonderful a young one could remember so many words, especially when she had a cold.

Out in the kitchen, Della was baking. She had a knack, as her mother said, with flour and spices and seasoning, and for the last two months or more had done most of the cooking for the family. Before that she had been in school, and this fall had begun riding horseback to the academy in the village, but since her old Polly had taken colic and died one night, Della had been at home, and her mother tried to save butter money toward buying another horse, but the fund grew slowly. It was not likely that Della could go back to school until the next fall, when she would enter with a new class, and she would be much older than the others, for she had never been quick at her books and was sixteen already. In the meantime she did the baking, ironed her little sisters' clothes, made embroidery with which she had filled a whole bureau drawer, and seemed content.

She looked up as her mother came out of the sitting room. In all the serenity of her round, pretty face there was one small wrinkle between her brown eyes, as if everything in the world were right for her except one little, insignificant thing. She leaned with her hands against the cakeboard, her sleeves rolled up, her dress turned in at the neck, and her body tall and sturdy under a yellow print apron.

"I feel as if I ought to offer to stay, Mother," she said, "but you see —"

"Why, there, you're in the play," her mother said. "I guess they can get along without me better than they can without you. Besides, you're not much more than a young one yourself. And you can look after Rachel."

"That's the trouble, though," Della explained. "I can't do that very well because Chuck is going to take me. I'd just as soon have her along, but I suppose he'd think —"

"Well, I should say it was a funny thing," cried her mother, "if you care more about what Chuck Wiggin thinks than —"

"I don't, but still —"

Rachel, eight, a lean, ungainly child, was writing a letter to Miriam. They had not been allowed together for four days, since Miriam had taken cold, because Rachel's colds often became tonsilitis or abscesses in the ear, and it was important she should not catch one. But it was difficult for her to manage a winter vacation without Miriam, and mostly she sat in the kitchen writing letters. Miriam had done the same when Rachel had mumps in the fall.

Dear Miriam,

Don't you think that stuff Mum burns on the stove smells very funny? I should think they could put a better smell in it, don't you? I will bring home what presents you get on the tree tonight. I know one you are going to get anyway. It is square. I will not tell you any more. I cannot think of anything more to say. I hope your cold will be better. I will write you another letter —

Rachel threw her pencil, and the lead broke off when it struck the floor point down. She had not appeared to be listening to her mother and Della, but she had heard every word.

"You don't need to bother about me," she said. "I don't want to go to the old social anyway. I don't care a thing about it. I think it's silly, and if Della's in love with Chuck Wiggin, *she's* silly. And I don't *want* to go."

"Yes, you do, too," her mother told her. "You put on your coat and go outdoors and don't you come in again until you can act like a lady. You shouldn't speak like that about your sister, and you don't know what you're talking about for she's nothing but a little girl just the same as you are. . . . Of course you're going to the social. If Della won't take you, Neal will."

Neal was eighteen, a tall, slender boy with a rough, dark-skinned face, and shoulders that rounded out in the back unless he remembered to straighten up. It was four years since he had left the district school, and he wanted to go to the city to find a job, but his father could not spare him off the farm. He had books that told about drafting, and a set of compasses and straightedges and other little tools in a broken box lined with blue velvet. Whenever his father did not need him, he sat at a table in his room over the kitchen and drew lines. He always felt

better natured in the winter than in the summer for he had
more time to himself, and it was not really cold if he wore
a sweater and sat by the wall where the chimney went up.

"Sure, I'll take her," he said. "That is, if she can stay
awake till she gets home. She needn't think I'm going to
lug her back."

Rachel liked to walk through the dark behind Neal, but
she did not say so. She did not say anything, kicking along
stoutly in the path he broke, her arms full of oddly
wrapped presents she had made at school for him and for
Della, and others that she had contrived the last few days
for Miriam, between letters. She could not have explained
why she felt she must carry Miriam's up to the church and
back again, but it would not be the same at all if they were
never hung on the tree.

The moon was out clear enough to lay shadows. Neal's
tall and Rachel's short one skulked along the road, sometimes slithering into bushes and trees and slithering out
again like snaky birds. Snow crunched under their feet, a
brave sound. *I'm not afraid; here I come; I'm not afraid.*
Rachel was afraid of nothing with Neal there. Her nose
tingled; her arms ached; she was perfectly happy.

They reached the church, which appeared first as two
rows of bright lights against the sky, and then as a warm,
bustling little room full of long tables and people who
stood in groups talking. Rachel took off her coat and held
it, staring around. The children who stared back at her
did not look the same as they did at school in the daytime;
night changed everything. There was the smell of spruce
and baked beans and snow and lemon pie in the air. By
and by Santa Claus would come and take presents off the
tree that waited somewhere even now, loaded with silver
and gold. He would call out a name. *Rachel Bradley.*

"Come on, folks. Sit down."

The children were given a table by themselves. Rachel
would have enjoyed this more if Miriam had been there,

for Miriam would have talked for them both. But what she had to eat tasted very good, and she could watch Neal sitting with two other boys at the far end of the room. He kept smoothing back his thick hair with his hand.

At another table Della sat beside Chuck Wiggin. Della wore a new brown dress with wide white collar and cuffs. It made her look very clean, and her hair curled a little, like her mother's and Miriam's; she was laughing, and her eyes kept going up to meet Chuck's. They were very warm and brown. Suddenly the way she loved Della made Rachel feel weak, as if she must lean against Della, or only touch something Della had touched, but she never did things like that because she was too proud.

"I hate him," Rachel thought. "I hate Chuck Wiggin. I should think she'd hate him."

But nobody else hated Chuck, Della least of all. Chuck was big, standing six-foot-three in his stocking feet, red-headed and freckled and good-natured; he could pick up a bag of grain as easily as Neal could a book; he walked with a long, sidling stride, self-assured and provocative; he was thirty years old and hardly ever knew where he could stay the next night, but anybody in the room, man or woman, would have been pleased to sit next to him at the church supper. Della was only sixteen, and he had brought her here and would take her home, had done so before and would surely do so again; no wonder she laughed.

"Now I believe everyone has finished," the minister said. "Will the children form in line and follow me upstairs? Children, we all know, have reserved seats tonight. The elders must take what is left."

Rachel stood between Gail Ross and Benny Jacobson in the line. Gail was one of the big girls and used perfume; Rachel could smell it. Benny kept bumping against her in the back and Rachel knew he meant to, but it did not matter tonight. Music began to play and the children marched up the stairs into the meetinghouse and sat down in the front pews, Gail at the end of one, Rachel beside her, and Benny next.

The tree filled the corner beyond Gail. It had been draped with strings of popcorn and cranberries hung droopingly, and with tinsel; and on the end of every branch swung a glittering ball. In among the decorations were packages wrapped in white and others in red tissue, red cheesecloth stockings full of candy and nuts, and toys with no coverings at all — a ship with sails, a harmonica, books, and dolls, and strings of beads. Every present had a label, and some — surely more than one! — read *Rachel Bradley*.

The entertainment came first. A quartet sang "Silent Night" and "God Rest Ye Merry, Gentlemen." Two girls recited poems, one of them in Miriam's place; she forgot very near the beginning and again toward the end, and had to be prompted. Then came the play in which Della took a part. Della was supposed to be an angel. She wore yards and yards of white and her hair hung down over her shoulders, yellow-brown and shiny, in big soft curls. She knelt beside a blue mountain with a star shining over it, and clasped her hands and tipped back her head with her eyes shut.

"It is sweet to be young, O God," Della said in her clear, happy voice. "May everybody in the world be young on Christmas Eve."

Della was beautiful. Rachel knew this. Her throat burned with knowing how beautiful Della was. She did not want to be sixteen years old herself; she wanted to stay small so that she could crawl in and out the cellar windows at home whenever she liked, and feel for the swing shelf with her toes; but she wished Della would be sixteen forever.

"Aw, angels don't pray," muttered Benny. "Do they, Gail? Do angels have to pray?"

Gail giggled.

Rachel pretended she did not care. She pretended she had not heard them. Della was her sister, and beautiful, and the blue mountain was not just a piece of blue cloth tacked on the wall, but really a blue mountain. The star was not just a painted star; if Della should put up her hand she could not reach the star, nearly. It would be millions of miles high.

A door off the platform opened, not the same door by which the minister entered every Sunday, but a different door — a magic door — and Santa Claus came in. He looked to Rachel quite as he had last year, still fat, still laughing, still dressed in red and white with his face almost hidden behind his beard. She did not notice that he was very tall, for Santa Claus.

"Well, now, that's my job," he said to Della, pulling off his gloves. "That's just what I'm for — to help everybody be young at Christmas."

"Indeed it is," the angel said. (Rachel had now forgotten that the angel was Della.) "And I am glad to leave it all to you. You have done the work well for hundreds of years."

Bowing, holding out her draperies at the sides, she backed away, smiling, and disappeared.

Santa Claus came down the steps to the tree. He seemed to Rachel for an instant to merge dizzily with it — red cheesecloth, red wool, silver tinsel, gray beard, green spruce, twinkling gray-green eyes — Christmas; the Christmas Eve social. She saw his hand reach for a package. What would the label say? She did not breathe.

"*I* know who it is *now*," Gail whispered. "I couldn't think at first. But of course it's Chuck Wiggin! That's his signet ring."

Rachel sat very still.

"Sure it is," Benny answered. "He makes a good one, don't he?"

"It's Santa Claus," Rachel said in a small voice.

The others looked at her.

"Say, she don't know," Gail exclaimed. "She thinks there is one. . . . Minnie! Ssss! Minnie! Rachel Bradley thinks there is a Santa Claus. . . . Sure, Rachel, that's old Santa all right; he's just getting his growth, that's all."

All the children laughed and looked at Rachel.

"I don't care," she said. "I don't either think — what you said. I knew it was Chuck Wiggin all the time."

After that Rachel sat quietly in her seat except when her name was called. Then she went up to take whatever was held out to her. Most of her presents were wrapped and she did not open them. The red coral bracelet she twisted between her fingers until Gail reached over and snapped it on her wrist; even then she did not look at it. When the others went downstairs, she went, too, and put on her coat and cap and gaiters and met Neal at the door. It was a long way home.

"Did you know who that was that took the things off the tree?" she asked as they turned into the yard at last.

Neal looked down at her.

"Sure," he said. "That was Santa Claus, wasn't it?"

"There isn't any Santa Claus," Rachel told him. "It was Chuck Wiggin."

Once inside the door, she spent a long time undoing her gaiters by the dim yellow light that crept into the entry from the kitchen. Only a part of her mind gave attention to the problem of pushing wide buttons through narrow buttonholes, and a still smaller part heeded what her mother was saying in the next room, but she was conscious of the sound of words.

"You folks back! You walked, did you? Well, I should like to know where Della is. She was riding, and that horse of Chuck Wiggin's goes like all possessed. She ought to have got here before you did."

"She's here," Neal said. "They're sitting out front."

"Sitting out front! This time of night! Cold as it is!"

Neal yawned and stretched.

"She won't freeze, don't worry."

"Well, I don't like the idea of it. What can she find to say to Chuck Wiggin so long? I don't know what folk's'll think, if any of 'em ride by. I'm half a mind to go to the door and call."

"Lord, Mother, let her have a little fun, can't you? It isn't very often there's anything going on —"

After a minute Mrs. Bradley spoke in a different tone.

"I know that, Neal. I know you don't either of you have anything like what I want you to. If you had any idea of the times I've begged your father to get us out of this place! If he'd try he could get a job carpentering in the village. He's as good a carpenter as he is a farmer, just exactly. Then he wouldn't have to keep you tied down to help him, and Della would be where she could get an education. I've always said she'd make a fine teacher, she's such a good hand with children. You'd every one of you get somewhere, if only you had a chance. But your father can't seem to see things the way I do."

Rachel heard a match flare at the end of the stove, and knew her father was in the room. Her mother was talking to him through Neal. She often did that, though usually through Rachel herself.

"I tell him," Mrs. Bradley said, "I tell him he'd be sorry if Della couldn't get graduated, now she's begun. But I don't know as he would. I don't know as he cares."

The outside door opened and Della came in, bringing a stir of snowy air. Rachel could see her quite plainly, but Della did not see Rachel. She was looking up over her shoulder at the person behind her.

"Come along," she was saying. "No, you've got to, Chuck. Do you think I'm going to tell them alone?"

The two went through the entry awkwardly, excitedly, brushing against each other, against Rachel and the doorframe. She could see them as they stood side by side in the kitchen, Della boldly holding Chuck's hand.

"Well, hello —" began Mrs. Bradley weakly.

"Hullo, Chuck, hullo," Will Bradley said. "Have a chair."

"I just brought Chuck in to help me tell you," Della said. "I guess you'll be surprised. We've decided to get married New Year's Day."

"Married!" cried Mrs. Bradley. "Della Bradley, you're nothing but a little girl. You're still in school —"

"No, I'm not," Della said. She stood away from Chuck now, her feet set apart, her back young and strong. She would win. Rachel knew that she would win, whether she was right or wrong. Della took what she wanted. "I've left school. I never meant to go back. I'm too old to go to school."

"Too old!"

"Yes, Mother, I'm too old."

"Well, what, will you tell me, is your husband going to do to support you?"

"I thought he could come here. You could use a big fellow like this, couldn't you, Father? He's worth three of Neal for haying and getting out wood. Then Neal can leave home and do whatever it is he wants to. You'll like that, Mother. Couldn't you use Chuck, Father?"

"Why, sure," Will Bradley answered. "Sure. I guess so."

"Well, you can't be married, Della," her mother cried. "I tell you, you can't. I won't let you. You're under age —"

Rachel did not listen any longer. She knew Della would win. She knew Della would marry this Chuck Wiggin who had been Santa Claus and bring him here to live. Nothing would ever be the same again.

She took off her shoes and tiptoed into the pantry, through the best bedroom and parlor and up the front stairs to the chamber she and Miriam and Della occupied together. It would not have been so bad if Miriam had been there, but Miriam was down in the sitting room with a cold. Rachel, too miserable even to shiver, pulled off her clothes and crawled into bed in the dark.

When she heard steps an hour or more later, she pretended to be asleep, but everything went suddenly so quiet that she peeked between her lashes. Della had set the lamp on the bureau, and now stood in her new brown dress, her hands clasped loosely before her, smiling at her reflection in the looking glass.

Della had won.

CHAPTER IV

hristmas 1918

Cynthia has been staying in North Hawley with her sister-in-law and small niece while her brother Hugh was in the Army overseas. This has been an opportunity for her to go to high school, but she has found it impossible to identify with her contemporaries there because of her intense feeling of involvement in the war and in the experience of fighting men and their families. Hugh, since his return, is concerned that she may have missed the joys of youth which he wanted her to know and which, in part, he has fought to assure. Betty Dixon has been Cynthia's only close friend of her own age in North Hawley, and is

now coming with her to visit the isolated valley where both Cynthia and Hugh grew up.

"There is the Valley," Cynthia said.

A year ago she had ridden out of it through a flurry of snow. Riding in she found the yellow fall stubble still uncovered but frozen in the fields. Willow branches beside the brook clattered together stiffly, and the ice below looked full three inches thick. The sun had set in a purplish film behind Jefferson Peak, Mount John, Two-Headed Hill, Little Two-Head, and Second Jefferson Peak. There were no stars. Only three lights shone at night in the Valley, and they set wide apart and lonely looking, like signals on a railroad through the woods.

"Say, you must have ghosts out here."

Cynthia started. For an instant she had imagined herself alone, walking along the Valley road with her skates slung over her back. She had forgotten that Betty Dixon of North Hawley rode beside her on the back seat of a wagon, while her stepfather sat in front with new brown leather suitcases and magazines and candy and all the travel-helps girls use on trains. Betty's curl-framed face hardly seemed familiar. Cynthia did not know what she had said. But Mr. Anderson was turning to answer, holding his worn fur collar away from his mouth.

"Well, we have dancing teakettles," he chuckled.

It would be the old story of the Valley's beloved and wicked Uncle Enoch who had frightened all the children and the simpler grown-ups by his elderly mischief years ago. Cynthia knew it word for word.

They passed the Silsbury place. The little house had sunk into itself, leaving only the old lilac bushes as a frail and passing monument. The Greenward house had now become the Valley ruins, its windows broken out, a hole in its roof, and its front door ajar. Cynthia could remember going there with her mother to visit in the evening, and falling asleep on a green couch with Don and a water spaniel while the grown-ups listened to music which never failed to begin with a voice that half roused the children, "Edison Record!" Old Mr. Greenward had been entirely bald. His wife had had a favorite chair in which all visitors had known better than to sit, a little reed rocker with a tidy on the back. Now the rocker and the green couch and the Greenwards were gone. Another group of Valley eight-year-olds peered fearfully in at the yawning windows and sometimes ventured through the door, as Cynthia and Don and Lollie and Tom had once done at the old Silsbury place, hoping, like Betty, for ghosts, but cautious of falling plaster. The Valley had changed in a year.

But it was not much changed. The near hills still looked fat and green, the far ones thin and blue. The road turned aside for the same three-cornered boulder, passed under the twin maples Uncle Enoch as a boy had set out, and grew sandy for a stretch at the foot of Perry's Lane. Two squares of yellow light in the white wall of the Anderson house meant the kitchen; the two adjoining revealed the dining room; the black expanse beyond showed where the stairs went up; and the one light on the end was the back parlor window, illumined for expected guests. The horse of his own accord turned in among the ash trees and drew the wagon into the yard, the muscles of his back spreading and arching for the steep rise of ground. He was old white Roxy, for whom Cynthia and Lollie had made birthday cakes of braided grass and sugar and quartered apples. Mr. Anderson pulled up on the reins.

"Hold on a minute, Roxy. Here we are, girls. Look natural to you, Cynthia?"

A door opened. Two children and a boy and a woman with a shawl over her head came running out. Cynthia climbed down from the wagon, was kissed, and went in, one of a crowd. The house confused her. The row of hooks on which she had used to hang her outdoor clothes was much too low, and the highest row of all none too high for her. In the living room a sewing machine stood where it seemed to her a toy box should have been. The place she had meant to take at the table was already filled by a small, black-haired girl sitting self-consciously upright. The food at supper had tastes that delighted her, but she could not eat much. People kept urging her; she shook her head and smiled. She was asked whether she had seen the ocean, what had happened at the Durands' in North Hawley when Hugh had arrived the week before, if she had noticed many gold stars from the train windows. Later, back in the living room, she was asked to choose the selection that Mary Ellen should play on the piano, to comment on the progress Jack had made in his first reader, to see the new rabbits, to stroke the old cat. The room seemed warm and there were many faces close together.

"You girls have had a hard day," someone said. "I think you'd better get a good long night's sleep."

Cynthia went upstairs, finding banisters and doorknobs without looking for them. A lamp had been left on a bureau. A blue oil heater lit up the opposite side of the room with yellow and gray checkers. The wallpaper was new, and the braided rugs and the spread on the bed; but wallpaper could not disguise the bulging circle which once had been an air register, or the spot on the floor where ink had long ago been spilled. On the plastering in the cupboard Cynthia had once counted off the days before she would be nine and receive a promised sled. The head board of the bedstead still had the crack which was the result of children's jumping. Below the crack, huddled among the covers, lay Betty Dixon of North Hawley.

"What *are* you staring at, Cy? Hurry up and get in here. I'm cold."

"Cold even in bed?" asked Cynthia.

Her voice sounded strange to her, as if she had not heard it for a long time. She could remember having spoken only once since the horse had stopped in the yard. "This is Betty Dixon." She hoped she had said more than that. The light flickered as a door blew shut somewhere downstairs. Standing on one foot, she unlaced the other shoe.

"I like it though," said Betty, shivering. "It's the first time I ever slept on a featherbed. It's puffy. It's fun. I like everything here, Cynthia. Really I do. I'm so glad you asked me to come. I'm simply crazy about the Valley and the house and everything."

"Are you?" asked Cynthia. The shoe was nearly off.

"Yes," said Betty, "and I just love your mother. I told her so when I said good-night. I simply couldn't help it, she's so sweet. Honestly, I just love her."

"You do?" asked Cynthia.

She dropped the shoe and turned toward the bed. Betty was nodding energetically, her curls flounced over the white pillow. Cynthia could imagine how easy it had been for Betty to say it. Everything was easy for Betty, who never seemed to have any feelings that she could not understand and express. Cynthia herself, at home for the first time in nearly a year, could not remember how she had said good-night, or whether she had said it at all.

"You wait a minute," she said hurriedly. "I have to go downstairs."

She did not stop to put on her shoe again but went, one leather heel and one stockinged toe, as fast as she could to the kitchen.

Her mother was setting bread behind the stove, a yellow print apron tied over her old-fashioned blue taffeta dress, the tins bright in her hands. Her hair was like Cynthia's, heavy and fair, and she wore it coiled softly just back of the top of her head. Cynthia remembered now the way she brushed it in the morning, stooping over from the waist and bringing up the strokes from the back and sides and front, then straightening, rather flushed, and twisting the thick mass quickly until it could be caught with bone pins. It left her ears bare, and they were small, and had been pierced many years ago. Cynthia knew the story of the roll of velvet held behind each pink lobe in turn, the needle thrust through, and the bit of silk threaded in and moved every day to keep the hole open. The thought gave Cynthia the same old sympathetic twinge for that young Ellen Durand of 1890. Mrs. Anderson laid a bread cloth across her pans and hung a blanket where it would keep the drafts away.

"Mother," said Cynthia.

"What? . . . Goodness, dear, I didn't hear you coming. What is it? Need more bedding?"

"No. I don't know. Mother, maybe I haven't acted as if I was glad to be home. Of course I am. You ought to know — I can't always *say* —"

"Cynthia, come over here and sit down. Why, you're in your stocking foot! Of course I know you're glad to be home. What in the world made you think I didn't?"

They were on the couch together. Mrs. Anderson had wrapped Cynthia's foot in her apron and held it against her side. Cynthia sat disjointedly, looking at the corner of her handkerchief which her fingers alternately smoothed and pleated.

"Well, but I mean, I don't know how to talk about it. It isn't as if it didn't mean anything."

"No, of course not, Cynthia."

"It gets me mixed up. Some things are the same and some are different. And some ways I'm the same and other ways I'm different. And they don't go together."

"Yes, I know, dear."

Cynthia raised her eyes in exasperation.

"Mother, you don't. What makes you keep saying you know, when you don't? I mean the war hasn't been in here at all, and where I've been that's all there was. And it's almost a year. And I'm growing up so fast, too. . . . No, mother, you *don't* know how it is."

"I don't suppose I do," her mother said humbly. She covered Cynthia's foot a little closer.

"I've thought so many things since I went away," said Cynthia, scowling and pulling at her handkerchief, "that

never came into my head here. Now I'm back there
doesn't seem to — well, be any place for them, kind of
. . . Where I was, I made a place, but here there isn't
any."

"Well, you're going back, you know, dear," her mother
ventured. "This is just your vacation, isn't it? I understood from Hugh's letter that they want to keep you with
them for your whole high school course. Didn't they talk
to you about it?"

Cynthia looked at her mother.

"Yes, but do you want me to?"

"Of course I do."

"Don't you miss me?"

"Yes. We miss you."

"Then I'll stay."

"No. You'll come home vacations."

"Oh, Mother —"

Cynthia turned and knelt on the couch, watching her
mother's mouth and eyes. They did not waver.

"I want to," said Cynthia. "But that doesn't mean I
don't like the Valley more than any other place in the
world."

"Yes, dear. The Valley is home. But you know the way
I always think of it? Homes aren't meant to *stay* in;
they're to *begin* in, and to come back to just every once in
a while."

Cynthia had forgotten that her mother talked like this
sometimes, kindly and from a mysterious height of experience, like ministers and teachers. She was not sure she
liked it, but, as if it had been an oracle, she probed the
depths.

"Does everybody feel like this, coming back? As if
there isn't any place? Not room enough?"

"No. I think that's only because you thought of it as for
always. There is just as much room as you always had,
and that is enough for a little while, but not for all the
time."

Cynthia considered, and changed the subject.

"You really didn't get much of the war in here, did you?"

"No. Not much."

"Mary Ellen will hardly remember it when she grows up."

"That's what your father says."

"She's lucky. Hugh's Rae won't either. Rae's awfully sweet, Mother. But she isn't so strong as Mary Ellen."

"Louise writes that she's frail. She may grow out of it."

"They're certainly lucky, though. I know a man who says, 'The best way is never to have lived through a war!' . . . I thought for a while I would marry that soldier I was writing to, but I don't believe now I shall."

"I wouldn't think about marrying for a long while yet. You have a fine chance for an education. And you want to have good times."

"That's what he said."

Curling her feet inside her skirt Cynthia slid down until her head rested on her mother's lap. Mrs. Anderson unbraided the long plait of hair and shook it out.

"Goodness, it is as heavy as mine, Cy."

"Mmm."

"Don't hurry about doing it up. It may give you headaches. They say short hair is coming in for older girls. If it does, you might have yours cut dutch. It used to be becoming that way when you were little."

"Wouldn't it seem funny? For a grown-up person, I mean?"

"I don't know. Your grandmother wore hers 'docked' when she was a girl. I've seen pictures of her."

"Did she?"

The room grew cooler. The faint smell of geranium leaves and food was spiced by the strong odor of yeast from the rising bread. The sounds of snapping nails and whistling wind and a mountain cat roving the woods were the ones with which Cynthia had gone to sleep every December since her earliest memory.

"Well, Cy, we'd better go to bed. What will Betty think?"

Cynthia sat up.

"I'm hungry, Mother."

"What do you want? I could get a chicken sandwich."

"Yes, and a glass of milk. And is there any cake?"

"Sponge."

"Oh, that's what I like best."

"I know you always did. That's why I made it."

They sat down together close to the stove. The cake was thick and very yellow. Nothing had tasted so good to Cynthia for months, not even the Armistice Day banana splits or the banquet with which Louise had welcomed Hugh home from overseas. Crumbs dropped on the rug. The cat came stretching from beneath the stove and sniffed at them.

"There! I came near forgetting to put you out, Fuzzy."

Cynthia took her dishes into the pantry and noticed there the iron sink which she had cleaned with kerosene surely a thousand times. The kitchen floor shook a little as always, with her weight. The backstairs door had swelled and stuck. She jerked it.

"Good night," she said, and paused. "I'll tell you, Mother. I wish you'd have Mary Ellen sit somewhere else at meals while I'm here."

Mrs. Anderson nodded, peering at her bread.

"Mary Ellen and Jack can go right back to their little table by the door."

"I just thought —" began Cynthia.

"It's your place," said her mother.

The next morning the chamber windows were buried deep in frost. The children came in caps and jackets to call the girls and sat like muffled satyrs on the footboard. Betty threw pillows at them. Cynthia rubbed her

eyes and reached for Jack to kiss him behind the ear, but
he wriggled and she let him go. Then they all threw pillows. It was fair because while Jack and Mary Ellen could
run about, Betty and Cynthia had the blankets to protect
their heads. They ducked and aimed, shivering and shrieking. Only Don's blow on the door brought them to their
senses.

"Hey, what's going on in there, you kids? You up, Cy?
Look, Mother's holding breakfast and I'm half starved.
It's after eight o'clock. You know Lollie's coming over
here this morning, too."

"Lollie! Oh, *is* she, Don? This *morning?* . . . Oh,
glory, you get out of here, you infants. Go on . . . Tell
Mother we'll be right down . . . Say, Betty, just wait till
you see Loll. You'll like her. She's a peach. Really she is.
Say, where's my other shoe?"

Ten minutes later Cynthia slid into her old place at the
table. She was warmed through once more. An open oven
door had revealed a hot mince pie, flaky and bubbling,
ready to be eaten when the fried potato and bacon and
muffins had been finished. The room looked small and full
of many familiar things, chairs and dishes and magazines
and the picture of red apples in a little boy's cap. The
sky was silvery gray; there might be snow for Christmas.
Mrs. Anderson passed plates this way and that, smiling.
Mr. Anderson had begun for Betty's benefit another Valley story. The children chattered at their small table by
the door. Cynthia interrupted it all without knowing she
was going to.

"Oh," she said, "it's great to be home!" Then quickly
because everyone was looking at her, "More bacon than
that, please, Mother. Three slices anyway."

Lollie came at ten o'clock. Cynthia and Betty watched
her making her way across the frozen furrows of the
ploughed back field. She had not grown even an inch in the
year; she would be small like her mother's people. Her
pale braid had blown over her shoulder and reached half-

way to the high waist of her green velvet coat, a brief
little pigtail of hair. She looked up at the window and recognized Cynthia. Her head tipped and she smiled.

"You wait here," Cynthia told Betty suddenly. "I'm going to the door."

When they came in, Lollie's coat and cap and leggings
had been left behind. Cynthia's arm lay across Lollie's
blue plaid shoulders. Lollie's hands dug into her pockets.

"Lollie, this is Betty Dixon," Cynthia said. "She's in
my class at high school. I brought her up to show her the
Valley."

"Do you think you're going to like it?" asked Lollie.
Her eyes fell under Betty's cordial gaze.

"Crazy about it!" Betty said. "Where do you go to
school? What class are you in? Sophomore, like us?"

"I don't go to school. Not this year," Lollie answered.
"I finished up the grades last spring."

Lollie had a soft voice and soft eyes. She looked at
Cynthia. Cynthia took up a gilt button that dangled from
Lollie's sleeve and twisted it in an excess of affection.

"Oh, Lollie, I wish you could go to school with me."

"I don't know," said Lollie tranquilly. "I don't care a
lot about school, you know."

"No, but with me, I mean. We always had such a lot of
fun. Didn't we? Remember that day you wrote a letter to
your mother, in school, and said you could have spelled a
word Jinny missed?"

"Yes, and the teacher found it on the floor. She said I
shouldn't tell stories on my schoolmates."

"You cried."

"I guess she let me go home, didn't she?"

"Yes, I took you. Old Mr. Poli gave us a ride. Remember Mr. Poli?"

"He still drives a wood team."

"Does he, really, Lollie? Does he still sing all the way
up and down the road?"

"That about 'the young man with a babe on his knee' —"

"Yes, *that* one —"

Once or twice Cynthia glanced at Betty. The glance seemed to say, "I ought to explain this to you. But even if I did you couldn't understand. Lollie is the only one who knows. Lollie may not like school. Lollie may not be cute like you. But Lollie's *Lollie*." Betty did not mind. After a while she went out to wipe the dishes for Mrs. Anderson, leaving Cynthia and Lollie by themselves. Betty, too, had had childhood friends.

When she returned the others had made plans for a skating party to be held on Christmas Eve.

It was like all other Valley skating parties. Clouds covered the sky, but even on nights when it was clear the moon took too long out-topping the hills to be of any use to the skaters. The meadows lay chilled and dim, with the black brook, hugged by the whispering willows, coiling through its heart. But at the edge of dark boys and girls bore down upon it from three directions, their supper lights bright yellow points behind them. Their heels crunched on the frozen stubble. Steel clanged against steel under their arms. They shouted greetings back and forth across the intervening spaces.

"Hullo, Tom!"

"That you, Cy?"

"Hey there, Raymond! Where's Jinny?"

"Oo-ouch! I'm in the ditch!"

"Hullo, you over there!"

They brought bags of coarse marsh-grass hay in their arms, and drew boxes of dry wood on their sleds. The boys crouched at the edge of the ice and laid a fire. Lollie poured on oil. It chugged and gurgled at the nozzle of her can. The smell was queer on the winter air. Tonight no one quarreled over who should drop the match, for Betty was the Valley's guest.

"Here," Tom Welsh said. "If yours don't light it, Cynthia's turn next." He scratched the match on a bit of kindling and offered both to her.

"Oh, good! Now don't anybody blow it out on me," cried Betty.

Nobody in the Valley would have thought of such a thing. They stood about in silence while she knelt, very small in her fur jacket and many pleated skirt. She looked intent. The best place for a match was between the hay and a small dry stick on the sheltered side. She tucked hers in there and shielded it with the bit of kindling.

"That'll burn," said Cynthia with regret.

It did. The red flame licked and lapped at the dry stick and rose above it. The hay sizzled and curled. Fire leaped into the wind.

"Say, I didn't know as it would!" triumphed Betty.

"You done fine," Raymond Perry said admiringly.

They all admired Betty, but Cynthia was one of their own. Cynthia used the quickest way to put on skates. She knew the curves of the brook and did not need to be guided. On the expeditions after wood with which to keep the fire going it was Cynthia who led the way on skates across the bare ground, gathered the first armful, and sped back along the ice, cracking tough branches across her knees. No girl in the Valley had ever skated so well as Cynthia. No girl ever would, or so Lollie thought, and Jinny and Tom and even Don. They watched her, skated with her, skated behind her, raced her.

"Try this one, Cy?"

"Bet you can't cut so close a circle, though —"

"Honest, haven't you been on skates since you left here?"

But they were polite to Betty. Tom and Don and both the Perry boys steered her with crossed hands in and out around the bends. Tom dried her mittens by the fire. She liked Tom best, and he would have liked her if he had dared, but he was not used to curly headed girls who talked so fast. Besides he belonged to Lollie. He had known that since he was ten. It made him very short and casual with her, though every cent he owned had gone yesterday to buy her hair ribbons for Christmas. A brown and a red and a flowered one. Brown and red he had seen Betty wear, and the flowered one was to boot. Yes, Tom belonged to Lollie. He meant she should have everything someday.

"Let's eat!" called Cynthia. "Let's eat! Let's eat!"

She stooped low and set off up the ice toward the fire that still lit up the fields and tinged the sky. Her arms stretched wide. Her skirts blew out. She was making a tremendous speed. The boys raced after but could not quite catch up.

"I had too good a start on you," she said.

"Say, though, you've got a dandy swing," Tom told her.

Their cheeks were stiff. They beat their arms and hands beside the fire. The timid, faithful Jinny had stood there stamping all the evening, and now passed out sandwiches and apples, and coffee in tin cups. Betty and Lollie came gliding up together, hand in hand, and stopped one on each side of Cynthia. She was much taller than either, and stood easily on her skates. They swayed a little, now and then catching at her arms. She smiled at them. They were very different and yet to her somewhat alike.

"What makes you teeter so, Lollie?" Tom demanded.

Reminded of herself, Lollie moved and nearly lost her balance. Everybody laughed.

"Leave her alone," Betty said. "I'm teetering too."

Don and Wesley Perry divided the last sandwich. The fire was dying down and the girls dropped apples into the red coals. Raymond caught Cynthia's hands and whirled her away down the brook, even across the Great Hole where as children they had never been allowed to go. Raymond's grip was hard. They did not talk, but skated as good dogs run, skimmingly. When they came back, the apples had finished baking. Wet sweet pulp sprayed out on their faces as they ate. Don cut a hole through the ice and each in turn lay down beside it to dip in his hands and scrub his mouth.

"Take your cups along," called Tom, "and bring back water to throw on the fire."

"What's the matter?" Wesley jeered. "Think the ice will burn?"

"The grass is dry," said Tom.

As he spoke the first snowflakes fell. But, all the same, water was splashed over the winking coals. Valley natives were good scouts. By the time they had finished, a thin white film covered the ice. While the girls tied bundles to the sleds, the boys made scrolls and paths and circles along the brook. The air was thick with the storm.

"We're going to have snow for Christmas, aren't we?"

"Isn't it great!"

"Big flakes too."

"It's good we got our skating in; this would be heavy to sweep off."

"I like snow for Christmas though."

The boys came back. It was impossible to tell them apart through the dark. Cold fingers fumbled with straps and buckles. Tired heels gratefully gripped the ground. The party was over. Each skater set off across the fields toward the point of light, dimmer now, which owned him. In this way families were united. Tom, who lived at the Grants', walked beside Lollie as if he were her brother. But he was not her brother. He thought of this, and secretly felt pleased. The Perrys sang as they went, "It's the last long mile," but nobody remembered it was a war song. Don, pulling a sled, made a trail for his sister and her friend, and thought himself gallant.

"Good night."

"Good night."

"Come over tomorrow and see what I get."

"Hope you have a merry Christmas."

"You come over, too."

"Good night."

Each figure took on an armor of white and blended with the snowy fields. Voices and sounds of footsteps died away. The patterns the boys had laid upon the ice already were blotted out. Down below the water still ran cold and black, with slender fish drowsy in the current. The willows on each side joined fingers with those on the other and swayed forward and back in the patient, peaceful dance of winter.

"Gee, I wish you'd always be like this, Cy," Betty was saying in a muffled voice that even Don could not have heard.

Cynthia bent her head.

"Like what?"

"Like this. Like you've been here. Not like you were all through the fall. Not as if you were shutting yourself away."

"Oh," Cynthia said. She flushed but the dark concealed her. "I will, all right."

"Will you, honestly?"

"Of course I will."

"Because if you are, you'll be chosen queen of the school festival in May as sure as anything."

"I won't. You will."

"No, *you* will."

They laughed. It was pleasant to know each other through and through again. They were excited to discover that while both wanted to be chosen, both also wanted the other to be chosen. This was friendship. Still Cynthia had one thought which Betty did not share. She was surprised at it, wondered where it came from, and let it go. It was not important.

"If I am, I hope Paul will be there to see me."

Don opened the kitchen door, and the three stepped through, brushing off the snow. The lamp had been turned low. The room was shadowy and silent. Children and grown-ups alike were asleep. Beyond the living-room door gilt balls and tinsel on a green tree caught the faint light. Two long-legged, short-footed stockings hung brimming behind the stove. The house was rich with the scent of meat and spice and fruit and popcorn, but above all the strong, live smell of spruce. Snow tinkled against the windows, filling the Valley. It was Christmas Eve.

hristmas 1922

From a journal kept by the author while a college student.

What a Christmas! I think it began early in December when the telephone was put in. My mother called me up at my dorm that night, and had Grammy there to speak to me, and of course my father came and talked. They were all excited, and so was I. It was installed in the back entry, to muffle a little the sound of the bell. There is a great deal of ringing for we are the sixteenth family on the line. Everyone rings one long for Central, and the party numbers go from two through six (long ones), from eleven through sixteen (one long and so many shorts), and twenty-one through twenty-five (two long and so many shorts). Ours is twenty-five. The last family to come on before us had a choice between sixteen and twenty-five and we are pleased that they chose sixteen, but we don't understand why. We think two longs and five shorts are much easier to count than one long and six shorts. We have learned that if there are more than two longs we can stop counting, also if shorts begin after one long. Though unless we have something more interesting to do we count anyway, because we know who every number belongs to; and we have also now learned how different people ring, so we can usually figure out who is calling whom. Grammy is likely to say, "There's Em calling Em Nason. Listen in and see how they are. You know Em thought she had a cold coming on this morning." Or my mother will say, "That's Central ringing Pearl. Probably her brother calling from Fall River." And when thirteen is rung about nine o'clock at night we exchange knowing smiles, because that means — (a young man) didn't go up the road to see — (a girl) tonight and is calling her instead for one of their interminable conversations in code, which always sets many receivers to clicking up and down.

These are the first blanks I have put in this journal. There will be more, and those to come are by special request. I told the senior English assistant that I am keeping a journal.

He asked, "Do you put people's names in it?"

I said of course I did.

He said, "I wouldn't want my name in anybody's journal."

I replied airily, "I can't think of any reason why it would be in mine."

He said, "So I can take that as a guarantee that it won't be?"

Thus pressed, I declared that he certainly could. And I

am a woman of my word. I am not sure whether he really meant he wouldn't want me to use his name, or secretly hoped I would. I'm not going to, anyway.

Now back to Christmas and the telephone. For us that telephone bell has joined sleigh bells and the chimes of Christmas records on the Victrola as the background music of this glorious season. For yes, my parents gave my grandmother a Victrola for Christmas, and Harold and Jennie and I and ever so many other people gave her records. She has McCormack records, Sousa records, Harry Lauder records, and several hymns. The one we all like most and play most is "The Holy City." We often wonder now how we used to get so much pleasure from the graphophone and the cylinder records. Christmas afternoon we played both machines, to compare, and the graphophone sounds so harsh, so tinny, it really isn't music at all. And what did we find so funny in "Uncle Jock"? Just the same, I miss that morning-glory horn on the old phonograph, and there is an excitement for me still in that familiar "Edi-*son Record,* Columbia Military *Band,*" with every syllable *snapped* out, that is equaled only by my excitement when I see a stage curtain going up. . . . Now the Victrola has banished the graphophone to the shed chamber, but we stored it carefully, the machine locked in its case, the records on their sides in their little round, covered boxes and strapped into a canvas valise, the horn and its stand inside an old flour barrel. I told my mother that I want to bring it downstairs and play it every Christmas.

She said I reminded her of the time she got up a Larkin order to buy me a big doll with real hair, my father made a doll's bed and spring, she made a featherbed, pillow, sheets, slips, a quilt, coverlet and matching canopy. They set the doll in her pretty clothes on the bed under the Christmas tree in the corner of the sitting room. When they opened the door to me Christmas morning I took one look, cried, "Where's my Margery? I want my Margery!" — and ran to get the doll I had had since I was two years old, and who had been dropped and broken and mended several times, whose elastic was sadly stretched, and who at the moment was wearing no clothes at all.

I told my mother I remembered that Christmas morning and knew why I had done that. It was because the new doll was so beautiful I wanted to run to her, but felt instantly that this would be disloyal to Margery and hurt her very much. I thought the new doll would not care yet whether I loved her or not; Margery was the one who would grieve unless convinced at the outset that I would never love another doll as I loved her.

"I was thinking only of dolls then," I told my mother. "I wasn't thinking of you. . . . And of course it isn't the same with the machines. I know the old phonograph doesn't mind being in the shed chamber. And I certainly like listening to the Victrola much better. But, like Margery, the old phonograph has a place that nothing else can ever take."

Our tree this year is in the parlor. I rode into the woods on the horse sleds with my father to get it. It is the tallest and bushiest we have ever had. The top touches the ceiling. To decorate it we used not only all the old ornaments and the usual strings of popcorn and cranberries and gilded nuts but a dozen new ornaments and yards and yards of tinsel which we bought in Dover on our last shopping trip. How it shines and glitters! We had it decorated three days before Christmas. It sets in a pail of water (hidden by balsam branches) and we shall keep it up until New Year's. After the fire in the parlor stove goes out at night, it gets very cold; when we build the fire again the next morning the fragrance of the tree begins to spread through the house, and I remember the way the district schoolhouse used to smell on the nights of our Christmas parties.

Harold and Jennie came on Christmas Eve and had Auntie's room, so the house was full again for Christmas. After supper Harold sat — the way he likes to — astraddle a chair in front of the open oven door with his folded arms resting on the back and talked with my father, who was smoking a cigar by the porch window (it was the first time I ever saw my father smoke in the house), while my mother, Jennie, and I cleared the table and did the dishes. I thought how fortunate it was that Harold had become a man before my grandfather went, and that he had brought us Jennie before Auntie went. There are as many Hasty men in our family as before, and as many Hasty women. It is only Hasty children we don't have now. And they will come.

Later on Christmas Eve Jennie and I sat on the sitting-room floor with disc records in our laps, telling Grammy the names for her to choose among, and handing her choices to Harold, who put each on, wound up the machine, set the needle, turned the starter, then sat down next to Grammy and held her hand while her music played. My mother sat in her rocker with hands clasped in her lap, listening. My father, passing, bending down, spoke low in her ear. I saw his forehead touch the pinned-up blue-black coil of her hair, above the silver pompadour. She looked up at him and smiled and nodded. Until this Christmas, she has always been very pale and slight, but now suddenly her cheeks are filling out and there is a soft pink which never leaves them but sometimes, in heat or excitement, deepens to the color of wild strawberries. Her skin, as always, is so fine textured, so translucent that the color glows and you are bound to think of rose petals. My father went on to the kitchen; between records we heard the clink of glasses, and he came back with Moxie for all of us and a plateful of Lizy Ann dropcakes, which are made by a very old recipe: big, soft, chewy spice cookies, with crumbled nuts and seeded raisins in them. The nuts are from trees on the abandoned farm where my mother and her mother lived with her grandparents after her father died. Harold goes up to get them for her every fall. She says no other nuts have the same flavor.

Since my grandfather is not here to build the fire in the cookstove in the early morning, my mother does it, but not at daybreak as he did. While my father is still sleeping, she slips out of bed and into a heavy bathrobe and slippers, and comes downstairs through the cold front hall to the sitting room, where in this weather there is still heat in the chunk stove. She opens the drafts in the funnel and below the door, puts in dry pine edgings and small applewood sticks, and the flames rumble until she closes the drafts partway and goes into the kitchen. Sometimes there are still red embers in the cookstove, too, for we are more prodigal with wood than we used to be. If not, she puts in kindling — chips and edgings — and sprinkles them well with kerosene oil; we are also more prodigal with oil now, as with eggs in cakes and cream for whipping. As soon as she can half-close the cookstove drafts and has the tea-kettle on, she comes back to the sitting room to bathe and dress, having left everything ready the night before, including a pan of water on the top of the chunk stove, which has an ornamental top on a hinge so that it can be turned back to leave a level surface.

My sleeping place is the bed-couch in the sitting room out of which Grammy's bedroom opens. I wake when she opens the door of the chunk stove. As soon as she closes it she turns to see if my eyes are open.

This morning I whispered "Merry Christmas!" as she turned.

She whispered back, "Oh, no fair! I should have said it when I came into the room, but you were *so* sound asleep I couldn't bear to. I thought maybe your grandmother had a restless night."

"No. She didn't ring at all."

"I didn't hear the bell, I know. But somehow I don't when you're here. When you aren't, it seems as if I stay half-awake all night long, listening for it. Anyway, Merry Christmas to you, and many of them!"

"No need to whisper on my account," Grammy called. "I'm awake. Merry Christmas, you two!"

We called back Merry Christmases to her, and my mother went in and put up her shade, saying the sun was coming up in a sky as pink as May's.

"No need to whisper on anybody's account," my mother said, as she finished dressing. "Jump up quick. Hop up, jump up, pretty little yellow bird! I'm going to call Harold and Jennie now."

With the stove poker she reached up and opened the register in the ceiling above the stove.

"Merry Christmas, Harold! Jennie!" she called. "Warmth coming up! Gladie'll be at your door with hot water in about ten minutes. Ham and eggs and hot mince pie for breakfast!"

Jennie's "Merry Christmas, Mrs. Hasty!" came prompt and clear. Harold's "Merry Christmas, Muddie," was slow, slurred, and muffled.

My mother glanced at me and laughed.

"What sleepyheads our menfolks are!" she said. "When you go up, pour your father's hot water right into the washbowl and tell him it will be cool enough to use by the time he gets to it, as cold in five minutes as if it had come straight from the well. He won't shave until after breakfast anyway. But I suppose Harold always does nowadays."

He didn't today, though. And after breakfast we wouldn't let them because we didn't want to wait any longer to go in to the tree. I must say they didn't protest much. I think men feel most loved when their women accept them unshaven. So as they all sat around the finest Christmas tree we ever had and I passed out the fruit of it, my father's face had a ruddy-gold stubble and my brother's olive skin had darker shadows. . . . I think they were as eager to open the gifts or see them opened as we were. I remembered when we children had to be satisfied with the contents of our long, black Christmas stockings until my father and grandfather had come back from a trip with the sleds for a load of cordwood, and then had had their dinner; because I *would* not have the tree touched until we were all together. . . . Though I think now that the process of distribution was tedious for my grandfather, who made no gifts and cared to receive nothing except the essentials which might have been provided any day, and that it was embarrassing for my father and mother, who knew my grandfather sat there at best forbearing, at worst disapproving of Christmas indulgences.

No one was bored here today, and no one was disapproving, though we all gave and received more than we ever had before. All gifts were wrapped in bright paper which we folded carefully after opening, and tied with ribbons which we rolled smoothly into balls — as we have always kept twine — to be put away for use again next Christmas.

Afterward we had roast pork with apple sauce as well as roast chicken with cranberry sauce, for dinner, with mashed potatoes (beaten up with cream), squash and creamed onions, coffee, pumpkin pie with whipped cream on top (I really like it better without, so we left it off mine: I don't like butter either — no dairy products, really), and the prime sponge cake Jennie had brought, which we all say is the best cake we ever tasted.

After more music and more talk and more admiration of all we had which was new, Harold and Jennie went home just before dark. Our supper was whatever each of us (except Grammy who had a tray) wanted to take of what was left from dinner, under a cheesecloth cover, on the kitchen table. Why does everything taste better eaten from your hand when you are standing up?

Tonight the telephone has rung many times, with everyone up and down the road wanting to hear about their neighbors' Christmases and to tell about theirs. Everyone knew there could be no secrets tonight, so often there were five or six families on at the same time, joining in the revelations, exclamations, and exchange of thanks for cards or little gifts sent and received. Those who have children in school still have school Christmas parties, and now we know that those on The Line have telephone Christmas parties.

At last everyone else is asleep, and I am sleepy. Mine is the only light in sight except that of the stars. Some other night I'll write of the not-quite-three weeks between the Thanksgiving holidays and the beginning of Christmas vacation. Among my gifts was a pair of pajamas my mother made for me of white seersucker trimmed in black and white plaid gingham with red braid. I am going to get into them and lie in the dark and think about all that is new in my life lately. That is, I'll think about it as long as I can stay awake.

CHAPTER VI

Christmas 1925

Mark Shaw's first wife was Minnie Foote, and George, Ed, Lize, Jen, and Olly were their children; also Ralph who became an aviator and went down with his plane last summer. Cora is Mark's second wife, Lois May and Bun her children by her first marriage. John is Mark's and Cora's son. Mil is George's wife, Margaret is Ed's wife, and Stan, a Polish boy recently arrived in the neighborhood, is courting Jen. There are five Shaw grandchildren.

After supper, on Christmas Eve, Mark Shaw went into the yard for the full-branched balsam which had been left

for good keeping in a snowbank by the shed since the day
a week ago when he brought it from the woods on the top
of his load. Coming back, he stopped by the steps, shaking
the snow off the tree, and looked through the window at
the family.

They were all at home, every one. George sat smoking
and talking to Stan who had a bit of white wood in his
hand and was cutting notches in it with his knife. It was a
thing to notice how even George, as well as all the rest,
had changed as time went on in his unfriendly feeling
about this man with a dark skin and a long name. Now he
was Stan. Ed stood at the tank end of the stove shelling
popping corn, grinding two ears together between his
palms. Ed was strong for all he was so lean and lank, and
strength grew in him every day now he had a son to think
of, another Ed come after him. Olly shook the popper
harder and faster than there was any need, and jerked his
head a little with the motion of his arm. But he was stead-
ier than he had once been, more easy in his ways; it was not
so hard to manage to make talk with him, and he had
more to say himself; he knew about the mountains and the
lakes, even deserts and the prairie country, and he would
be a lawyer in good time, like Minnie's Uncle Jeff. A
strange way to do it might seem, but his way and reason-
able enough when looked at from all sides; not everybody
laid his plan like everybody else. Lize and Lois May were
wrapping boxes at the table. They had fine clothes and
curly hair and shining fingernails, and the paper they used
was gold color and the ribbon wide and red; it looked extravagant but they were doing well and made good pay,
both of them. Mil and Cora Shaw sat by stringing popcorn and cranberries, talking fast as women will, with
quick changes on their faces every word or two; Cora
looked brighter and more cheerful than she had in years,
but Mil was going gray again and getting big; there
would be another mouth for George to see to; he must
learn to think less of that pipe and more of working; five

was too many for a laggard and this George would come
to understand; he was a young man yet. Margaret, out of
her room for the first time, sat in a sheltered corner by the
stove holding the baby on her lap; young Ed was a likely
child; he took a stout grip on a finger; he would do. Jen
went back and forth between the pan of hot molasses for
the popcorn balls and the children undressing on the
rug before the stove; she had planned beds for everyone
tonight and when Mark Shaw lay down in his he could be
thinking that they were all asleep beneath his roof and so
would be safe until morning. All who had ever lived in this
house were here; all who could come; and even Minnie
Foote and Ralph slept not far away, inside as stout a
stone and iron fence as any man could build; they were
safe too, at last, not flying high nor sick with wanting to.

Mark Shaw took up the balsam tree and carried it inside.

"Now ain't that a handsome one?" Jen cried. "My,
that's handsome, father. You put it in the sitting room.
You'll find the base is there, and Lize and Lois May will
be right in to trim it. My, I'll bet that'll hit the ceiling,
won't it?"

She turned back to the children.

"You young ones hustle up. It's full time some folks got
to bed in case Santa comes around early! Come now, see
which one is undressed first."

"Esther," Mil called. "You help Georgie with his shoe-
strings and his buttons."

"Say, you know, they're sweet," Lize said, watching
them. "Esther makes me think so much of Jen as she used
to be."

"When are you going to get married, Lize," asked
Cora Shaw, "and bring home some of yours? And where's
that Bobby you was telling for?"

"Bobby's been given the air," said Lois May. "Bobby
was a gay deceiver, wasn't he, Lize?"

"Bobby was a mess," Lize answered briefly.

Jen heard this and remembered how differently Lize had spoken of him that day not a month ago out in the entry. Lize was not the marrying kind, she thought. Lize would still be a trim, smart office girl when she was fifty. It would not be so with Lois May.

"Look, Ed," said Margaret. "He's waking up a little."

"He'd better go back to sleep," said Ed, "or Santa Claus won't bring him anything. . . . There, that ought to be enough corn, Ol. Did you go through the corn belt on that trip you took? Iowa, and them places?"

"Yes," Olly told him. "Just after harvest. It was stacks as far as you could see in all directions."

"I guess they use it mostly for their hogs," George said. "It must be a big job to raise up all that stuff and feed it out and like as not get nothing for it in the end. From all I hear they cover a lot more territory out that way but most of them don't get ahead much faster —"

The children stood, a row of six, Mil's Vera wavering between her older sisters, all in their striped outing flannel nightgowns, each holding a stocking he had just taken off. Jen did not approve the hanging of stockings from a drawer. Let each child hang his own, with the imprint of his foot still in it, a bigger foot each year. She had always done so, and Olly had, and Lize and Ed and George and Ralph.

"Now then, father! Where's your nails? We're needing six this year. No, seven, it is."

Mark Shaw brought his hammer and leaned across the woodbox to nail each stocking in place from the shelf behind the stove. He took Bun's first because she was the oldest; it hung long and wide; then Esther's, Betty's, John's, Georgie's, Vera's, and young Ed's. The children watched with solemn eyes, each breathlessly waiting for his turn to come, and Margaret held up her baby's small white sock until Mark Shaw came to it in his due course and fastened it as carefully as the others next to the funnel.

"Mine's most as big as John's," cried Georgie. "Next year it will be; won't it, Daddy?"

"I guess you'll have to hyper," chuckled George.

"It won't," John retorted doubtfully. "I guess. Will it, Bun?"

"Course not," Bun answered. "It'll just be longer than it is, and so will yours, and so'll the baby's." She eyed her own.

"There!" Jen exclaimed. "And now you're going to bed, as fast as you can scoot. Lois May'll take up the hot rocks for us."

"It don't seem as if I'd go to sleep," objected Betty. She was all blue eyes and yellow curls to-night, unreal beside the others.

"No," laughed Jen, "but you'll find you will."

She had seen wide eyes before on Christmas Eve.

With the children gone, the elders had their brief turn at being young again. Filling the stockings and decorating the tree with strung popcorn and cranberries and tying little packages for one another on the boughs, they talked and laughed, remembering what had been in the past and hoping for the future. Lize curled up on the floor like a kitten, wearing an old plaid dress Jen had brought down for her from the attic, and leaned against her father's knee as she had years before; he kept looking down at the top of her head. Jen and Margaret worked fast at pressing corn balls into shape and heaping them on platters here and there about the sitting room and kitchen. There were bowls of candied popcorn too, and sugared orange peel, and pans of polished apples. Lois May kept tasting first one and then another, daintily, but still her glance would travel in the direction of the tree; she wondered what it bore for her, especially what Lize had put there. Mil was in high spirits, with much to say to tease Ed and Stan and Olly, and even George. Jen listened to her with amusement; this was like the old Mil who had come here for Christmases while she was still the oldest Ross girl, and sometimes brought her younger sister with her, the grave, sweet one who went to normal school.

It was close to midnight when Mrs. Shaw broke in with, "We going to hear that new machine of yours before we go to bed, Stan?"

"His new machine!"

"Shall I?" Stan asked Jen.

"He got his Christmas present from his folks this morning," Jen explained. "It's an accordion. . . . Why, yes, Stan, play it, if you think you can."

He brought it out and it was a strange thing to see in the Shaw kitchen, but still it looked like Christmas for it was red and black with squares of mother-of-pearl set in the ends. Stan lifted it tenderly, his eyes intent, his mouth smiling, and tried a note or two, pushing it in and out from the ends, an odd way to make music. Suddenly he straightened, throwing back his head, and began to play a Christmas tune, "Hark, the Herald Angels Sing." He played it no more like a hymn than like a dance, and no less; his shoulders swayed with every note; he sang with it, laughing as he sang.

> *Hark, the herald angels sing*
> *Glory to the new-born King* —

Olly saw the strange, wild look in Stan's eyes that he had seen there in the summer but none of the other Shaws seemed to notice it, or be afraid. They were laughing, too, and singing; even Mark Shaw smiled, watching Stan.

"Now wasn't that fine?" asked Mrs. Shaw. "You can't imagine the pleasure we've took with his music all the fall. And I declare I think I like the way this works full better than the fiddle."

"It's just lovely," Margaret said. She was tired and leaned against Ed's arm but her face was bright from the singing. "I don't see how you knew how to play it, Stan!"

"Oh, I've tried one a few times before," Stan said modestly.

"It seems to come awful natural to him some way, playing tunes," Jen said. "Now I think *we'd* better go to bed and get ready for tomorrow, like the young ones. It's almost tomorrow now."

They yawned and nodded, wandering off, one alone, two at a time, as Jen told them where they were to sleep.

"Good night."

"Good night, everybody."

"Good night."

When twelve o'clock came, it found only Jen and her father in the kitchen, she clearing away the litter of paper and string and cooking dishes, he taking a lantern from the shelf and going toward the barn. She wondered if he would find the cattle restless, having heard they were so on Christmas Eve. Quietly she carried her plants away from the windows, wound the clock, and set the chairs in order. Her father's step was slow and steady coming back.

"Everything all right out there, Father?"

"Yes. All right."

He hung the lantern in its place and sat down to take off his shoes.

"Cold night," he said. "Clear as a bell."

"I see the stars are all out bright."

She closed the drafts of the stove and turned down the light.

"You put this out when you come up, won't you?"

"Yes. I'll put it out."

As she opened the stairway door he looked up at her. She smiled.

"We got a full house, Father."

"Running over, ain't it?"

"Just the way it ought to be. For Christmas anyway."

Alone Mark Shaw sat for some time on the end of the couch, looking down at his feet in their brown cotton stockings. Then he rose deliberately and with his thumbs stretched his suspenders until he could ease his shoulders out of them. Now he was more comfortable, and he stood idly by the window looking out at the snow and the woods and the blue, starred sky overhead. The glass was already frosting over, but the room felt warm. He turned back into it, hearing Minnie Foote's steeple clock ticking, smelling the apples and the molasses and the green life of the tree. Yawning, he went over to where the stockings hung behind the stove, seven in a row. His face, as he surveyed them, was serene, proud, meditating. Thoughtfully he slid his fingers into his overalls pocket and withdrew a handful of change, selecting several small silver coins and dropping one into each stretched top. He had done so every Christmas Eve for nearly thirty years now. It was his part.

christmas 1942

It was snowing hard, with a high wind. Not a day for anyone to be out, who had cover to keep under. Every time a
woman opened the vestry door, it slatted back fiercely
against the inside wall, as if trying to take off the plaster;
and the woman would gasp, and grope for it, unable to see
for the steam on her glasses, and unable to pull against
the wind, for the bulging bags and boxes which were balanced on her breast, even up to her chin, as children carry
stovewood. Somebody else would have to run to get the
door shut, and all the women would feel a chill like ice
water wash over their feet and up their legs, even though

they had kept on their overshoes and their long-skirted coats.

"Now ain't this a day?" Lou Mordaunt greeted each new arrival, spitefully poking sprays of bittersweet into crude little brown baskets filled with pine. "I want to know, ain't this a day? We never ought to have had it."

She meant the Christmas Bazaar. She always thought they ought not to have had it. She did not think December was a proper time of year for any self-respecting woman to leave her kitchen, except to go to bed. If it didn't happen to be windy and stormy, it certainly would be cold, or slippery underfoot, or a lot of sickness around. She knew. She could see ahead. She didn't know what was the matter with the rest of them that they couldn't. But no, every fall somebody would be bound and determined! This time it had been Nellie Brand, seemed as though, who went ahead. Nellie always had the Food Table, and stood on a chair behind it now, tacking up the placard her brother Pierce had made for her, before he first left home. Pierce was in the Navy this year, off fighting somewhere, probably, halfway across the map, but here was his fancy shaded printing going up again for the hometown Christmas Bazaar.

EVERYTHING WE COOK IS GOOD!
MERRY CHRISTMAS!

Lou cast a derisive glance at Nellie, who was too broad-hipped and full-bosomed, perhaps from the very goodness of her cooking, to look as trim and neat standing on a chair as Lou felt she would have. But thinking of Pierce took the stingers out of even Lou Mordaunt's eyes. There was a fine boy. Fine and handsome a boy as the Navy, or the Army either, had got out of any town in the country, Lou was willing to bet. There; *boy!* No, of course he wasn't really a boy any longer. Born the spring the river washed out Brands' bridge, that would make him — well, there, thirty-five; that's just how old Pierce Brand was. But womenfolks who had known him when he was a boy would never think of him any different. He was that kind. Always bright and polite and friendly whenever he came around; seemed to like to talk with everybody; remembered any little thing you used to have or do, even the kind of flowers that spread down the bank from under your garden fence. There was something about Pierce Brand's mouth, something just as young and sweet-looking as it had been when he was twelve years old. . . .

"Nobody'll come," snapped Lou, bringing herself smartly out of her daydream. "Not a soul. See'f they do."

Nellie pounded in the last tack.

"Oh, pull in your horns, Lou," she said good-naturedly. "Somebody always comes. Somebody's coming now."

"Some of ourselves," returned Lou, "I'll warrant you. Year after year I kill myself frying doughnuts and putting cross-stitch on dishtowels and you kill yourself baking lemon pies and running up aprons, and we drag 'em over here so you can buy doughnuts and dish towels you don't want and I can buy aprons I don't need and pie I never ought to eat—"

"After all which killing, we're still alive," Nellie laughed, easing herself down off the ladder. "I call it wonderful."

"But for once we had such a good excuse to save ourselves," mourned Lou. "It's wartime. You ain't supposed to do the things you generally do, in wartime. We ought to stay home and knit. Then if your feet gets cold, you can tuck them into the oven, and not risk chilblains."

She stamped significantly, as the door creaked again.

"Even in wartime," Nellie said, unperturbed, "seems to me everybody needs a change of air once in a while."

This was Sue Garland coming in now.

There had never been a lovelier girl grow up in this town than Sue Garland. Nor a lonelier one either, Nellie Brand believed.

Everybody knows how it is in a small place. Every so often there is a surge of life and excitement; two or three new families move in, a number of different ones are having babies, the district schoolhouse is overcrowded, and the church opens up with a series of revival meetings and right away after that a baptism; there are Sunday School picnics at the beach and sleigh rides up the mountain, kitchen parties, and Saturday night dances in the Town Hall, and older folks are nearly crazy with so much to see to, but they can't leave it alone, and they worry over the young not taking enough sleep. Then as the years slip by, somehow it all dies down again, like lively water settling into a mill pond so still that birch trees reflected in it are bewilderingly like themselves, caught like a framed picture clear and perfect in every detail of bark and leaf. One house after another gets its windows boarded over, the schoolhouse closes up for lack of enough children to be worth a teacher's full attention, the faithful of the Church are hard put to it to pay an itinerant preacher for Sunday afternoon services, and most of the traffic is in summer when strangers from hotels along the coast drive out in proud, cold, shiny cars pointing their fingers at roof lines and doorways and the old-fashioned flowers which bloom by cellar holes; knocking and bowing and inquiring the best way out of here to the next town.

Pierce Brand had seen the beginning of the last ebb of the tide in East Derwich and then he had gone away to take a business college course and work in an office in Boston. It had never really touched Pierce. Still he knew what it was and what it could do, for he had come back for weekends once in a while as long as he was near, and Sue Garland had shown him.

Sue Garland it had caught.

Sue had been ten when Pierce left home. She was an only child, a slim little girl with an oval face and big, grave eyes the color and the texture of blue pansies, and she had long, soft, dark curls which her mother combed over her finger every morning, dipping the comb in a cup of water set on the windowsill. Sue wore white aprons with Hamburg ruffles over her plaid dresses, and she would stand for hours gently swinging on the front gate, perhaps because this was a kind of play at which she could keep clean, the way her mother had brought her up to want to be. She made a picture.

But to Nellie she had seemed a strangely deserted little figure even then.

The Garlands lived next door to the Brands, and Pierce would talk with Sue while he worked in Nellie's flower garden, or offer her an orange or some candy if he was bringing some home from the store. He thought Sue was wonderful, and he thought the same about everybody else in town. He had that disposition. And though he was wrong about many of them, as Nellie had means of knowing, she agreed with him about Sue. The child was not only lovely. She was the soul of honor. She was quick to learn, and not afraid to work. By the time she was twelve, she could bake as well as any woman, and dust and make a bed, and wash a pair of socks to suit even her mother, who was the neatest housekeeper in town.

But there wasn't another girl Sue's age in the place, nor boy either. She rode to school in Derwich Center on a bus which came from Northville, and when she got off it at her gate at night, and stood and smiled and waved as the bus went on with its shrieking, swarming cargo, she was like a remnant of some old royal line set ashore on a safe, solitary isle where nothing at all could reach her, either good fortune or ill.

Pierce still thought of Sue sometimes. That was his way. He sent her postcards once in a while. At Christmas he generally brought her a little gift. If he was home over a spring weekend he might take her mayflowering with him, or, in the fall, for nuts. She knew the woods around as well as he, and loved them as he did. Pierce told Nellie that child would speak sometimes, as natural as breathing, in such a way that your heart rose up with a deep thump and almost choked you, what she said was so beautiful and, you knew from the way she said it, so true. Then he would go back to Boston, and maybe, send her a picture of the Public Gardens with his name scrawled across the back.

One day Sue brought over to Brands' a box which Pierce had made for her of birchbark one day long ago when they went picking pond lilies, and showed Nellie what she kept in it. She had everything that Pierce had ever given her. Every card, a few bright wisps of handkerchiefs ("I use them often," Sue said gravely, sweetly, "but then I wash them and put them back in here"), the card from her graduation roses which Pierce had ordered because he did not want her to be the only girl on that foreign Northville platform without flowers, a cheap little blue ·enameled watch which no longer ran, a cloisonné locket in which she had put two snapshots she had taken of him, a round Swiss music box which played a tune when the handle was turned, a paper where he had figured a problem in algebra, scraps of worn-out dresses he had noticed enough to speak of, a book of poems by Robert Frost ("He read some of these aloud to me one day," Sue said. "He read them the way he said he had heard Frost read them. I don't believe Frost could read them as well as Pierce did. Frost is an old man. I think he would like to hear Pierce's voice read them"). There were the wrappings of two or three candy bars, and some pressed maple leaves.

"Pierce is the most wonderful person I ever knew, Nellie," Sue Garland said quickly. "I think he must be the most wonderful person in the world. He is so kind. And so wise. He is really good. I want to be just as much like him as I possibly can."

Sue was seventeen then. Nellie Brand knew she was no longer the child Pierce thought her. And she was afraid for Sue, because what was to turn out to be true of Pierce

Nellie even then suspected. Pierce was not a marrying man.

"He is good," Nellie thought grimly, "But he is not wise enough, it seems. And he is too kind. Being kind makes Pierce happy. It never occurs to him that even kindness can do harm. And how can I tell him? Bless his old heart—"

She had never found a way to tell him.

And now Sue Garland was twenty-four. Pierce Brand was thirty-five and off riding a torpedo boat in the far Pacific, keeping guard over Australia, and doing it so well that he had been commended and commissioned, and his picture put in all the papers only a few weeks ago — the same gentle, handsome face and sweet, boyish mouth as before he had become a hero. But Sue was twenty-four and had been nowhere and dwelt on nothing since she was a child except how much she loved Pierce Brand. As far as she knew he was the only man in the world.

Here was such a one as older women must manage to have Christmas Bazaars for, if they can do no better, even in wartime.

"Hi, Sue!" Nellie hailed her, and all the other women looked up from their food and fancywork exhibits and smiled at least a little, and all tenderly. Even Lou Mordaunt.

Sue said softly, warmly, "Hi, everybody!"

But her eyes went quickly to Nellie Brand and stayed there, their wide, purplish pansy-blue darkly scalloped around with excitement.

"Can't guess what I found in my mailbox, Nellie!" she said like singing.

Nellie could guess. She had seen those dark scallops in Sue Garland's eyes before.

"No," Nellie said shortly. Why did it have to come today? The Bazaar would be as good as wasted. "Shut the door, child, for heaven's sake. You'll freeze us all out."

"My goodness," Sue exclaimed. "I'm sorry —"

She got hold of the door and pulled it to, but not until the wind had swept the point of her fringed kerchief into a peak on the top of her head, and blown out a ruffle of embroidered white muslin apron like a crisp fan between the flaps of her red coat.

Sue's part in the Bazaar was to serve the tea, and she carried her mother's fat brown teapot cuddled into the curve of one arm, and gleaming merry with its pattern of varicolored dots and scrolls. The other arm hugged a pile of boxes. She hurried across to set these down on Nellie's table, and drew a card from her pocket as if it were a love letter, as if it were a ring.

Nellie Brand could have cried.

Oh, Pierce Brand, Pierce Brand, you and your cards! Not even a trinket, this time, not even a few lines sealed! He should have his ears boxed, that one should, hero or no hero. If she just had him here — oh, but if she did have him here —

"There! And his own sister without a word from him for six solid weeks," lied Nellie. "What a guy!"

"You stop talking like that," Sue said. She clenched her small teeth threateningly, but her eyes were shiny and proud. She knew Nellie loved Pierce almost as blindly, as idolatrously as she herself, if such a thing could be. "I guess, reason he wrote to me, this time, he got that sweater I sent him," she explained. "And the other things. He says the sweater fits fine. He says he's well. See what he says —"

Nellie glanced down at Pierce's card and saw black words on it but they swam into one another. All she could see clear was how Sue had looked, bending grave and sweet and pale over that knitting in blazing August heat, the needles so weighted down that the girl's slender arms could hardly lift them.

So. It fitted, did it? And Pierce was well, was he? Oh, of course it was fine he was well, but if he only knew, if a

man could know . . . Still, what was there now that
Pierce could do, even if he did know better than he was
doing?

"I'm a fool," she thought. "A silly old fool about them
both. I'm soft. That's the trouble with all three of us.
We're too soft."

She pushed the card away.

"There, no time now," she said brusquely, "for reading
cards. Get off your things here, quick, and start your ket-
tle boiling in the kitchen, and set your table up. First
thing we know, there'll be a carful here from Northville
half froze —"

"Won't be a soul here from Northville, and you know
it," declared Lou Mordaunt, gloomily twisting red ribbon
through a wreath. "Nor wouldn't be, even in good
weather. Folks over there always thinks we ought to come
a-runnin' to all their doin's, but if ever we get up anything,
they manage so they don't even hear of it till afterwards.
. . . No, day like this, we shan't see a soul but what's
here this minute. You see'f we do . . ."

"Mother planned to come," Sue said, coming and going
about her table on light feet, "but she had to give it up.
Her back is bothering again lately, and one of us, anyway,
would have had to leave by four o'clock, to get Dad's supper."

"My back'd bother me all the time if I paid any attention to it," Mame Travers said. "Anybody's back is just
like a young one. Either it's going to be boss, or you are,
that's all there is to it. Just depends on how you start in."

"My husband," observed Ethel Kent, "is going to get
crackers and milk for his supper. And no fault found either. At least, there better not."

"Mother says she knows she spoils Daddy," Sue admitted, holding a match to a red candle. "He likes his hot
supper, and he always gets it, too. She says he'd feel he
was abused if ever it weren't ready for him when he got
home and she would feel the same way. She knows she

spoils her husband!" Sue looked at Nellie smiling with a half-secret intimate delight. "And I don't doubt," she finished, "I'll be exactly the same about mine!"

Nellie did not doubt it either. But who was Sue's husband going to be? And how would she know him if she saw him?

The whole room seemed now to swirl about Nellie as Pierce's writing had swirled on the postcard. She could feel the other women, roused by Sue's words and lovely, shameless smile, turn and look at Sue, speculatively, and then at Nellie herself, inquiringly, shrewdly. How much is there to this, their sharp eyes seemed to say; isn't it pretty one-sided; and just who is in love with who. Nellie Brand's stout, kind heart filled up with a dull, throbbing misery, a quick hatred of both man- and womankind. She wished she could kick something and then walk away and leave it there, broken and scattered. The vestry was bleak and chilly and none too clean. Glass rattled in the windows. The food on the Food Table looked as any food looks when nobody is hungry. The fancywork was limp and silly, like the gifts laid back around a Christmas tree after they have been opened, a brave, sad little display. The decorations — the looped evergreen strands, the wreaths with their red ribbon bows, the lettered sign — were shabby, meaningless. Nellie agreed now with Lou Mordaunt. She knew at last what Lou Mordaunt had known long before. There was no good reason for a Bazaar in a forgotten place like East Derwich. They might as well not have had it at all.

Then suddenly the door opened. Nellie thought afterward that it couldn't have happened at exactly that instant. But it did.

The door opened and a soldier came in.

He was tall, rather slight, and very young. His face was as deeply tanned as if it had been in the tropics, his eyelashes and eyebrows silver white with snow which had blown into them and frozen there. Against this deep brown and silvery white his eyes were as blue as seawater on a bright winter day, blue and alive and strong like that, undeniable, and — for — always. The shoulders of his khaki coat and his boots and the cap he held in his hand were heavy with snow. He must have been out a long time. He must have come a long way.

Nellie Brand knew where he had come from. He had come in from the coast where strange men had been walking up and down for months, watching and listening. Nellie had seen them a few times in the summer and thought of them often, especially in bad weather, but she had never spoken to one of them, or heard anyone else. She believed she had had some idea that probably they were not allowed to speak while on duty, and, so far as she knew, they were always on duty. Fine, strange young men walking the American coast, studying the American sea and sky. Godlike was what Nellie Brand had thought, though of course she would not have said so, even to herself.

But this one did not seem so strange, here in the vestry. He had closed the door quietly. Now he stood outlined against it, looking around the room, at one face after another, half smiling.

"Am I right?" he asked cheerfully. "This is public? Okay to come in? Three other fellows outside — told them I'd find out."

"Oh, yes," Nellie gasped. "Oh, yes, of — of course it's public. Bring them right in, quick, before they freeze. It's a — a terrible day to be out."

"We didn't mind it," the boy said. It was easy to see now that he was only a boy. More of a boy, that is, than Pierce Brand would ever be again. "We're used to weather," he said. "We came over the mountain. It wasn't so far . . . Thanks. I'll tell the fellows —"

He went out.

The women looked at one another.

It wasn't so far over the mountain as by the road, from

the coast. But still it was eight miles, at least, and through thick woods. It was three o'clock now. These boys must have been on the way since noon, or earlier, walking to East Derwich . . .

The women saw their duty, and with acute pleasure.

"Rustle up that fire out there," one exclaimed. "Where is some pans? I'm going to heat these rolls —"

"Sue, clear away that mess of tea. They're going to need their coffee — a good, stout cup."

"I'll run over home for cream. It's just a step —"

"Better pick up a cut of cheese. To go with the pie."

"Best way to warm doughnuts is in a toaster. Makes them as if they'd just been fried —"

There was stamping and laughter, the fine, urgent sound of men's footsteps and voices in the vestibule, and then where there had been one soldier suddenly there were four, hunching out of heavy coats which they folded neatly and laid on benches by the wall, rubbing their hands together hopefully, a little shyly, and glancing around.

This changed the room. Instantly it turned warm and bright. The rattling of the windows became a snug and cozy sound. The red candles flared up with new life. The food looked as good as the sign said; it smelled good, too; it smelled wonderful. And even the fancywork took on the magic of before Christmas instead of afterward.

Men — boys — American boys — were here to be done for. After walking the American coast for so many days and so many nights, they had come inside at last, for a little while, to see just what this was they had been guarding, whether it was worth all that they had done and would have to do, just what was here that was so precious. They had come in, young and cold, with snow on their eyelashes.

This changed the women as it had the room.

They all knew now why they had had the Bazaar. It was part of some scheme far more subtle and less selfish than any of their own. What they had made and brought here was not to be sold this year. It was all gifts. It was for these boys. The women had no need to step aside and talk it over in whispers. The feeling ran from one to another as if on an invisible chain; and not only rolls and doughnuts went off the Food Table to be made hot, but meat loaf, too, and escalloped potatoes. These boys must have their supper. And from Fancywork they must have the scarfs they could wear, the handkerchiefs, the painted boxes of fudge and stuffed dates; even aprons and pot holders to send to their mothers, the bright dusters, embroidered dish towels, and braided lamp mats which any girl would like to keep in her hope chest — or whatever girls used nowadays instead of hope chests.

"Gee, ma'am," the boys kept saying. "We thought this was a sale. You ought to let us pay —"

"Pay," cried Ethel Kent. "As if we would! We're only too glad —"

"Well, I should say so," snapped Lou Mordaunt. "Hadn't been for you, it would have all gone to waste."

"Have another piece of pie," coaxed Nellie.

They were all lost in the happy whirl of such service as only women who know how can give to the brave, the cold, the tired, and the hungry.

Nobody noticed Sue Garland just then, or for some little time.

Nobody, that is, except the first soldier.

He stood near the kitchen door when Sue came in the first time, with a tray of steaming coffee cups.

"Let me take that," he said to her. "It's too heavy for you."

"Oh, no," Sue told him. "It isn't heavy at all. You just sit down and take your cup —"

But he took the tray, and stood holding it, looking at her. The others might have rubbed their hands because of shyness, but not this one. There was nothing shy about him. He was smiling, a smile so wide that it cut a line into either hard, thin cheek, and looking very straight at her.

This was the one with eyes like the seawater he had been watching, and the snow had melted off his eyebrows and lashes now, showing them fair and crisp as the sand on the beaches where he walked.

Sue's eyes fell.

"What's the matter?" he asked her.

There was nothing the matter.

"You don't mind my looking at you, do you?"

Of course she didn't. Not really. Not the way he was doing it. She shook her head. But still she could not get her eyes up.

"It's what I came here for," he told her, low. "Please don't mind. Don't look like that. I mean, don't not look at me, like that. It isn't just that you're a girl."

She knew it wasn't.

"We see a good many girls," he said. "More girls than ships. Or subs. In the coast towns they ask us to supper. They get up dances for us. They're awfully nice. But I don't care about dancing with strange girls . . . I'd like to dance with you."

Sue said carefully, "I don't dance."

"Why not?"

"I — just never learned how. Please —"

"I'd like to teach you —"

"Please let me take my tray."

"It's too heavy for you."

"It isn't heavy at all," Sue said again.

"It might slip and you'd get burned."

"Nobody will ever get burned with that coffee," Sue told him. "Another minute and we'll have to take it back to the kitchen and make fresh. Which isn't right. We aren't supposed to waste coffee. Or — or anything."

"Not even time?"

"No. Not even time."

"No," the boy said. "Okay. Where do you want this coffee put?"

"On that table. And then I want you to marshal your

— your company, and sit down, and drink it. And eat too."

"Okay —"

Sue heard nothing more from him until someone asked for a second cup, and as she bent, brushing a khaki shoulder, to pour it, his face looked up over her arm. His dark face with the sea-blue eyes and the sandy brows and lashes. He was not smiling now. He was quite grave.

"— only get one thing straight," he said, low, as if they had not been interrupted. "Believe you me, this time isn't being wasted!"

"Eat your meat loaf," she told him. "You haven't touched it."

"Did you make it?"

"No."

"I'd eat it if you'd made it. Did you make anything that's here?"

"I made a cake."

"Please may I have a piece of cake? That cake?"

She brought it, white squares, chocolate-topped, on a blue plate. And while the other boys went on eating meat loaf and escalloped potatoes and rolls, and then doughnuts and pie in great quantities, making all the women very happy, this boy asked only for more and more cake, and more coffee.

"You'll be sick," Sue whispered anxiously.

"Oh, no. I feel fine. I feel wonderful. Did you make any of the things on that table over there? Those sewed things?"

He looked earnest. Eager. She bit her lip with pity, and at the same time felt it curve with pleasure that it took so little to make him so happy.

"Some of them," she admitted.

"Come show me which."

All the boys had finished eating now. They eddied about the tables.

"This apron," Sue said.

"That's a fine apron . . . Lady, can I buy this apron?"

"Nothing here is for sale," Grace Morrison told him. "Just say what you would like. This apron, you say? Well, it's a nice, big, sensible apron. For your mother, maybe? I'll wrap it up all ready to hang on the tree —"

"You needn't wrap it up," the boy said. "I haven't got any mother. But you can't tell. I might have sometime. I'll take this right over my arm. Thank you." And then he said to Sue, "What else did you make — that I could have?"

She was embarrassed. Not of what the other women might think. None of them seemed to notice. But of what he might think.

"Don't be silly," she said. "Unless there's somebody you want to give such things to —"

She wished suddenly, terribly, that she had knit a scarf. She could have knit a scarf.

"Would you feel better," he asked her gravely, "if I made up somebody to give them to? I could do that —"

"Isn't there anybody, really?" she whispered incredulously. "Anybody?"

He shook his head.

"No. Nobody. Really."

"Not anywhere?"

"No."

"Why, I — I can't believe it!"

"You'll believe it when I get a chance to tell you my whole story. It's kind of a long one. But you'll believe it, all right, when I tell you."

"But — but everybody — has somebody!"

"Not me." After a minute he added as if to comfort her, "See, I was brought up by the state. The State of Texas. I had a good bringing up, too. And then I was in the C.C.C. for three years. Now I'm in the Army. See, the country took care of me a long time. Now I'm taking care of the country. Okay?"

She thought it was okay enough. But dreadfully lonely. And sometimes she had thought she was lonely. She felt ashamed.

"I couldn't send the C.C.C. an apron," he was saying meditatively, "but hey — suppose the State of Texas would like a fine apron like this? I'll send it there, if you want me to? To the State House! Okay?"

"Maybe," Sue began huskily, "— maybe you'd better send the State of Texas a wreath from the State of Maine! I'll show you one I made."

She was surprised to find, crossing the room, that she had put her hand on his arm. But not surprised enough to take it off.

Sometime later she heard him say, contentedly, "I knew this was how you would be. I knew you would be just like this."

"How?" Sue asked him.

"Gentle. Thinking. Sort of prim — just nice. Bossy — just a little; the way a woman is bossy. But especially thinking. Not about yourself. Or about ideas. I mean, about other people. So that somebody else would have to do the thinking about you —"

"But I meant," Sue said, "how did you know about me? Anything about me? I mean — did you make me up?"

"Oh, no," he told her quickly. "Why — haven't I told you that? I thought I had. I saw you walking on the beach last summer. I saw you sit on a rock down by the water, under a big hat, writing a letter. I kept walking by you, to look at you. I didn't think you would mind. I did it very politely. I mean, not noticeably. And you didn't see me at all, I guess. You were writing a letter."

"I remember," Sue said slowly.

"And when you went to mail it, I followed you. Not close. I was very careful. But I was just going off duty, and I — I really couldn't help it. I went into the post office, and stood behind you while you bought a stamp. I heard the clerk talking to you. I knew he knew you. And after you had gone out, I asked him who you were and where you lived. I didn't know as he would tell me; he hesitated; and then he did. I guess he thought I looked okay. I was very careful. I even bought some stamps. . . . And after that, through the fall, I got to drive a truck up through here. After gravel for some roads we were building —"

She had seen the trucks go by.

"I hardly ever saw you. Once I did. You were picking flowers in a garden. It was an awfully pretty garden. In front of a big brown house with deep piazzas all around it and vines growing over. I didn't stop. I only drove slower. But not too much slower. I was awfully careful. . . . And last week when I drove through I saw the poster up saying there would be a Christmas Bazaar here today, and everybody was welcome. Believe you me, that looked pretty fine to me. Everybody welcome! . . . It's funny. I feel as if I had told you all this before."

"You haven't even," Sue said carefully, "— even told me your name!"

"It's Claude," he said. "Claude Reynolds. But everybody calls me Tex."

"Come here," Sue told him. "Come over here."

She took him straight to Nellie Brand.

"Nellie," she said. "Nellie, I've just found out who this boy is. He's Tex Reynolds."

Nellie Brand, behind the Food Table, leaned against the edge of it, heavily. It seemed like days and weeks that she had been waiting here and, yes, praying. Praying that Sue Garland could go at least as far as to look at and listen to one of these boys. She knew she was an old fool. But she had always done the best she could. She went to church every single Sunday. She had a class in Sunday school. She often washed the big windows, and even the painted pews upstairs. And now she was going to find out what it had availed her. Nellie could not see far ahead, yet, any more than Sue could. Nellie did not ask much.

Just that Sue's eyes and ears and heart had not been closed. . . .

"Well, for goodness sake," she exclaimed, thrusting out a quick, sturdy hand, smiling a broad, warm, Brand smile. "So you're Tex Reynolds!"

And suddenly he was no stranger to either of them any longer, really.

"Nellie Brand," Sue explained, "is the nicest woman in this town, Tex. And probably the nicest woman in the world."

Was the child quoting herself, Nellie wondered? Did Sue remember that she had said something like this before?

"You're telling me?" Tex Reynolds asked, smiling back at Nellie.

"I'm telling you," Sue said, with a new spirit. "Just in case you wouldn't know." She explained to Nellie, "He's had a funny bringing up. The State of Texas and the C.C.C." And she said to him, "I made a handkerchief that's on that table over there. A blue-and-white checked handkerchief with flowers embroidered in the corners. If you want it."

"Of course I want it," he said. "I'll go and get it."

When he had gone, Sue said, "Nellie. Nellie, he really hasn't eaten anything here but cake and coffee. I think he — I think he's just the kind that needs a — a hot supper. Cooked fresh, you know. A real man's supper. And who knows when he ever had a home-cooked meal?"

"God knows," Nellie Brand said feelingly. She thought He should. She had been telling Him all afternoon.

"I thought maybe I might," Sue said, "ask him to come over home to supper. It wouldn't hold him up long. Mother'll have it all ready. The only thing, I feel as if I ought to ask them all, and still I can't do that, with Mother's back the way it is, and I've been over here all afternoon —"

"There! Your mother," Nellie exclaimed. "Of course

your mother never could stand doing for a crowd like that. Don't you give it another thought. Besides, if those other fellows should eat any more than they have, I wouldn't answer for it. No, don't you worry about them, Sue. But I had noticed this — this Tex was kind of picking. And of course none of the rest of us have got a hot supper to offer. But I'll take the other three home with me to make molasses candy or something."

"Well, there," Sue decided, on a soft breath of relief, reaching for her coat, "it's settled. I'll take him." Then, tying on the flowered handkerchief, tucking the teapot into the curve of her arm, and seeing Tex coming back, she leaned suddenly, trustingly, across the table to Nellie and whispered, "You don't think — Pierce would mind?"

Nellie gripped the edge of the Food Table with her hands and the floor with her toes.

"Sue," she said solemnly, "I don't have to think about that. I know. And so do you! Pierce would be disappointed if you didn't!"

And silently Nellie Brand promised, I'll wash every one of the big windows, God, before ever another Sunday rolls around. And the pews, too, the very first chance I get.

CHAPTER VIII

hristmas 1943

Esther remembered how in spring, the blossoms of the crab apple tree brushed the screens of the upstairs windows of the furnished cottage behind her father's house.

She thought they must smell wonderfully sweet at night. She had always wanted to sleep there. As a child, she had planned that when she married, that cottage would be her home. Whenever it was vacant, she went in to play. She would take the dishes with the yellow flowers from the apple-green pantry shelves, and set the little table under the window which looked out on the back porch of the big house, where her mother might be sweeping rugs if it were morning, or knitting if it were afternoon. (Knitting up balls of khaki yarn. That was during the other war.)

She would go to her kitchen door, turn its loose white enamel knob, and call her six children in to supper. She washed their faces very clean, no matter if they cried, and set them up straight at the table. Then it would be time for her husband; she could hear him coming up the narrow walk between the peony beds, and she would take off her apron and go to meet him, gently but quickly, like a lady who is glad . . .

It would be different now, but still it would be wonderful.

Esther folded her mother's letter. The clothes out on the line were dry. She had better bring them in, and she might get them folded and put away before Essie woke up. Then she could wheel Essie down to the chicken house as soon as Paul came from school. If she helped Paul with his chickens, he might still have time to go across the field to play ball a little while with Bobby Ryan before he had to feed his dog and get in wood. She tried to plan on play for Paul as often as she could. He was so good, and she found herself depending on him for so many things, more and more all the time, since his father went away. She must not forget that for all his grave manly ways, Paul was still only a little boy, only ten years old. In wartime, especially in the country, boys seem to grow up so fast.

It would be different in Kenford. Paul's school would be only a few city blocks away. He wouldn't have to leave at eight o'clock every morning and ride four miles on a bus. He wouldn't be another hour getting back in the afternoon. He could even come home for lunch.

Her mother had written: "Esther dear, it seems almost a miracle, the Peabodys really asking to be let off their lease. Why, for years they have acted as if that cottage belonged to them. Anything they wanted in the way of repairs, if we couldn't manage it, they would just go right ahead and do it themselves. Like last spring, they built on that sleeping porch . . ."

Paul would love a sleeping porch. They all would. How nice it would be for Essie, sleeping out! They would be as good as in that crab apple tree, the three of them! And so near the big house that if Esther should just speak ("Mother! Dad!") at night, the chances were they would hear her. It would be a different thing, a very different thing, from lying alone in a big bed in a house a quarter of a mile from any neighbor, and listening, listening, thinking she heard — deciding she hadn't — looking at the clock, finding it still only midnight, or quarter past, turning over, and beginning to listen again, finding she only half-breathed, she was listening so hard. She did not think she had really slept — not wholly, not soundly — an hour since Don went away after his last furlough. More than five months ago.

". . . I guess the Peabodys began to feel crowded after the new baby came. The cottage really isn't big enough for much of a family. But it will be just right for three. And I can't tell you what it will mean to your father to have you and the children so near. You know it was always our dream."

But Don Furbroke had had a dream of his own, from the very first: Don wanted to live in the country. He wanted a farm. He talked about it before they were married. It was nothing Esther had not known.

After they were married, while they were living in holes-in-the-walls of New York and Chicago, while Don studied and wrote and took oral examinations to earn a graduate degree, he had kept on talking about that farm they were going to have. At wayside auctions, when they were on vacation, he bought things; queer things, Esther thought; crowbars and wheelbarrows and ladders and china eggs. It was going to be a chicken farm.

And before he had taught two years at the State University, a chicken farm was what they had. Other faculty families might live cheek by jowl on the campus fringes. The Furbrokes lived ten miles out, in a big brown isolated farmhouse with porches all around — a house big enough for a dozen — and a creaking old elm at the curve of the driveway, a great gaunt empty barn, and two tar-paper brooder houses. Other professors might play golf on warm afternoons; Don Furbroke left campus in a beach wagon to set hens, to whitewash, to scatter shavings and oyster shells; he planted, hoed, cut poles for beans, and strung wire for peas. Other professors' wives went to teas and club meetings, worried about being seen too often in the same dress, left their children with coeds and went to movie matinees. Esther Furbroke did all the work in her big old house, and took care of her children herself, for there was no help this far out, unless Mrs. Ryan could spare a day, now and then, to come over and clean. Esther sowed the fine seed, too, held the ladder, washed the eggs, hunted for the lost tools, bound up the cuts . . .

It had been fine while Don was here. It had been all right as long as he was likely to come back on furlough almost any weekend, and be happy to see it all again, proud of all she and Paul had managed to do.

But now Don had not come for five months. She had not heard from him for two. All she knew was that he must be very far away again, that it would be a long, long time before he could come back, and that she was left alone on a bleak hilltop, among rambling and ghostly buildings, alone with a small boy and a baby.

She heard the school bus coming; and from the kitchen window, from behind the table where she was folding clothes, she saw Paul get off and stand well to the side of the main road until the bus had rattled on. As it disappeared she saw him raise his square brown hand straight up, more like a salute than like waving; then he turned and started slowly up their lane, a little road so rarely touched by wheel or hoof that grass grew in a green line through the center. She could not see him all the way, for the bushes were thick in places, especially where the road followed the curves of the brook, and by the little stone bridge.

He seemed to take a long time.

"I suppose he's tired," Esther thought. "School is a strain. Parents forget how much of a strain just going to school is for a child . . . And he's beginning to realize how much is waiting for him to do, as soon as he gets here. It isn't right. He shouldn't have so much on his mind."

Her mother had written: "Dad says to tell Paul your old bicycle is still up overhead in the garage. It may be old-fashioned but it's just as good as it ever was, and folks are glad to get hold of anything with wheels these days. I tell your father we know now why we've kept so much stuff, the last twenty years, that we couldn't see we would ever have a use for. I guess it will all come in handy."

Esther thought: "He wouldn't even have to do errands. Prescott's store is just around the corner. I could take Essie along in the stroller. How easy it would roll on the sidewalk! And Mr. Prescott would like seeing us come in."

Mr. Prescott must be quite an old man now, but whenever she had been home, it seemed to her that he changed hardly at all. A little grayer, a little fatter around his always fat and jolly waist, that was all; and the smiling lines cut deeper around his mouth and eyes. He had always offered a box of broken cookies, and sometimes a frosted cupcake, to Esther when she was a little girl. On the nights before holidays he would even throw open the door to his penny-candy counter and tell her to take her choice. He would do the same for Essie.

It was sweet in Kenford the night before a holiday. Never too noisy but always busy, and everybody friendly, even with strangers. You could hear the happiness, the eagerness and anticipation, even in the footsteps of people passing, after you had gone to bed at night.

She heard Essie raise her voice softly, trustingly, in her one conversational achievement:

"Gar-den!"

She could have called "Ma-ma," but she hardly ever did.

"Gar-den?" she would inquire, on an almost lyric note.

And Esther would answer. "Yes, that's the garden, darling," or, "Do you want to go out into the garden, darling?" or "Are you thinking about the garden, darling?" depending on circumstances.

It could not be that it took much to make Essie lyrical. The garden here, so far, was only a mowed patch in the middle of a tangle of old lilac and syringa bushes, and a few hundred-leaf roses which hugged rosebugs tight to their hearts as they began to open. Esther always wondered how the bugs got in there. It was as if buds and bugs were born together. There had been no time yet to work with flowers here. Vegetables, chickens, and building repairs had taken all and more than all the Furbrokes had had to spend, in both time and money.

The cottage behind her mother's house was grown all over with tiny pink roses, Dorothy Perkins roses. And there were the peony beds and the tulip borders; and the row of hydrangeas across the back. Esther could not remember when they had not been there, every twig and leaf and flower whole, bright and perfect. Her father tended them. He always had, even when he had tenants, as he generally did. He loved flowers and nursed them like children, protecting them faithfully from wind and frost and dogs . . .

Don had said, before he went away, very grave and gentle, like Paul: "What you do while I'm gone is all up to you. You're letting me go. You're taking on the responsibility for our family. You'll have to decide how you want to take it and where. Mother is alone, has plenty of room, and would be glad to have you there. Living in somebody else's home is a problem — but I don't have to tell you.

It's your job, and I know you'll do it the right way. Whatever you do will be the right way, as far as I'm concerned.
You know that."

Esther had said, "I wish the cottage were vacant. But
of course the Peabodys will never leave."

Now they were leaving.

"It won't really make any difference in this place,"
Esther thought. "Paul and I can't keep it where it is, even,
however hard we might try. And there's no help to be
had. Don is bound to have to start all over new when he
gets back . . . All I need to do is sell the chickens, pack
our clothes, lock the windows, pull down the shades, lock
the doors, get into the car, and drive away!"

"We've kept your crib and your high chair, you know,"
her mother had written. "And your father says he will
make Essie a playpen. You know how handy he is at
things like that, and he needs something nowadays to take
up his mind. Don't bring a stick of furniture."

It would be as wonderful for her mother and father as
it would be for her.

"Gar-den!" called Essie, rather less lyrically, more im-
periously.

"Yes, darling," Esther answered, running in. "And she
shall have a garden. A real garden. A lovely garden!"

"By-by?" Essie chuckled unexpectedly.

"Yes, darling," Esther cried. "We will go by-by. A long
by-by." Paul came in and she said, feeling her face flushed,
"Hello, son. Did you hear what Essie said? She said 'By-
by'! A new word!"

"I heard her," Paul answered.

He put down his red lunch box and stood on it to look
over the foot of the crib. They were big, heavy shoes to
rest on so small a metal box, and metal was precious, but
Esther restrained herself from speaking of it. In Kenford
he would not need a lunch box. She forbore too, to remind
him that his hands were not clean, nor the front of his
sweater, probably. What might he have leaned against

last? How many who were on that bus tonight would be down with measles tomorrow?

Never mind. She would get out a clean blanket for Essie. Blankets would wash. Essie's blankets were always being washed. It took a great deal of water. Sometimes Esther worried about the well. There had not been much rain this spring, and the pipe went only within six feet of the bottom. She ought to have measured the water, but she had not dared. Never mind. In Kenford the city sent in the water, tested every morning, and guaranteed pure.

"Say 'By-by,' Essie," Paul said. "Say 'By-by' for Brother."

He might have been sixteen, except that he had to stand on his lunch box to look over the footboard of the crib.

"By-by," said Essie, tipping her head sideways and smiling at him.

Nobody with only one child can know how much more than twice as precious are two together.

"She does just like Paddy does when I speak to him," Paul said. "The way she tips her head."

Paddy was his dog, a lean and rangy hound with whiskers.

"I've got a chicken does that same way too," Paul went on. "Only he does it quicker, and jerks it right back. I named that chicken 'Ickin' Head.' It seems as if that's what he does; he icks his head."

"I think you're horrid, Paul Furbroke," Esther told him. "Essie thinks you're horrid too. Come along with your mother, darling. Mother doesn't think you're like a dog, nor like a chicken, nor like a duck. Mother thinks you're like a —"

"Gar-den," Essie said confidently.

"Yes, darling."

And Esther thought: "Now there is Paddy. What can I ever do with him? Will Paul think Bobby Ryan — Bobby doesn't have a dog since his Foxy ran off —"

Essie held out her arms to Paul.

"She wants me to take her," Paul said.

"You wash your hands first," his mother told him. "Brother's a dirty boy, Essie. That dirty old bus."

They went into the kitchen, and Paul put his hands deep into a full washbasin.

"I kind of like the bus," Paul said. "It isn't specially dirty. I didn't like it, when I first went, but now I do. I like the things I'm used to."

"You're lucky," Esther said. "Because there'll always be new things to get used to, and as soon as you're used to them, you'll like them, won't you? That's nice to know."

"It isn't nice getting used to them," Paul said, slowly scooping up water and letting it run down his arms below his sweater sleeves pushed up. "That part isn't nice."

You never know what makes a child's mind discover a small trail and follow it.

"I'm glad I'm ten," Paul said, drying himself. "I've got used to so many things. Now I can just keep on for a long while and like 'em better all the time."

He looked at the baby in her clean pink dress, holding out her arms to him.

"I'm kind of sorry for Essie," he said. "She isn't used to anything but just us, and this home, is she? She isn't even used to Daddy."

He took Essie's hands and helped her slide off her mother's knees to the floor, and steadied her while she walked about. Her feet looked too small to stand on.

"Maybe Essie'll be different," Esther said, folding clothes. "Maybe she'll like changes. Lots of people do."

"I don't believe she will," said Paul. "She's one of our family. She's like us. None of us like changes. Not even Dad. I think Dad hated to go away, don't you?"

"Yes," Esther agreed. "Yes, I know he did, Paul."

"He won't hate to fight," Paul said, "He won't be afraid. He just hated to leave here. Us and this place."

"I expect he's getting used to it by now, maybe," said Esther. "Don't you?"

"No," Paul said. "I don't. Some things I guess you couldn't ever get used to."

After a minute Esther told him: "While I lay the clothes away, you put Essie into the stroller and we'll go down and help you with the chickens."

When she came back, they were out under the elm tree, and Paul had his egg basket and pail of table scraps. Esther bent to the angle that was needed to push small wheels through the grass, and Essie rode ahead of them like a princess, reaching out her hands for daisies, and laughing when she caught them. The wind blew out her hair like feathers.

"I was just thinking," Paul said. "Essie's lucky she's got me. Because I can help her get used to all these things I'm used to. I can explain them to her. I can show her. It won't be as if she had to do it all alone."

"Did you have to do it all alone, Paul?" Esther asked. "Weren't Daddy and I any help?"

He looked at her. They were by the chicken houses now.

"Tell me truly," Esther said, smiling. "I'm just curious. I really want to know."

"Well," Paul said gently, "grown-ups help all they can. But there's so much grown-ups don't think of."

"So much, I suppose," Esther said, "grown-ups have forgotten."

"I guess that's it." He touched her hand. "You don't feel bad I said it? I know you and Daddy tried —"

"I don't feel bad, no, darling. Only for you. It seems so sad — a little boy being unhappy — and maybe mixed up and afraid — all alone. In a big, kind of empty place like where we are."

"It never seemed empty to me," Paul told her. "It seemed — it seemed awfully full of things. Only I didn't know what kind of things, at first. And I can remember when it seemed so new. As if nobody had ever been here before. I suppose we'd just come. I can't remember coming, or living anywhere else, but of course we had. That's why it seemed so awfully new, at first. It won't ever seem as new as that to Essie. She's always been here."

"Yes," Esther said.

"She's got room in it right now," Paul said. "I kind of had to make room for myself. I had to push something else out to make a place I could get into. Like a chicken coming out of an egg. I had to push so hard at first, it seemed as if it took all my breath away. Essie won't have to do that."

"No," Esther admitted.

"That's lucky, too," Paul said. "Because I don't know as she is strong enough. Being a girl."

(Oh, girls are strong, Paul, his mother thought. They'd better be.)

"Let's get your chickens fed," she said. "I want to pick strawberries for supper."

His chickens were white, and they came like doves and stood on his shoes and wrists while he filled the hoppers. Esther, pouring fresh water, heard him talking, calling the chickens by names he had given to them. His own choice of names — Ickin' Head, Silver Chief, Little-hen, Agruelda, Bantaneriopple. One he took in his square brown hands and carried over to the door where Essie sat looking in with wide blue eyes.

"This one," he told her, "is Essie-chick. See? This is the nicest little pullet chick we've got. Next winter she'll lay an egg every day for Essie. She'll sing a song. She'll say, 'Cut-cut-cut-ca-da-cut! Just-laid-an-egg-for-Essie!'"

Essie smiled suddenly, delightedly.

Paul said: "See. She understands."

She understood the Essie part, her mother knew. Perhaps she was not quite clear about the rest. Essie's round arms in their red sweater sleeves shot out as suddenly as she had smiled, and the pullet's back reared, her wings fluttered, she essayed a sort of squawk; but Paul held her secure and set her down on her feet, carefully, where she could race back to the others.

"You mustn't be so quick, Essie," he said. "Not with chickens. I guess not with anything. Like we were just saying, you have to get used to everything, and everything has to get used to you. That takes time. And the more you jump around and try to hurry it, seems as though, the more time it takes. You wait. You just wait till next winter. Then you'll know how to put your hand on Essie-chick, maybe, so she'll stay right there and like it. You just wait."

Esther thought a little wildly: "He's a philosopher. He — he really is superb. How does one cope with a ten-year-old philosopher?"

Essie's arms lay quiet on the rod which encircled her, her dimpled hands grasping it tight in front, her eyes watchful on Paul's face.

"See," Paul said again. "She understands. I explained it to her."

"You don't think," Esther ventured, "you'll be too old to know, always, what to explain, and how to explain it, to Essie?"

"No," he answered confidently. "I think I'll be just right."

Who was this — was it Paul, or Don? Esther's heart — and glance — went out in swift yearning to find the white pullet, but she had disappeared now among a hundred others, all of them eating busily, apparently content, at the hoppers Don and Paul had made for them. When they finished, they would go up to the roosts Paul and Don had built, so thoughtfully and happily, with such tender care that the home they provided should be the best a domestic bird could have. To those roosts the pullets would cling all through the dark hours of the night without protest, almost without moving, waiting for dawn. Esther hoped they would sleep.

"Now," Paul said, coming from the next building with eggs, "we're going to pick strawberries, you say?"

"You needn't," his mother told him, looking at her watch. "It's late. You'll have just time to go over and play ball with Bobby. You run along."

"I'd rather come with you," Paul said. "I can play ball any time. I like to be out here with you and Essie. Besides, I probably know where the strawberries grow better than you do."

He probably did.

"They're biggest along the ditches," he told her. "You have to get right down in the ditch, on your knees, and lift the little bushes up that's hanging down. That's where you find them."

That's where they found them, long, red and sweet. Esther could not remember having seen such berries growing wild.

Essie sat playing with a trayful of buttercups and daisies, talking to them as Paul had talked to Ickin' Head and Bantaneriopple. Sometimes she laughed, as if in excitement over what the flowers told her.

"Gar-den," she cried. "Gar-den?"

Once Paul found a berry bigger than all the rest.

"Can Essie have this, Mother? Can I give this to Essie?"

He was so good. He had looked it all over for ants, and taken off the hull. Esther tried not to think how lately he had held the white pullet, and picked up the eggs. She nodded.

"Here, Essie," Paul said, "see what Brother's got for you."

How many little girls had such a brother? What would most women give for such a son? Wouldn't most boys want the biggest, reddest berry for themselves?

Essie opened her mouth, wide and trusting.

"Now chew, Essie," Paul told her anxiously. "Chew!"

She chewed, her eyes on him.

"See," Paul said, relieved. "She understood." And then he added, "That's like the baby swallows in the barn cellar, when I brought berries for them. Only course they couldn't chew like Essie can. And when they open up their mouths, mouths is all there is of them. They're all gone now, anyway. They're all grown up and gone. When I looked yesterday they'd gone."

Grown up. And gone. So soon? . . . She seemed to see his hands on the old stones of the cellar wall, his grave round face peering over the edge of that empty nest.

"Paul," Esther said, "don't you ever get lonesome? You're alone so much, since Daddy went away."

"I miss Daddy, of course," he answered politely. "But there's Essie now. Besides I like to be — alone."

She noticed his pause before the word "alone." Something told her that he used it only because it was a word she had used. Something told her, with sudden peculiar distinctness, that Paul was never alone, here.

"You like to be with other boys, too," she reminded him. "And the only one you've got is Bobby."

"I like to be with other boys sometimes," he told her. "I wouldn't like to be with other boys too much. I couldn't, anyway. I have my work to tend to."

"Maybe," Esther suggested, "there's too much work for you. I worry about that, a little. You're only ten years old."

Paul laughed indulgently, affectionately.

"I guess mothers always talk like that," he said. "When you're six, they say you're only six. Then when you're ten, they say you're only ten. I s'pose when I'm twenty, you'll say I'm only twenty!"

She would, of course. She felt her face flush. Who was this — Don or Paul?

He crawled up, on his knees, to where she was kneeling, her fingers lifting up the little bushes that hung down, and his face brushed roughly for an instant against her cheek. His brown eyes studied her with faint concern.

"Course it's all right for you to say it, Mom," he assured her. "It's perfectly all right. I even kind of like it. Only, you know, course a fellow can't pay too much attention —"

If Esther had spoken aloud, she would have either laughed or cried. Most likely cried. So she only shook her head, smiling at him, and gave him a little push.

"Go 'way," she whispered. "Smart aleck!"

He liked that. He grinned.

"You look pretty, Mom," he told her, "the way you get all pink sometimes."

(Oh, Don Furbroke! It isn't fair. It isn't fair. You're thousands of miles away!)

The basin in which they had brought grain was nearly full of berries.

"I had a letter today — from Grandma," Esther said, in a rush, as sometimes before in her life she had forced herself to make a difficult revelation. "Grandma Clark. She and Grandpa would like for us to come and — and stay with them a while . . . Would you like to?"

It seemed a full minute before he answered.

Then he asked warily: "How long?"

"Well — how long would you like to stay?" She added quietly, "Gramp said to tell you he had a bicycle overhead in his garage."

"I don't know how to ride a bicycle," Paul said.

No. Ten years old and never had a bicycle, because it had not seemed worthwhile. There was no safe, smooth place here where he could ride it.

Reassuringly she said:

"It wouldn't take you long to learn."

"Well, longer than there'd be," Paul said. "We couldn't be gone more than a day or two. I really don't see how we could be away at all. What about the chickens?"

"I guess we could get somebody to — to take care of the chickens."

There was a pause.

Then Paul said suddenly, triumphantly, "Maybe. But what about Paddy? He'd miss me so — even one night! Hear him yelp right now — just because I didn't go out to talk to him soon as I got home!"

Esther could hear him. That whiskered hound!

"I suppose," she said weakly, "we could take Paddy with us."

Paul was picking no more berries. He was standing up, and even pacing like an anxious man, treading the tall grass down.

"Do you believe," he asked quietly, with an admirable control, "Grandma Clark would like hairs on her carpets? And that silky green sofa she's got in her parlor — I could keep Paddy from jumping up on it. But if ever I was sitting there, he'd be almost sure to just come and rub his nose on it. And lots of times his nose is wet."

Never a truer statement.

"We might stay in the cottage," Esther suggested. "Remember that cunning little cottage behind Grandpa's house? The Peabodys are going away soon. We could stay over there."

"It's a cunning little cottage," Paul agreed condescendingly, "but it isn't big enough. Not for Paddy and us. Why that cottage is just about hardly big enough for Essie!"

Could he be right? It had seemed plenty big once, but then Esther had been small.

"Besides," Paul said, "Paddy is used to being out."

"He could be out. We'd have a yard."

"There isn't hardly," Paul reminded her, "enough of it so you could call it a yard! And if ever Paddy got out into the street, he'd be run over."

That would be sad. For Paul.

"We could keep him on a chain."

"No," Paul said quickly, definitely. "Paddy couldn't be kept on any chain. . . . Besides, I don't think Gramp would like the way Paddy would dig!"

He waited for a response, but Esther could think of none. A child who had seen so little of his grandparents — how did he know them so well?

"Besides," Paul added finally, "isn't that quite a piece of work to go through, just to stay there a day or two? . . . And we couldn't possibly leave these chickens more than a day or two!"

After a minute she said gently: "Grandma and Grandpa want us very much. You see, I was their little girl. Like Essie. The only one they ever had. They've been lonely since I went away."

"Well, that's been years and years. They must have got used to it," he countered. But she saw his eyes rest on Essie.

"Maybe," she suggested, "that's another of those things nobody ever gets used to."

A troubled look came around his mouth, but he said stubbornly, almost sternly: "People must have to. When their children grow up. You'll have to, when Essie and I grow up."

Oh, yes, she would too . . .

"They have to, Paul. But what if they can't?"

"I don't see why they can't," Paul said, now inexorable. "That's where they live. In Kenford. That's where their house is. That's where they picked out to live. I don't know why they picked it out, but they did. Why can't they — just live there?"

"They can," Esther said quietly. "They do. But they're lonely. Grandma always says they're lonely."

"Well, they ought not to be," Paul declared. "And she ought not to say so, if they are. I bet you won't, to Essie and me!" He looked at Esther proudly. "You won't go worrying us, trying to get us to turn everything upside down after we get it planned out nice!"

(Oh, Paul, I'll try not to. I will try.)

"Besides," Paul finished, strong now as a judge with the verdict in hand, "what good would it do, our being there a day or two? I bet they'd be all the lonesomer soon as we went again! Grandma'd be writing letters to you about how big the table looked with only two plates on it, and how bad she felt when she found your handkerchief in her apron pocket, and what Grandpa said when he took down the gate at the head of the stairs! . . . And that's foolish! They ought not to — to hang onto us like that!"

How did he remember? It was three years since they had visited in Kenford. Essie had never been there. They had not seen Essie since just after she was born, in the hospital. They would love Essie. Much as they loved Paul, they would love Essie even more. Because once they had had an Essie . . .

"No, Paul," his mother said. "It isn't foolish. Whatever else it is, it isn't foolish. It may be selfish. But aren't we all at least a little selfish?"

That pricked him. And she was sorry. He really did not deserve it. But that was her last argument, the last appeal she had to make. If he would not go for his own sake, perhaps he would go for theirs. She would never ask him to go for hers. He should never know, and Don should never know, how much she wanted it, needed it, just now — that shingled cottage in the yard behind her father's house, the tended roses and peonies, and hydrangeas, the crab apple tree, Mr. Prescott's spick-and-span store around the corner, and footsteps passing, alive and friendly, in the night . . .

"I s'pose maybe we are," Paul said after a minute, humbly. "I didn't think of it that way." He was so good. "It's hard to think about everybody. I wasn't thinking only about me; honest! I was thinking about Essie, how she likes everything the way we have it. And what a lot of work it would be for you to get us all there, without Daddy to help you. And about Paddy and the chickens. I guess I really didn't think enough about Grandma and Grandpa. I s'pose if they want us so bad, we could go there — for a day or two . . . Sometime."

That settled it. That ended it.

Esther got to her feet and turned the stroller round in the tall grass. She had to push it with one hand, holding the basin of berries in the other. Paul had his eggs and scrap pail to carry.

Ahead of them the big, brown farmhouse loomed grim and solitary against the pale spring sky. A little like a deserted fortress Esther thought. Only it was not entirely deserted, and would not be. A small force, a very small force, would hold it for the duration, whatever the odds.

"We'll go when you want to, Mom," Paul offered humbly, bravely. "Soon as school finishes, we'll go whenever you say. I could fix up the chickens in the morning before we started, and the next night when we got back. Prob'ly I could get Bobby —"

"Well, there's no hurry," Esther told him in a quiet voice. "After all, Essie's pretty little now for a long trip like that. Maybe we'd better wait and go Thanksgiving. Or Christmas, maybe. I shouldn't wonder if the holidays are when they want us most."

She was quite sure she heard him make a small, choking sound behind her. She looked around quickly, and saw his cheeks had whitened under his tan.

"All right," he said after an instant, in a tight voice. "All right."

She had an impulse to cry out suddenly, almost to shriek, "Well, what's the matter with that? What's the matter now?"

But she kept quiet. She bent lower, pushing the stroller over a sharp rise of ground. Paul came up beside her. The grass nearly reached his bare knees. She did not look again as high as his chin.

He said evenly, politely: "Only — the traveling might not be very good, that time of year. And Essie might get sick. She might get a cold . . . Besides, maybe there won't be any gas . . . And if they want to see us so bad, that would be a long time for them to wait. Wouldn't it?

Why don't we go pretty soon, Mom? I think it would be nice to go pretty soon. As soon as school's out."

Esther felt very tired.

She said again: "Essie's too little."

They had reached the porch, grown over with its dark woodbine. She bent to lift the baby, and felt herself sway. It seemed that she was always bending nowadays.

"I couldn't," Paul said miserably. "Mom, I couldn't — I guess I couldn't stand looking ahead to it so long! I'll go — I said I'd go — I know we ought to. But — but I guess I'd just have to — go pretty soon! Then we'd get back —"

She glanced once at his quivering child's mouth, his wide urgent eyes, white streaking his cheeks, and then away, quickly, at the big, old brown house, the bigger, empty barn, the creaking elm, the broad fields with the grass lying dark against the setting sun and blowing in waves like a deep green sea, in the night wind. What was it that Don had found here, that he had known he would find? What was it that they had given to Paul, by bringing him here to live? Some magic surely. Not only a sweet but a strange, strong magic. Would Essie find it too? . . . Would even Esther, if she waited — if she were not too quick, if she got used to everything, and let everything get used to her: if she did not run away?

"Gar-den," said Essie softly, to the woodbine.

Esther said: "Paul! Paul, darling. Listen to your mother. I've just had a wonderful idea!"

Paul looked at her. She could see that he steeled himself. He did not know what her next idea might be, but he knew he must be brave. He was the only man on the place.

She laughed. She knelt suddenly, setting Essie down on the step, and put her hands on Paul's shoulders, turning his face up to hers.

"I don't see why I didn't think of it before," she said. "We won't go to Kenford at all! We'll have Grandma and Grandpa come here, to visit us! That's much the best way! They haven't any dog or chickens to leave, nor children to pack up and take! They can come here so much easier, and stay just as long as they like! . . . Which probably won't be very long," she added ruefully, "because Grandpa does like his own bed! And he'll worry about his flowers!"

"Mom!" Paul breathed, grasping her elbows. "Why, Mom! That's — that's just swell! Why, we'd love having them here, wouldn't we? And we've got lots of room! And — and we can show 'em all our things — the chickens, and Paddy, and — and the brook — then the bridge — and down under the barn! Oh, Genie! And then when they want to go, they can just go, and nobody'll — I mean, of course we'll miss 'em, but we won't cry — and things like that!"

"Oh, for goodness sake!" Esther exclaimed, pushing him away and getting up, laughing. "Us! Crying!"

She took Essie's hands and balanced her while she walked the length of the long porch. Essie loved to walk, and Esther loved to see her, the way her small feet flew out, a little like wings. Her small fingers clung fiercely, like a bird's on the edge of a nest . . . Esther could hear Paul going around to the backyard for Paddy's dishes, to wash them clean before he put supper in them. He was trying to whistle — that sibilant hollow whistle of a small boy . . . Maybe her father could do something about the well, if the water really was getting low . . .

They had their supper, the three of them, under a window which looked out into tangled lilac and syringa bushes.

When Esther came back from putting Essie to bed, Paul had taken his bath, without having been told, and was in his pajamas down on his knees on the kitchen floor, wiping out the tub. He looked up and smiled through the dusk.

He was so good!

"I like to sleep in my own bed, too, Mom," he told her

happily. He turned and sat there on the floor, his legs hunched, his fingers locked around his ankles. "And, you know, I'm awful glad we won't be away for Thanksgiving! Or Christmas! Because that's just the time I like to be home best. I look ahead to Thanksgiving and Christmas all the year . . . Besides, it's just the time Daddy might come, I think."

hristmas 1946

A novelette first published under the title While the Angels Sing.

It was as quiet in my daughter's house that early December afternoon as it had been all summer and fall in my own home in the country. I was alone here as I had been alone there since my husband's death the winter before. Yet, as a matter of fact, I never feel alone, or separate from Alvin. We have been together too many years ever to leave each other, and though I say "death," like other people, I do not believe in it. Alvin is just outside my window, while I am inside, as we have always been, more often than not. Alvin was a farmer all his life. I have little doubt he still is. I am the onetime district schoolteacher who surprised herself by kissing him back when he found a red ear at the husking bee she did not want to go to. We were married after school closed. We lived together fifty-four years, had five children, lost two at birth and one of scarlet fever when he was ten, brought up the youngest two — Julia and Robert — always had what we needed, and gave away all we could spare. I am spending this winter in the village with Julie, but the farm is waiting for me, and I shall go back to it in the spring.

I talk to Alvin when I am alone — or suppose I am. I think Julie knows it, or suspects it, but she has never said anything. It would make no difference to me if she did.

I sat by the window of the second-floor room which the children call "Gramma's apartment," knitting ruddy-brown mittens for Pete, and watching the street run down into the sky. It may sound queer, but that is what it does, and I like it. Julie's house is on a hill a quarter of a mile from the Square. The brick-fronted stores are so far away that they cannot be seen, at least by my eyes, except as a streak along the horizon, ruddy-brown like my yarn; and my window, facing west, is high above it. Julie looked anxious when she showed me into this room. She said, "I wish it got sun in the morning, Mother. I wanted to give you the study. But Horace is so used to it. And, as we said, you will enjoy seeing the people go by." I agreed calmly. "That's right. I shall. And I enjoy looking into the sunset, Julie. It has only beauty and no terror for me."

There was no one at all going by that afternoon. We were in the midst of an early cold wave, and the few country people who had ventured into town in midmorning had gone home as soon as they could. It was not yet time for the school bus. I always watch for that. The children from out our way know I am here and never fail to wave to me. But the sun was setting as it does every clear day, untouched by cold. The sky billowed like a length of old China silk I tied and dipped in pastel dyes to make Julie's first party dress, and I held it by the silver string which was the empty, icy village street.

I said, "Alvin! Have you looked at that sky?"

"What?" he asked. "The sky? No. I hain't."

I have never tried to improve Alvin's grammar since the first year we were married.

I told him, "Well — look!"

After a minute — I suppose he had to set down his milk pails or a basket of wood and felt none too agreeable about being bothered for a woman's whim — he said, "Hm. I've seen 'em brighter."

"Of course you have," I agreed. "But none prettier."

"Prettier!" grunted Alvin. "Say, you keepin' up your fire good? This wind has got a bite in it."

"Fire's blazing like all get out," I told him comfortably.

I had learned, after a while, to talk the way he did, when I talked to him. I never have to anybody else, and I admit I miss the sound of it, lately, when I am in other company so much. It is a very natural, cozy kind of talk, when you are used to it.

"Anybody'd think," I told him, "if once I did let the fire die, we'd have to run to the neighbors for coals to light it with. Matches have come in, Alvin. Can't you get that through your head?"

But I saw then that my little hearth did need attention and I went over and coaxed up a flame. I had not realized my hands were getting cold, but when I fanned the fire, the warmth felt good and the stiffness began to go out of my fingers. I stood there feeling it, smiling to myself, I guess, and thinking that nothing gives anybody such deep-down satisfaction — really unutterable joy — as having some simple thing he needs, when he needs it. Getting warm after you've been cold; having something to eat when you are hungry; finding you do have a handkerchief

when your nose begins to run; sitting down and taking off
your shoes when your feet hurt . . .

Julie came into the room without my having heard a
sound of her at the front door or on the stairs.

Julie was forty-five years old the ninth day of last
month and still looks as much like a girl as she ever did,
but quite a different type of girl than she used to be. If you
put one of the photographs she had made when she was
president of the Woman's Club last year beside the one
she had taken when she graduated from college, without
ever having seen her, very likely you would think the college girl was the older of the two. You might suppose
they were sisters. You certainly would never guess they
were the same person, with twenty-five years, nearly, between sittings.

She used to be — well, I called her plump. She had a
broad face and broad hands and short fingers like her father's. She was a nice, wholesome-looking girl. I never
thought the clothes of that period were becoming to anybody; those long, pipestem-straight dresses with a wide
girdle around the hips, ribbed tan cotton stockings and
heavy, brown, laced walking shoes with brass-bound eye-
lets, the hats like small enamel kettles turned upside
down. And the short, straight bobbed hair! I used to feel
a little sorry for Julie when she was growing up, thinking
of the lovely gored skirts and saucy bustles and tiny sealskin muffs and velvet hats with plumes of my young days;
our pompadours, and the "scolding" curls at the backs of
our necks. But she wore what the others did.

When Julie was about thirty, though — a few years
after she was married — she began to change in her
looks. I have wondered what happened to her. I never
knew it to happen to anyone else. She grew, or seemed to
grow, a little taller. She had always been small boned, but
as she became thinner, her fingers grew not only slender
but long, like mine, and her feet, on which she had worn
4B shoes, gradually narrowed and lengthened into size

6AAA. Her cheekbones are still high but there are soft little hollows below them and her chin is pointed now. Her eyes look very large and they are darker than they used to be, and bluer. A short, curly haircut was becoming to her in her thirties, and when she let it grow long and curled only the ends, a few years ago, everyone admired it. Julie's hair is thick, like her father's, dark with reddish lights, and she brushes it so much it shines. There is something electric about Julie's hair. Her father's was the same. I often think of that. But wearing it long gave her a theatrical look. I never really felt at home with it that way. Lately she has been pinning it up, with little combs in the back, very much as I do mine, and I hope she always will. It does not make her look any older. Sometimes I think it gives her face an almost childlike sweetness. And I think this style is of all the most suitable for a woman.

Yes, Julie is beautiful now, at least by local standards. People often say to me in the village, "Isn't Julie gorgeous! And at her age! Nobody would believe it! What must she have been when she was eighteen?"

I always say, "She was a dear girl."

I do not show them her old photographs.

Julie is simple in her nature, like her father, but not shrewd and down-to-earth like him. Horace calls her idealistic and declares repeatedly that the idealistic person is always riding to a fall. Horace says these things but I don't think he has ever worried about Julie, much as he loves her. I believe he expects Julie to fall without hurting herself too much, and that thereafter life will be easier for him. But I do not want her to be hurt at all, and so I have worried about her. I tried to persuade her to take out her idealism in thinking and in reading poetry, as I had; even in writing poetry. At college she was told she had some talent for writing. But Julie rarely thinks. She is a doer and a feeler. And she is more outgoing than either her father or I; more frankly emotional, and far more indefatigably optimistic. Perhaps I can sum it up by saying that Julie is keenly confident of more essential goodness in those about her than most of us ever see or care to risk believing in, and that by this confidence she has not only brought out much that was hidden before, but perhaps has even produced some which was not inherently there; and while she was so doing, there arose within her a fount of good will and courage and faith in the future from which others drink more often and more deeply than she because they are thirstier.

I admire my daughter without reservation. Yet I love my son better. I can give no reason for this unless that, for so long, I felt mine was the only love he had, while love comes to her as, between brief showers, the sun shines on grass and flowers.

She came in wearing her old tweed suit and matching coat with the krimmer collar, which looks better every year she wears it ("Like anything else that was good to begin with," Julie says), and carrying a few packages and the mail. Her nose was very cold when she kissed me.

She said, "Christmas cards already! Isn't it fun?"

Julie and I have always loved Christmas. Alvin never had much patience with it, and from the time Robbie was twelve years old he never wanted anything but money or something that would turn into some. Alvin used to give the children each a calf or a pig if he had new stock coming along at about that time, and that ended his responsibilities of the season. I suppose it was a sensible gift, for farm children; those calves and pigs helped to educate them; but Julie was the only one who dwelt on the wonder of their kneeling down at midnight on Christmas Eve. (She never went out to the barn to see if they did. She said she knew they did. Robbie went out once, knowing they didn't, and came back, shivering and triumphant, to assure her he had been right. But Julie said, "Course they didn't, front of you. They waited till you went. I don't say my prayers front of you either. But I say 'em just the

same. Every night. And so do you, I bet — when nobody'll know." *Did you, Robbie?*)

I used to go to the woods with the children to get the
tree, until they were old enough to go by themselves; and
helped Julie decorate it until she could reach to the top by
standing on the stepladder. Even then I always sat by to
watch her, and we would speak about which balls were
prettier and where the prettiest came from and how good
the popcorn strings smelled against the spruce — or
sometimes it was fir. And she would ask, "Just three balls
left? Where do we need them most, Mother?" And I
would consider and say, "Why, maybe in there, to the
right — and another by the window where the sun will
strike it in the morning — and — and . . . Oh, Julie,
you choose the place for the last one. The tree doesn't
really need another single thing!" Until at last she would
run back and hug me, and we would stand looking at it,
and half whisper, "It's the loveliest one we ever had!" I
think this is a part of every Christmas Julie has had since.
I know it is of mine.

Alvin never saw a Christmas tree until after we were
married. I had never had one in my childhood home
— it wasn't usual in those days in a private house — but
I had seen them in church vestries and schoolhouses. And
I had always hung stockings behind the kitchen stove with
my brothers and sisters. Alvin was an only child and
he had never even hung up his stocking. His mother usually had a present for him Christmas morning; sometimes
two or three; but, as I understand it, he would have been
quite as pleased with them on any other day of the week
— or year — and much more proud of them if he had
earned the money to buy them or hire them made, as he
earned nearly everything else he ever had, including his
little jackets and school readers and spelling books, from
the time he was eight years old.

Alvin was always concealed by the weekly paper on the

Christmas Eves when Robbie and Julie were little and hung up their stockings. I don't know whether he was really reading it or only pretending to. I used to wish, after they had gone to bed, that he would at least drop a piece of silver into each stocking toe as I had often seen my father do, when he went to wind the clock and thought I was asleep in my trundle bed. But Alvin never did. He would read items aloud to me from the paper, or sit at the table peeling an apple while I filled the stockings, exactly as he did other nights when I was skimming milk or darning. It used to make me exasperated with him, but I did not mention it — or anyhow, not often — because I was sorry for him, too. And when I was through, he would pass me a slice of apple on the point of his jackknife with that sideways grin that always crinkled up the corner of one eye. No apple ever tasted half so good any other way!

On Christmas morning Alvin would be in the barn before the children woke and came running out, barefooted, in their nightgowns. I was more likely to have to call him to his breakfast than on other days. And as soon as he had eaten, he was sure to have some special work planned. Ten chances to one, he was going into the woods to haul out limbs before the next storm. If he was, Robbie would be all high to go with him. Many were the Christmases Julie and I waited until midafternoon to take the presents from the tree in the parlor, because Julie would not touch them until we were all together.

That did make me cross, in those days. "I don't see what is the matter with them," I used to scold. "I believe they just want to plague us!" But not Julie. Standing at the window, she would turn from watching for them, and say, laughing a little, "Oh, no, Mother. They sort of really don't like it. I guess it makes them feel funny. But they've got to do it just the same. Because it isn't Christmas without the whole family, and *we* like Christmas!

. . . I'll tell you what, Mother. Some day I'll have a different family and you'll come and have Christmas with us!"

Well, here I was, beginning Christmas for the first time with Julie's family. All the family I had now. We had not seen Robbie for many years, and had heard from him only in rare, brief letters which told me almost nothing of all I wanted to know.

"Isn't it fun?" asked Julie, opening cards.

It has always been fun, with Julie.

Four of the cards were from the most distant friends, as usual, and the other two from neighbors just down the street. I suppose it all depends on who reads and reacts to the appeals of the Post Office Department.

Julie said, "Here's a picture of Mimi's grandson, actually! Remember Mimi, at college? I wonder what she's like now. She was my senior sister and I thought she was the most beautiful thing in the world. . . . The only thing I like better than a snapshot on the front of a Christmas card is a note on the back." She yawned and stretched. "Isn't it awful? I haven't even taken our cards out of their boxes. I must start on them tonight. Did anyone call?"

I told her that Lorna had telephoned but left no message except that she would ring up again later.

Julie said, "That's what she always does if I'm out. She says she doesn't want me to feel her hanging around my neck like a ribbon. Like a ribbon! Who but Lorna would ever describe herself like that? But it does rather fit her, doesn't it? Slender, feather-light, almost ethereal, very pastel, and faintly quaint in the most becoming way . . ."

Not faded, I hope, I thought. Not beginning to be just the least bit frayed —

For I was very fond of Lorna, too. When she and Julie were in high school together, and she came out with Julie to the farm for overnight or the weekend, I had been happy about their friendship and perhaps a little boastful to myself — since Lorna West was the daughter of the president of the village bank and her mother was past-president of the Woman's Club, and all Lorna's coats, hats, and dresses were bought in Boston; while Julie's father was only the farmer who delivered their butter and eggs and dressed chickens, and Julie's mother did the weekly mending for the Wests and sometimes was engaged to make Lorna's everyday slips and bloomers out of finer material than the Monroes could afford for their daughter's graduation. But if Lorna was aware of any difference between herself and Julie, she thought of it as all in Julie's favor. Lorna, a lovely-looking, sweet-dispositioned child, was shy and lonely, and from the first admired Julie ardently for her capability, determination, and obvious promise, while adoring her for her loyalty and readiness — even eagerness — to give of whatever she had, whether it was much or little. And now that Julie (my Julie!) was mother of three and past-president of the Woman's Club, and her husband was president of the village bank, as well as owner of the twine factory which is our principal local industry, while Lorna lived on alone in the Victorian mansion with the gingerbread façade and the cedar-darkened lawns at the lower end of Main Street, never doing anything but grow older, it seemed to me that life had been very stingy with her, and I felt compassionate. Lorna deserved better than she had got, in nearly every way. Though nobody could deserve or want — I thought — a better friend than Julie.

But what, I had often wondered, came back to Julie in return for all she gave to Lorna? Not that Julie seems to lack anything she wants or needs, but how many ribbons can a woman wear around her neck before they become too heavy a chain? Lorna is a creature of moods. Sometimes she is merry, and then Julie is merry with her. Sometimes she is sad and Julie sympathizes with her. There are weeks when she is at the house every day, and Julie welcomes her joyfully, lets her go reluctantly. There are other weeks when, for no apparent reason, she withdraws into herself or into the company of ghosts and vanished dreams with whom she shares her mansion, and then it is Julie who goes to her again and again, calls her every night before she goes to bed, and writes her little notes, until one day Lorna comes up the hill again, her own sweet self. . . . Does Lorna realize how many other people Julie has to think of beside Lorna? Should I wish she did? I am quite sure Julie does not wish it.

At last I had a chance to inquire casually, "How did the meeting go?"

Julie raised her eyebrows.

"Ho-hum," she said. "Only two of us there. Freddy didn't come. Just Mabel and I."

The situations my child gets herself into!

In the church of which Julie is a pillar, there had lately been a storm. Dear old Mr. Stacy, who had held the pulpit for twenty-seven years, retired last June, and all summer and early fall the parishioners listened to candidates and substitutes. When the time came to make a choice, many of the members felt it was time to select an able, liberal-thinking young man and contrive together to raise a sufficient salary to engage him. Julie and her next door neighbor, Frederica Augsburg, were of this group. However, nearly an equal number of members — the ancient and orthodox — wanted to take an old man who looked as much as possible like Mr. Stacy and would come for far less money, though, as Julie and Frederica said, "Mr. Stacy was as young in his mind as he was old in his body. This man isn't. He never was. He is a strict fundamentalist. He would make no contribution to the town. Our church would stagnate under him." Feeling ran hot. Through Julie's finagling, there was a compromise rather than a deadlock. The Mr. Ransome who was called to the pulpit in November is a middle-aged man, vague, gentle, innocuous. Since he had offended no one and accepted a modest salary, everyone was reasonably satisfied except Frederica. Frederica was furious — with *Julie*.

"But Freddy," I had heard Julie say soothingly on the telephone, "at least he'll do no harm!"

(The Augsburgs and the Thompsons — Horace and Julie — both have private lines.)

"Harm!" Frederica responded in a voice I could hear across the room. "We needed somebody who would do some good, and you know it!"

"I know it," Julie answered quietly. "So now we'll have to do the good, Freddy."

"You do it, Rabbit!" snapped Frederica. "I'm *through!*" She whacked the receiver into the cradle.

And when I was a child I was taught to call all women "ladies"! Even when Alvin was delivering butter and eggs and dressed chickens at their back doors, I continued to call the village women "ladies," despite some of the rather surprising things he told me about a few of his customers.

Julie turned from the telephone that night, rubbing the side of her head ruefully.

She said only, "What a spitfire!"

I said nothing at all. I did not trust myself.

And the next day Julie nominated Frederica to serve on the church Christmas party committee of which Julie had been elected chairman.

Now the committee had held its first meeting, with Christmas only three weeks away and recitations to be typed and coached, songs to be rehearsed, a tree to be cut, hauled, and decorated, gifts to be bought and labeled, candy bags to be made and filled, a Santa Claus to be found — and Frederica, who was strong as a horse, a widow with only one child, and time and money to burn, as they say, had not deigned to be present! Nobody there but Julie — and Mabel Saunders who is as willing as Barkis, but has "a crazy head," by her own description, and two thumbs on each hand, and likes children only in pictures, for which she won't forgive herself; works in the twine factory all day (tangling the twine into knots, I assume), and really wonders whether it is quite — well, *religious* to have parties, even Christmas parties, especially with — well, *you* know — Santa Claus!

I said, "Oh, Julie. I'm sorry."

"Don't worry, Mother. I think Freddy'll come round. Even if she doesn't, Mabel and I'll work it out. Mabel says she'll do anything I think best. You know how Mabel is. And there are others who'll help us, in a pinch. I'm sorry for Frederica. . . . And of course I'm sorry for Honey — I mean, Young Horace. This won't do anything to solve his problem, poor dear. I'm afraid it'll only make things worse. . . . I'll call Lorna now."

I sat thinking about Young Horace. It is not difficult for me to cease calling him "Honey." It was Julie's baby name for her first-born. He is sixteen now, and very much like his father whom Julie used to call "Honey," too, before they were married and for the first year or so afterward. Later she shortened it to "Hon," which she still uses when she speaks to her husband. I think "Horace" fits them both much better.

They are tall and lean, with copper-colored hair which once was pinkish-blond. They are narrow shouldered, slightly stooped, and wear glasses. Young Horace's mouth is shaped like Julie's. This makes it all the more surprising to me that so few light or tender words ever issue from it, and that it so rarely smiles. I have often thought that Horace could — and probably should — have been a laboratory technician. Certainly he is not happy in business, though he has made such a success of it. He has no regard or respect for money, though his income seems to me a small fortune annually, and he makes almost no direct, personal use of it. He occasionally says we should all be better off if we had the philosophy of Thoreau. Yet he is not careless of money. Far from it. To

Horace expense is an academic matter of bookkeeping, and in that he takes what I can only consider an unholy joy. He sets aside annually, having perfectly balanced his own books, an amount he considers sufficient for the maintenance of the family. This is placed in Julie's account and from it she pays all household bills except for such items of clothing as Horace buys for himself. She has never overdrawn it, which — knowing Julie — I consider a major triumph, but that is routine to Horace. He goes through her stubs and canceled checks methodically at the end of every month, correcting an occasional figure, asking for a more detailed description of one item or another, with a shrewd expression and an amused indulgence which I consider both absurd and faintly insulting. But Julie is not troubled by it.

It is not that she is pretending not to mind. She does not mind. I can read her thoughts. But I do not understand it. I feel grateful to Alvin for much that I took for granted for fifty years. He never asked me how I spent my egg money, nor seemed under the impression that he could add or subtract better than I could.

But Julie mentioned Young Horace's problem.

For six months, she told me, he had been desperately in love with Frederica's daughter, Madelene. At first I could scarcely believe this. I could not imagine either of the Horaces desperate about anything, least of all love.

I asked, "How do you know?"

She spread her hands.

"Oh, Mother, I just know!"

And after a few weeks, I, too, saw the curious but unmistakable signs of hopeless infatuation, all unbecoming. He oiled his hair. In the evenings when he should have been doing his homework — his grades were dropping until his father warned him that he might not be certified for college — he was in his room writing letters which he covered with his hand if anyone so much as passed his door. In the mornings he ate little or no breakfast, snarled if he spoke at all, and from his place at the table kept a brooding eye on the Augsburg house until Madelene emerged on her way to the office where she works. This was always too late for him to be sure of reaching school before the first bell rang, but he never budged from his chair until he saw her. Then he would spring up as if stung, reach for his parka, sneer at Julie for suggesting that he turn up the hood, jerk his schoolbooks (unstudied) from her hands, and hurry out, leaving the hall door wide open behind him, having turned over every rug in his path.

Madelene is two years older than he is; attractive, I suppose, in a modern way; the village glamour girl.

"Poor Honey," Julie would say, looking after him.

"Why — especially?" I asked. "More than other boys who go through this stage trying to outgrow themselves?"

"Yes. Because Madelene laughs at him. Openly. Though I don't think he knows it. Yet."

"That is very unkind of her," I said politely.

I admit I saw no reason why someone should not, at one time or another, be rather unkind to Young Horace. I thought perhaps it was what he needed.

Pete is my favorite of the children, though even a grandmother cannot afford to show favoritism.

One of the reasons, no doubt, is that Pete's real name is Alvin. But the other — and far stronger — is that, just as Young Horace is Horace over again, Pete is Robbie. It is almost uncanny. He looks like Robbie — square-built, big head, solemn gray eyes, reserved, even grim; and underneath he *is* Robbie, with such strong emotions that he dares not show them, cynical almost from birth, withdrawn, and brilliant. At the age of twelve he is a freshman in the high school where Young Horace is still only a junior, and Pete leads his class without effort. Pete is brilliant to the point where probably none of us could follow his thinking even if he would divulge his thoughts, and perhaps that is, in part, why he does not. Not many may ever try to understand him. It is one of the most heartbreaking situations into which a human being can be placed by capricious Nature. I had hoped never to see another child in it. Yet here is Pete. Such children — such people — are saved for the world only if they are greatly loved.

Alvin and I saved Robbie as long as we could keep him. Somewhere, after he went away, he became lost. He left college and went out West. He did not marry. He never kept any job long. He wrote less and less, each time from a different address. He had been in the service some time when we received our first allotment check, and put it in the bank for him; it was the first we knew of his enlistment. He was a good soldier. The checks increased in size very rapidly as he rose in rank. He led his men on several fronts and was frequently decorated. At the end of the war he was a colonel. He was discharged in California, shortly before his father died. I wrote him there about his father, and he answered briefly. I had not heard from him since.

I said, "Alvin! Where's Robbie?"

After a minute — I thought he yawned — Alvin answered, "Hm? Oh, I don't know. Somewhere around. He'll turn up."

Alvin never worried about Robbie, but I did. And I worry about Pete.

Though Pete has Julie and me, now. And she says he has Horace. I don't know, but Julie says he does. Certainly he has Babe.

They came in while Julie was talking to Lorna on the telephone. High school is dismissed before the grades, but Pete always waits for Babe.

"Mum-mie?"

"Just a minute, sugar pie . . . It's only the children, Lorna. Babe can take off her own things now. Even her boots. Isn't she the smart child? It's her teacher, really. Miss Atwood's making a big girl out of my baby, and I really am grateful. Though I didn't have the heart to do it myself . . ."

I noticed it was Pete who was taking off Babe's boots. Babe sat on the hall bench with her feet stuck out, smiling at him until her dimples showed, her eyes bright with sheer admiration.

Babe is another miracle. A small one, but I have noticed that the smaller the miracle, the more miraculous it is.

Babe is Julie in miniature; same big, dark blue eyes, same dusky, electric hair, though Babe's is cut short with bangs across her forehead; and full of the same celestial spirit. But she is not Julie as she used to be; that is the wonder of it; she is a piece of Julie as Julie is now. Babe is beautiful *now*. She has a slight body and long slender fingers *now*. She is not only friendly and cheerful and trusting, but she is outgoing and intuitive *now*. Julie in her childhood comforted me by her ability to stand square and straight on her own feet, against any wind which blew. It was not until she grew up that she developed the flexibility and grace of a fern which can reach tall or bend low, even be beaten from left to right and back again without injury to a single frond, and which keeps green and growing wherever it has put down its roots, however dry the season. But Babe is both yielding and strong already, at five.

Sometimes I worry about her too, though no child could give less cause for worry. I wonder what the life span of a fern is, in a stormswept world. I wonder if she has everything Julie has — not only the disposition and the desire, but the energy — and how long it can live in a mortal creature. I never want to see the sun come up on a day when Babe does not see it. I never want Julie to. I never want Pete to.

For Pete is my favorite grandchild.

They came into my room together.

Babe flew to kiss me, light as a butterfly. Pete dropped into a chair just inside the door, hands hunched in pockets, hair standing on end, solemn eyes on us both.

"Oh, Gramma! I've had such a happy day! Misatwood says we're going to have a Christmas tree right in our room. Misatwood says we're each to bring a present. But I'm going to bring lots of presents. I want to take a present for Titia — a book for Titia; Titia's only got two books in *all,* she told me so . . . and one for Molly — ribbons for Molly; Molly lost her ribbons and she don't seem to get any more; she just wears 'lastics . . . and one for Leslie — a bracelet for Leslie just like mine; she likes mine . . . and something for Jean, and Simone, and Eveline, and Betty-May, and Rupert — money for Rupert because he never has any money for candy after lunch; he gets in the candy line and has to get out before we come to the counter because he doesn't have any money —"

"You can't give money to other kids," Pete said.

"Why can't I?"

"Not s'posed to."

"Misatwood never said —"

"No, but you're not, just the same."

"I *do,* though. I give Rupert part of mine lots of times. So he won't have to go out of line."

"Shouldn't think he'd take it."

"Well, he does."

"That's because he's just a little kid. You aren't s'posed to do it. Miss Atwood would tell you so if she saw you doing it. So would Dad. So would Mother, even."

"But they never saw me. I won't let them see me."

"That's sneaky."

"I don't want to be sneaky. But if I *have* to be sneaky . . . It's my own money, isn't it, Pete? Isn't it, Gramma?"

I said what I thought Julie would have said.

"You're talking this over with Pete, Babe."

"Well, isn't it, Pete? I don't like for Rupert to have to get out of the line! You wouldn't either!"

Pete moved uncomfortably.

"You could give him some candy, couldn't you?"

"What's the difference — only to Rupert? I might not pick out what he likes best. Besides, he likes to buy it. It's fun to buy it. It's fun to be in line. It must be awful to have to get out!"

She was close to Pete now, with her hand on his knee. Her under lip was turning out.

"Oh, gosh, Babe . . . Look, what if you didn't have any money?"

"Then I couldn't give it to him. We wouldn't either one of us be in line. I wouldn't even *get* in."

"You think that would make him feel better?"

"It might. I'd feel better, anyway, than to be in line and not let Rupert in too!"

Pete said suddenly, half roughly, "I bet you would at that. Okay. I'm out of it. I said you weren't s'posed to and you're not. But looks like you're going to."

He stood up, pushing her off, and grinned at me, one-sidedly. Whenever I see that grin I know everything is all right. It is not only Pete's. It is Alvin's — and Robbie's.

"Gosh, Gramma! What's going to become of a girl like that?"

I said what I knew Alvin would have said.

"Oh, she'll get along all right."

I thought, And Rupert? Can she see that Rupert, too, gets along all right?

Pete said, "We hope. Well — I'd better get out of this rare atmosphere. My classifications are calling me."

Last summer Pete collected five hundred and thirty-one different kinds of insects within the boundaries of my farm and has been at work ever since, classifying his collection. Just for his own satisfaction. I told him if I had realized there were that many bugs around me, to say nothing of that many kinds, I should not have dared to go to bed at night. When I think of all I've swatted and trod on, too! I hope he has made a clean sweep, I tell him. The first time I said that, he told me solemnly:

"Gramma, listen. There are millions of times more in-sects in the world than there are human beings. Do you realize that the ants already have a very high state of civi-lization? If the ants should grow to our size they almost certainly would control the world. And if they did, it would be a much better world than ours."

"Not for me," I told him quickly.

Pete has learned to expect answers like this. He does not hold it against us. But he goes right on thinking.

It is strange how a boy can be so old in some ways and so young in others. Alvin and I used to speak of that in Robbie.

Pete is already grown-up in his mind but very young in his heart. Perhaps he always will be. Perhaps Robbie still is.

While Julie — and Babe — are all-of-a-piece.

His feet had hardly hit the top stair when Babe, feeling herself freed, knowing herself right, dizzy with triumph, ran to the foot and sang after him:

> *I see England, I see France;*
> *I see a hole in Petey's pants!*

He did not take another step. Even before he spoke I could hear the rumble of thunder.

He said, "Babe! That's not a nice thing to say! Don't you ever say it again!"

"What do you mean?" she cried in astonishment.

"I mean what I say," Pete roared. He has a very big voice when he lets it out.

"Why, it is too, nice! It's funny! Everybody says it to everybody else at school."

"So what? It's not funny, and it's not nice. Don't you ever say it again!"

Babe considered this ultimatum. After a minute she began tentatively:

"I see England —"

"Mother!"

Julie said, "Good-bye, Lorna. See you tomorrow? Fine
. . . What is it, Petey?"

"Listen to Babe. I won't."

His door slammed.

Julie came in and sat down, smiling at Babe.

Babe did not smile.

She said, "Pete's mad."

"Why?"

"Because I sang about 'I see England,' and he told me
not to."

"Why did he tell you not to?"

"He said it wasn't nice. And it is. Everybody says it at
school. But he doesn't like to hear it."

"Why, do you suppose?"

"I don't know. It is nice, isn't it, Mummie?"

"It can't be altogether nice if Pete doesn't like to hear
it, can it?"

"You like to hear it, don't you?"

"Not especially. But I don't mind. You may sing it to
me if you like."

Babe began, but desisted.

She said, "Well, maybe it isn't funny at home. It is at
school." She leaned lightly against Julie's knee. "Mummie, is everything only funny in the right place?"

"I think so, Babe."

"Why isn't this the right place for 'I see England' to be
funny?"

"Because Pete doesn't like it."

"Why doesn't he like it?"

"I wonder."

"Course it isn't true, and Pete only likes true things.
He doesn't even like talking about the Man in the Moon.
Because there isn't any man in the moon. It's mountains
we see up there. Gigantic mountains. The other children
didn't know that, but I did. Pete told me. Misatwood was
s'prised I knew."

"Pete's a big help to you, isn't he?"

"Oh, yes . . . But sometimes I see things Pete doesn't see. Then they're true, aren't they, even if he doesn't see them?"

"Yes, of course. Did you see a hole in Pete's pants?"

"Oh, Mummie, no! If I had, I wouldn't have sung about it. That wouldn't be — wouldn't be —"

"Kind."

"Yes. Kind. If he did have a hole, I'd — why, I'd whisper! . . . Oh, darn it! Maybe the darn song isn't nice."

I am an old dog, full of old tricks. I should probably have said, "Darn isn't a nice word either." But Julie is not that old. She said nothing.

Babe twirled a little about the room.

She said, "Did you hear, Mummie? We're going to have a Christmas party at school!"

"Oh, Babe! Your first school party!"

"Misatwood wants me to bring a cake. A whole cake."

"What kind of cake shall it be?"

"Mm. White?"

"White."

"Jelly between?"

"Jelly between."

"Chocolate on top?"

"Chocolate on top. And Babe — I got a package of shredded coconut today! The first in years!"

"Oh, Mummie! It'll look like snowflakes!"

"It'll look like Christmas, sugar pie!"

"Oh, I love Christmas; don't you?"

"Love it, love it, and lo-ove it!"

Babe stood by the window, pinching the drapery, smiling to herself. She went in slow little twirls to the foot of the stairs, her lips moving silently.

She called up, tipping her head, "Pete! . . . Pete! . . . *Pete!*"

"What?" Pete answered grudgingly.

"I want to sing something to you."

"Don't want to hear it."

"Yes, you do. This is nice. It isn't funny, but it's nice. Listen, Pete. Open your door."

The door opened a little.

"Listen, Pete:

I see England, I see France;
I see Santa's reindeer prance!

There, isn't that nice, Pete?"

After an instant Pete agreed sheepishly, "Sure. Sure. that's all right." He cleared his throat. "That's fine. . . . Look here, Babe. Come up a minute, will you? I thought of something I wanted to tell you."

"G'bye, Mummie — Gramma! I'm going up with Pete!"

She was already on her way.

Julie looked at me, when we were alone.

She said, "Could I be prejudiced, Mother? Or do I have the most wonderful children in the world?"

I knit rapidly, pretending I had been doing so all along, and blinked back foolish tears.

When I could I said, "Don't pay any attention to me. I'm nothing but a silly old woman."

I always have my dinner on a tray at Julie's. It seems to me quite a formal meal in the dining room when Horace is at home, as he usually is, and I am not accustomed to formality. Besides, I feel that it is the only time of day when the president of the bank has his family all together and that it is only right he should have them — and they him — without being obliged to cater, in conversation, to a grandmother from up-country. Julie was afraid, when I first suggested it, that I would be lonely, eating by myself. But I explained to her that it was quieter, that I enjoyed it, that my food digested better, and that I was not lonely at all.

"After breakfast with you all and lunch often alone with you," I told her, "I like this time to think back over the day. A person of my age has so much to think about,

Julie, that unless she can do it before she goes to bed, it keeps her awake at night!"

Julie nodded.

She said, "I can believe that. I've felt for a long time that everything that happens to me is a treasure I lay away to take out and enjoy when I am older, and not so busy. If it is that way, and things keep right on happening — even when you're older — "

"They keep right on happening," I told her. "Seems as if things are always piled up in my mind like a basket of mending ready to topple over."

That night Horace had to go to a directors' meeting, which hurried their dinner, and Pete came in for the tray before I had quite finished my dessert.

He said, "No rush, Gramma. Ellen's just beginning to clear the table."

He sat down on the floor beside the fire, his arms looped around one drawn-up leg.

He said, "Look . . . You think Babe still believes in Santa Claus?"

"Why, yes. Don't you? She's only five."

"She's smart, though. What if she figured we're lying to her?"

"I'm sure she knows you wouldn't lie to her."

"I believed in him, literally, till I was eight. I can't see now how I did it. But I was different. Things get by me. Nothing gets by Babe — for long. . . . Be funny when nobody in the family believes he actually comes down the chimney. . . . I s'pose that's when we stop hanging up stockings."

"Why? Your mother didn't. Even your Uncle Rob didn't. They liked being Santa Claus even more than having Santa Claus, it seemed to me."

"Horace doesn't. He hates hanging up his stocking now."

"Then it's time for Horace to stop. It doesn't have anything to do with you and Babe."

"I s'pose not . . . Gramma, what was Uncle Rob like?"

"Like you. Very much like you."

"Mother said he was a hero in the war."

"Apparently he was."

"Do you suppose he's glad he was? I'd hate it. All the fuss."

"I imagine he hates it, too. If there is any fuss."

"Why doesn't he ever come? I never saw him."

"Maybe he's afraid there'd be a — fuss."

"Huh! Doesn't he know you and Mother better than that?"

"I don't know how well he knows us, Pete. If he did, maybe he has forgotten. It's been a long time."

"Is there anything — the matter with him, Gramma?"

"The matter? No, there's nothing the matter with him." (*Is there, Robbie?*)

"Sometimes I see Mother look — and you — when you speak about him — as if . . ."

"It's only because we love him and he went away. Completely away . . . How do you think Babe would look, if you went away, like that, from her?"

"I'd never do that to Babe."

"Of course you wouldn't." (*Would you, Pete?*)

"I do know," Pete added slowly, "how a fellow can want to. Sometimes. Things get so thick. . . . But I wouldn't do it."

"As long as you wouldn't do it," I said.

Young Horace came in and sprawled on the sofa, knuckling his head.

"Thought Mother might be in here," he told the ceiling.

"She was putting Babe to bed," Pete responded. "Guess she's upstairs."

I knew he hoped Young Horace would go up to find her.

But Young Horace mumbled, "Heard her come down."

Julie had passed my door a few minutes earlier without coming in. She understood at a glance that Pete was in one of his rare talking moods and had chosen me as a listener. She makes me very proud and happy by saying sometimes that she thinks it is good for Pete to be alone with me.

I recalled that I had never considered Young Horace intuitive, but probably he would feel it an insult to be considered so.

After a minute Pete got up, overcasually, and took my tray to the kitchen.

Then Julie came in.

She was looking especially lovely in a thin gray wool dress with gold clips and a pair of chased gold earrings which were my mother's and which will be Babe's someday.

She said brightly, "Oh, Honey! You're in here!"

She sat beside him on the sofa. When he did not move closer to the wall, she began pushing his hair back from his forehead. He still did not draw away. I thought this was surprising.

She said, "Why is Gramma's room the homiest room in the house?"

He did not answer. I doubt if he thinks so. It is natural that she should. I believe Pete does too. Babe is at home anywhere.

He said, "Look — Mom . . ."

"Yes, Honey, darling?"

"Mom, for Pete's sake!"

But he did not sound angry. The tone was indulgent.

Julie laughed.

"What is it, Young Horace?"

"Got any extra money lying around?"

"Extra money! At this time of year? Don't be ridiculous. . . . Honey! You have saved your Christmas money, haven't you?"

Horace has insisted for years that the boys work in the summer to earn money for birthday and Christmas giving. So far Babe makes what she gives.

"Sure," Young Horace responded gloomily. "I saved it. I've got it. But it isn't going to be enough."

"Not enough? Of course it is, Honey. Don't get big ideas. You know we're always pleased with whatever you get. The best part is having you choose for us. It doesn't have to be anything much."

"Yeah," Young Horace admitted. "But this year I . . . well, I've got my eye on something special. And I'm short — well, about twenty dollars."

"Twenty dollars!" Julie looked at him in amazement. "Why, you don't need more than twenty dollars in all! For five people — and Aunt Claire!"

Aunt Claire is Horace's only sister, Clara, whom he has never liked because, being much older, she interfered with his life constantly until he disowned her. Julie has not disowned her, nor allowed the children to. They send her little duty gifts every year. Horace disapproves, but Julie says firmly, "Family is family." I know what she means, but Horace doesn't.

Young Horace rolled over on his stomach and drove his fist into a cushion.

"That's another thing! I'm not spending any money on Aunt Claire this year. I never saw her. I never hope to see her. I'm lining up with Dad on that!"

Julie sighed.

She said, "Very well, Honey. I suppose I can't expect you to go on forever."

Perhaps she thought this concession would distract Young Horace. It did not. It fired him to further self-assertion.

He sat up scowling.

He said, "You're right you can't. And you can't expect me to go on buying all my Christmas presents for twenty dollars either. I'm no kid any longer. I've got thirty dollars and I'm going to blow it all on one present, this year. If I don't get more money from somewhere, there won't be any presents for the rest of you from me, and you might as well know it now."

After a minute Julie said faintly, "Your father would tell you that if you needed more Christmas money, you should have earned it."

"Sure," Horace growled. "Sure he would. Sounds just like him. Well, it happens that last summer I thought thirty dollars would be enough. Last summer I was — still a kid! . . . Different, now."

He got up and walked around, stumbling into things.

Pete had come back from the kitchen and was hunched by the fire again, staring into it. Young Horace nearly fell over him.

"I'd have earned more since," Young Horace reminded Julie. "I wanted to get a job for afternoons and Saturdays. But he wouldn't let me."

"He didn't think you should take the time for it," Julie reminded him. "He thought your grades looked as if your schoolwork needed more time instead of less."

"Schoolwork!" snorted Young Horace.

He came back and sat down beside his mother, taking the cushion on his knees and picking at the corners.

"Look, Mom. Couldn't you possibly scare up —"

"I'm sorry, Honey. You know I couldn't. You know your father wouldn't permit it."

He did know that. His shoulders slumped.

He said, "Okay." Then, "Here's one last arrow into the air. How about you, Pete? You earned more than I did last summer, helping Gramma on the farm. I consider you were overpaid, but we won't go into that. . . . Help a fellow out, would you?"

Pete said, "No soap."

"Why not? What're you going to do with fifty dollars? Buy more silver napkin clips, three times around?"

Pete gave us all silver napkin clips last year. Julie uses

them at every meal. I doubt if I could eat properly if I did not have mine. But Young Horace sneers whenever he picks up his. "Merry Christmas," he sometimes hoots. "What fun. Jiminy Cripes!"

"Don't worry," Pete said. "You won't get another one. Not from me."

"Then what are you going to do with fifty dollars that thirty wouldn't do? I'd pay you back, you know."

"You bet you would. Only I'm not lending."

"Then what *are* you doing, for Cripes' sake?"

Julie said, "Now, Honey —"

But Pete was on his feet.

He roared, "If you *mean* Christ, why don't you *say* Christ? You make me sick. I don't have to tell you what I'm doing, but I will. I'm buying what I want to buy. It'll cost plenty but not all I've got. Any I can spare I promised to Babe this afternoon. She wants to get things for little kids in her grade. Little kids that won't have too much, no matter what she gives 'em. Little kids that don't even have a nickel to buy a candy bar —"

"Oh," mimicked Young Horace. "So you're going away back to the little kids in first grade to scatter your blessings."

"One sure thing," Pete retorted, "I'm not going up to the Electric Light Office! I'm not helping anybody buy a snakeskin bag for any moon-eyed dope that works there, either!"

He stood another instant, swaying slightly with impotent rage, and bolted, nearly knocking down his father as he passed him in the hall.

Horace said, "Hm," speculatively, and bent his head to come through my door. He looked from one to another of us.

Horace does not often come into my room. I usually see him only at breakfast. He looked tired and distinguished and brought the smell of good tobacco and a crisp, outdoor chill.

I said, "Good evening, Horace. Pull up a chair to the fire. I suppose it's pretty cold out."

Horace sat down a little stiffly, as he always moves. With one toe he gingerly straightened a rug Young Horace had kicked up.

He said, "Thanks, Mrs. Monroe. What just went out of here? A tornado?"

I knew he thought Pete had ruffled the rug. For some reason this was more than I could stand.

I said, "Pete went out. But he did not disturb the rug. I think it was your older son who did that." I added, "It's of no consequence."

But it was to Horace. He turned a narrow eye on his older son.

He said, "Until a boy can pick up his feet he should be stabled."

Altogether, this was more than Young Horace could stand.

He said, "Okay. You don't any of you want me in here. So I'll get out. You don't care whether I have anything for you for Christmas. So you don't get anything; see? Some time I'll be out of your way for good, and it may be sooner than you think. I'm getting fed up. Of all the —— —— families a guy ever had!"

He walked stiffly out into the hall, his back absurdly like his father's. I thought Horace must see that, and be embarrassed, I cannot say whether he did or not.

He barked, without turning his head, "Horace!"

"Yes?"

"Horace."

"Yes — sir."

"Go to your room and stay there until you are called tomorrow morning. No communication of any kind."

Horace plunged violently upward.

"Horace —"

The plunging stopped.

"I gave you an order. Reply to it."

"Yes . . . sir."

Horace waited, motionless, until Young Horace's door closed.

Then he asked Julie in the same level tone, "What's the row?"

Julie — *laughed*.

She said, "Oh, Hon, relax. You're not in the army any more. This is me — remember?"

Be it recorded that Horace relaxed, visibly. He did not go so far as to begin a smile, but he did look faintly sheepish.

He said, "I remember. Also that there has obviously been a struggle here. What was it all about?"

Julie said, taking a cigarette from him — she had never before smoked in my room — and balancing on the arm of his chair, "Growing pains, Hon; that's all."

"Who's growing now?"

"Honey — or he thinks he is. And Pete. Looks like we've just got to grow along with 'em, darling."

Horace shook his head.

"I was through with that long ago. No intention of repeating the process. Come on, Julie. What's it all about?"

She told him as much as anyone could have told him.

"If Honey really is thinking of doing such a ridiculous thing as Pete says, we must prevent it by some means; mustn't we?" Julie finished anxiously.

Horace said, "By *no* means."

"But he's sure to be horribly embarrassed —"

"Fine. He's in over his head. Now let him flounder."

"Oh, Hon! It seems cruel!"

Horace said, "Only way to learn to swim. Don't mention the matter to him again. . . . Look here, Julie. You've learned to let them settle their own problems while they're little. Don't tell me you're going to start interfering just when they're determined to — as it is called — lead their own lives?"

"We-ell," Julie said, "I never let them drown when

they're little. Or burn themselves up. Besides, were you letting Honey lead his own life when you sent him to bed, the poor lamb?"

"Yes. Only seeing that he led it out from under my feet. I've got my life to live too. He may be a poor lamb, but I'm an old ram, used to my way of life, and none of last spring's flock is going to gambol on my green."

"Oh. I see. Old ram . . . What about telling him he couldn't get a job for after school and Saturdays?"

"That's just a different kind of gambol. That would be *gambling,* with my money. The money I'm paying for his keep and education against his money for a Christmas gift for Madelene Augsburg. Poor risk. No taker . . . If he wants to blow in what he has in a vain effort to win the fair lady's favor, it's his business. I've no objection at all. And don't you raise any."

"All right," Julie agreed meekly. "I won't, Hon. Want some hot chocolate?"

Didn't she know yet that that way does not work with her Horaces?

He said, "No. But something else now. Speaking of Augsburgs. Frederica came into the bank today. She had quite a bit to say."

"That does not surprise me," murmured Julie. "Knowing Freddy."

"Well, all she said sounded very sensible. She's worried about you."

"Worried about me? Freddy? She isn't even speaking to me!"

"So she said. That's why she's speaking so much to me. She wanted me to use my influence on you. I told her I hadn't any."

"Oh — Hon!"

"As I told her, it's obvious I haven't any. I asked her if she supposed I needed to be told that you are half killing yourself trying to raise that church which is a sunken ship; that you are going to have to put on the Christmas concert singlehanded except for Mabel Saunders's extra thumbs; that I am probably going to have to cut the Christmas tree and drag it to the vestry on my back, unless I'm willing to watch you do it; that you will doubtless have Lorna West here labeling horns and wrapping rubber balls and writing out recitations and popping corn until *she* pops again in one of her recurrent pops, after which you will have both the concert and Lorna to carry — which will be more than enough without dragging the Christmas tree and the Yule logs in? I told her certainly you would half-kill yourself. Maybe three-quarters. That you are always doing it. That you appear to be possessed of evil spirits which make you do it, with no consideration for yourself, which in the end means no consideration for your family —"

"Half-kill! Oh, Hon! And I feel so well! Don't I look well, darling? Any dark circles? Any gray hairs?"

Horace pushed her off the arm of his chair, and stood up, tall.

"See?" he said to me. "No influence! I'm going up and tell Pete I consider him the only person in my family with a grain of common sense, at the moment. Then I'm turning in. Somebody has to keep up his stamina for the grueling miles yet between us and Christmas night. O, blessed night!"

He went out. We could hear him climb the stairs with his neat, quick step. His shadow moved swiftly along the polished banister, narrow but opaque.

I picked up my knitting. So far grandmothers have always had knitting. My wish for future generations of them is that they may never find themselves without it.

Julie said, "Poor Hon . . . Mother, do I really spend too much time and thought outside my family?"

I held onto my tongue.

I said, carefully, "You are as you are, child. You have to be doing. And, according to Horace, you are already in danger of doing more for at least one member of your

family than he thinks wise. What does he suppose would
happen if you concentrated all your energies on the four
of them?"

"But what if I never had any ideas at all? What if I
just gave myself to making them comfortable all day and
every day?"

"That would be some other woman, Julie. Besides, it
couldn't be done. Nobody ever is comfortable all day
every day. You know that. We weren't intended to be.
Nothing could be worse for us."

"But everybody could safely be a little happier than
they are."

"Yes. And that's what you're trying to make them. Everybody. And in sum total, more can be done for the
many, I suppose, than for a few."

"It does seem so." Julie sighed, and smiled. "Oh,
Mother, you're such a comfort! The church isn't a sunken
ship, is it? We do need a Christmas party, don't we? It
wouldn't be right to give it up and let Freddy win, would
it? Why, it wouldn't be fair to Mabel! To say nothing of
the children! Babe is going to love that Christmas party!
Those parties in the vestry are built right into all our children. They're a part of their heritage. That makes me
think — I'd better talk to Pete, too. He'll be in a better
mood after Hon gives him a pat on the back. And Pete
was sweet about offering Babe part of his money, wasn't
he?"

I said, "Pete is sound. What are you going to talk to
him about?"

"Oh — little Sue Halsey."

Sue Halsey is a strange child from the lower part of
town, the section which in some places is called "across the
tracks" or "the wrong side." She was adopted as a baby
by an elderly man and his wife, a stout, bluff good-natured, ignorant couple, after their own children were
grown. Nobody knows her parentage. Some people hint
that she is the child of their unmarried daughter, but Julie

has never believed it. Certainly she does not resemble the Halseys in any way. She looks like a gypsy. Very thin, very dark, with big, smoldering black eyes, and a witchy manner. Julie has been fascinated by her since the Halseys first brought her to Julie's Sunday school class when Sue was the age Babe is now; and Sue openly adores Julie, follows her about, makes up excuses to come to the house, and will look at her worshipfully as long as she is within range, sometimes without saying a word, and sometimes chattering like a magpie.

"There's something about that child," Julie has said a hundred times. "I don't know what it is. I can't figure it out. She is plain, and still she is beautiful. The quality of her voice haunts me. She puts out her hands, but never touches anything. She is so — alone. I wish she were mine!"

Sue is fourteen now, in Pete's class at school, and apparently she has seen at least a reflection of the halo she long ago gave to Julie shining about Pete's dear, square head. She talks to Julie about him, in terms Julie would not dare quote to anyone but me; she nominates him for offices; she sends him valentines and birthday cards; and she trills, "Hello, Pete," wherever she sees him, however public the place. I have heard that myself, but never heard him more than make a growling sound in his throat by way of reply. Pete sees no possible relationship — none whatever — between himself and any girl but, because of these cards, nominations, and trilled hello's, probably the only girl he troubles himself to dislike actively is Sue Halsey.

So perverse is fate.

I asked uneasily, "What about Sue, now?"

"Oh, the poor darling, Mother. She came into the vestry where Mabel and I were meeting this afternoon and waited until we were through to walk up to the village with me. I was afraid she would freeze. She's still wearing that old greenish-black coat she's had since she was ten —

they must have cut it over from something they had in the
house — and honestly, the sleeves are so short now
they're half way to her elbow. Her wrists are like pipe-
stems and horribly chapped. And her long, scrawny little
neck goes up and up and down and down, all bare, until
you think of illustrations in *Alice in Wonderland*. But she
was so happy and so excited that she was trembling. At
least, she said it was trembling, not shivering. She had
some money in her pocket. She showed it to me. Five half-
dollars she had earned as a baby-sitter through the fall.
And this was the great day when she was going to spend
it — on a present for Pete! To put on the Sunday school
tree. She wanted me to tell her what I thought he would
like best of anything!"

"What did you tell her?"

I knew I should have told her to keep her money toward a sweater, one with a high neck and long sleeves. I
should have said, "Listen, child. You are shouting down a
rain barrel to Pete, and you don't even get an echo. Don't
go on making a fool of yourself. Where is your pride?"

Julie said, "I know what you think I should have told
her, Mother. But I didn't. I couldn't. If you had seen her
eyes, you couldn't have either! I told her Pete would like a
book. I told her the title of a book he does want. It made
her so thrilled her feet hardly touched the sidewalk. . . .
Now Pete simply has to get her something. Something
warm — and lovely! Oh, I hope he's still in the mood —"

I doubted that he was, ever had been, or would be.

She ran upstairs.

I finished a row around Pete's mitten, my hands fum-
bling like Mabel Saunders's. I dropped the needles in my
lap and said:

"Alvin! I'm as jumpy as a cat!"

After a minute he said, "Don't addle your brains, Old
Woman, about what's none of your business. Better go to
bed. Tomorrow'll be another day."

"That's what you always say," I told him. "What does

it mean, if anything? It'll be another day nearer to Christmas; that's certain. And what kind of Christmas is Julie going to have with her own, different family? I've always wondered what her Christmases were like. Now I'm going to find out, and I'm not sure I want to. . . . But it's no use to talk to you about Christmas, Alvin. It never was in your line. Any more than it is, apparently, in Horace's."

Going to bed, of course, was the best thing for me to do, and about all I could do.

I took off the handwoven spread from the sofa — the spread Alvin's mother made and that we always had on the bedcouch in the sitting room at home — and turned back the blanket, opened the windows, snapped off the lights, and went into my bathroom.

As I unbuttoned, untied, bathed, and finally pulled my cotton flannel nightgown over my head, I said, "Alvin, running hot water is a wonderful thing. To a woman who has lived all her life without it, running hot water feels as good as the pool in the brook used to feel to your bare feet when you were a boy; as good — almost — as your lips felt against mine at that husking bee. An old woman who likes to be clean is in love with running hot water. You may think that's silly. I don't care if you do. . . . And snapping lights off and on is like the bonfires we used to go to on the mountain, Fourth of July, when we were young, and like the fireworks we used to drive to the edge of town to see later on. Every time I snap on a light I want to dance. Every time I snap one off I want to whistle in the dark. I know you think I'm foolish!"

I snapped off my bathroom light and groped to the bed, whistling all through me, but not making a sound.

I thought, "If I had running hot water and electricity out at the farm, I'd never set foot off that place again as long as I live. . . . Oh, well, can't have everything."

I had almost completely forgotten about Julie and her Horaces and Robbie and Pete and Babe. I did not even miss Alvin as I settled myself in bed. I always do at home, but Alvin never slept with me here. There is only room enough for one anyway. But it is very comfortable for one. How all-in-all physical comfort can be when you are old, only the old can know.

It was a minute or two before I realized that Julie was standing by the hearth. Then I thought perhaps I was imagining her.

I said, "Julie! You there?"

"Yes. Did I startle you, Mother? I'm sorry. I thought you would turn on a light when you came out of the bathroom."

"I like to watch the fire blinking out," I told her. "Makes me sleepy. Julie, this is the best bed I ever slept in."

"I'm so glad you like it, Mother. Good night, darling." She came over and kissed me.

Her touch roused me from absorption in myself. I remembered that she was still too young to be able to afford to lose herself in comfort.

I asked, "Did you talk with Pete?"

"Oh — yes —"

"What did he say?"

"Must you know?"

"I might as well."

"He said, 'No soap' again. Said it very firmly."

"Horace would approve of that, too, wouldn't he?"

"I know. But Sue —"

I reached for her hand.

"And you. Oh, Julie! I want you to have a perfect Christmas —"

She kissed me again.

She said, "I will. I always do."

I let her go. I heard her move, through the dark, and saw her face silhouetted against the window as she paused there, looking out.

She stayed quiet so long that I began to slip away again.

She said softly, "Don't worry, Mother. The angels are singing all the time."

It seemed like part of a dream.

When I woke from it, the sunshine was streaming in. It was another day. One day nearer to Christmas.

Julie was at my desk writing cards that afternoon when the side doorbell rang, Ellen — the maid — opened the door, and Lorna came running upstairs.

Julie's face lighted at the sound. She turned quickly, but before she could get up, Lorna had crossed the room and they were in each other's arms. As they clung together, I caught a glimpse of what Lorna gave to Julie, as well as of what Julie gave to her. I realized dimly that I had never experienced an intimate friendship with another woman of my age. It would be difficult, I suppose, for any farmer's wife, and more so for me, perhaps, than for others, for I am naturally reserved and independent. Julie is neither. I saw that she was leaning, in her own way, as much on Lorna as Lorna was on her, physically and emotionally.

She cried, "Oh, Lorna! It seems weeks since I saw you. Was it really only the day before yesterday? And it's getting so late I was afraid you weren't coming. I was just going to call —"

Lorna said softly, "Darling, of course I was coming. I told you I would. But I met Frederica Augsburg and she held me up, practically at gunpoint."

Still within the circle of Julie's arm, she began drawing off her gloves, and added in her characteristically low, gentle voice, "What a beast that creature is!"

"Oh, no," Julie laughed.

They drew apart. Lorna kissed me and sat down on the sofa, her hands folded and her ankles crossed. Julie left her chair and curled up like a kitten in the sofa corner opposite her. I thought they must have sat like this many times, so different and yet so close . . . while they were

in high school . . . when they came home from college
on vacation . . . while Julie was teaching and Lorna was
caring for her father in his last illness . . . when Julie
came here to live as Horace's wife and Lorna stayed alone
in the house where she had grown up . . . when Julie
was waiting for her babies . . . while Julie's children
were napping . . .

How much had they told each other? How much did
they know about each other without ever having been told
in words?

Julie said, "You know Freddy, Lorna. She is opinion-
ated and has a furious temper. That prevents her from
taking a very long view of anything and it is a handicap.
But when she's good she's awfully good. It's only when
she's bad that she's horrid."

"When she is horrid, she's beastly," Lorna said gently.
"And when she's being beastly to and about you, I hate
her. All the time she was talking I could have choked her.
I could have pushed her over a precipice. I could have
locked her up in a cell with water dripping on her head
and a bright light in her eyes —"

"Lorna!" Julie squealed. "What on earth was she saying?"

"I hardly know, darling. I was so preoccupied with my
thoughts about what I could cheerfully do to her if only
you wouldn't mind. But I knew you would, so I didn't
even choke her. Really, Julie, you have no idea of the ex-
cesses from which your tender heart and forgiving nature
restrain me whenever people in this town oppose you in
anything. Sometime I am going to make a long list of
them, for my relief and your amazement."

Julie toppled over, laughing, her head in Lorna's lap.
Lorna fingered the dusky topknot, stroked the sleek dark
wings springing up from Julie's white temples.

She added in the same sweet monotone, light and fleet-
ing as her touch, "I believe she said you were cooperating
with Old-Time-Religion to close the church to intelligent

people. I told her that was nonsense. She said you would be down sick if you tried to put on a Christmas party with nobody but Mabel Saunders to help you, and that she wouldn't lift a finger. I told her that sounded friendly on her part. She said she wouldn't speak to you again until you came to your senses. I told her that was wise, considering her state of mind; the less she said, the less she would have to regret and take back later on. She said — but somewhere in there, I walked away. Now I doubt if she is on speaking terms with me. I hope not. If I had known how easy it was to bring that about, I should have artificially induced it long ago."

I thought how different was Lorna's report from Horace's, and wondered if any man could face a woman's attack on another woman with such fierce loyalty expressed so imperturbably. And even if he did, could he tell the maligned woman how well he had defended her, without displaying personal embarrassment or seeming to boast? I thought not. I believe a man is honestly terrified by the ferocity with which women fight, and feels he saves his skin only by pretending in public that feminine wars are silly and futile; in private he blames the woman he loves for being found available for attack, regardless of how right her position may be; he thinks she is safe enough in the struggle because of some extraordinary armor she wears, while he, unarmored, resents the risk she makes him run of being struck by glancing blows, all vulnerable as he is. Only a woman can see other women's quarrels in proportion and contribute her own thrusts exactly where they will tell, with a kind of scientific detachment and with an inner ecstasy which is her high and complete reward.

Julie said, "Oh, Lorna, you're wonderful!" She sat up and shook Lorna's knee. "Darling, with or without Freddy, we're going to have a bang-up Christmas party in the vestry of the Congregational Church!"

Lorna said, "Of course you are. And you're going to let me in on it. Sotto voce. Just so I can always remember I had a hand in proving that Frederica is not indispensable."

Lorna is not a member of Julie's church and does not attend it. Lorna is not a member of any church or organization. She is not active directly in any of the affairs of the town. She has worked only with and through Julie, very much, I imagined, as she would work with and through her husband if she were married. She is naturally self-effacing. She cherishes, apparently, no personal ambition. She has, I believe, all the qualities intended to aid and abet and content a husband, some of which, as I have shown, Julie does not have in so great a degree as she has others. How often this is true of spinsters! What the middle-aged man most craves, the young man is utterly blind to. He chooses a wife for the very characteristics he later longs to eradicate. I wonder if this is not the main reason why, in these modern days when marriage no longer forces a woman to become less of an individual than she was as a girl, but rather tends to develop her more fully along her foreordained lines, there are so many broken homes.

Julie said, "She certainly isn't indispensable to me. Especially since I have you. But Lorna — should you get into this? Horace said last night he knew I could count on you —"

(Now exactly what was it Horace had said?)

"— but it will be a strain. There's so much to do, and with the feeling what it is this year—you mustn't think you have the slightest obligation! Of course you haven't. And I wouldn't have you hurt for all the Christmas parties in the world!"

Lorna said gently, "There is nothing this town can do to hurt me, Julie. There isn't a person in it who means anything to me except you and your family. I'd really love helping. Behind the scenes. It will — keep me occupied — for a while."

This wistful, resigned note comes easily and often into Lorna's voice. Sometimes it is very touching. Sometimes I have wondered if it could not also become boring and even irritating to a positive person like Julie who never resigns herself to any situation which is other than as she would like it. Even if, actually, she cannot alter it, she keeps on trying with unflagging zeal and optimism. As far as I can see, Lorna has never tried to do anything for herself. But Julie knows when — and how — to pass off Lorna's wistfulness.

She said, "Okay, sweet. Let's go. Just remember you can pull out whenever you like."

She pushed aside her cards on the desk and brought pad and pencil. They literally and figuratively put their heads together, making lists.

I thought, "Now they can be children again. People are always saying it is only men who are boys forever. I don't think so. Men grow up in their feelings toward everything and everybody except themselves. And even there they are never little boys as once they were little boys; they are grown-up little boys. They want what they want but it isn't what they used to want. Women can be anything, if they will. They can be whatever the people they love need most — wives, mothers, nurses, teachers, disciplinarians, entertainers, club presidents, program chairmen, school board members, politicians. And they can be children with and for children, with all their hearts. Perhaps that is what they like to be best. And that must be what has kept up the tradition of Christmas and steadily enlarged upon it all down the decades. Boys outgrow Christmas so quickly that, as men, they do not even remember what it means. Girls never outgrow it. Every year it reaches out its arms, lifts them upon its silver wings, and flies them direct to the workshop where magic is in the making."

I thought of how many times Julie and Lorna had put their heads together before: translating Latin, working out equations, designing dresses, making posters, reading letters, looking at snapshots, pasting souvenirs, leafing catalogues, reading handbooks, decorating place cards, counting ballots, studying timetables, figuring proceeds, choosing from samples, spreading canapes, tracing genealogies, checking records.

I said to myself, with quiet delight, "Now Christmas transcends it all. Now they can be children again. Good, busy — but children."

I felt a mother to them both; a young mother who would be a child with them, for Christmas. Is this annual renewal of youth and vigor one reason why a woman's life expectancy is greater than a man's? If so, God, why did you not plant in men, too, a capacity for sharing, over and over again, the birth of the Child? Why are they driven to close their eyes just when He is nearest? Would His brilliance blind them?

As the days passed, the fall of cards grew from a few fluttering flakes to a whirling storm. Julie's and Horace's overran the living room and banked the dining-room mantel. Babe's obscured the toys in her playroom and the brushes and combs and little boxes of talcum and little bottles of cologne on her dressing table. Mine made a Christmas panorama around me, framing the fireplace, covering desk and windowsills. Even the boys had a good many, though Pete hardly glanced at his and Young Horace only looked through those which came for him with the same swift, accurate precision which his father accords a row of figures. The boys' cards dropped from their hands like whittlings and were left for Julie to pick up and spread on trays on the table in the upstairs hall, just outside my door.

"Honey got more than Pete," she told me. "I know Pete doesn't care, but I do. Of course Honey has always sent more. He's more social. At least, he has been until lately. But Pete simply won't."

I wondered what she meant by "social." I thought I knew. But it seemed to me a superficial sense of the word.

It was difficult for me to grant Young Horace any desirable characteristic which Pete did not have. I supposed I was prejudiced.

One of Pete's cards was from Sue Halsey. It had the picture of a girl's face looking through a holly wreath, and there was mistletoe in her hair. She had drawn it herself, presumably, and tinted it with watercolors. And she had printed in neat script:

> *When Christmas comes around each year*
> *I like to say "Hello"*
> *To folks I think a lot of —*
> *And one is you, you know!*

She could hardly have done worse for herself. Julie sighed when she read it.

There were times when Pete's resolution to make no Christmas gift to Sue, and Young Horace's grim determination to make no Christmas gifts to his family — though neither was openly referred to — seemed to fill the house with clouds so dense that I wondered if Christmas could ever break through. And I was sure that the atmosphere of the church vestry, where Julie went to work with Mabel every afternoon she did not work at home with Lorna, could not be much brighter. Frederica continued to make her absence as noisy as possible, the janitor was grumpy because of the extra heating and sweeping he had to do, the more willing children had colds or measles or chicken pox, and the less willing stumbled through their parts, drummed on the piano while others recited, and went with their parents to talk to department-store Santa Clauses in Dalton City on rehearsal afternoons.

And surely Horace's disapproval of all Julie's seasonal undertakings, never muted to anything more encouraging than a show of complete indifference, would have dampened any less buoyant spirit than hers.

But Julie went from one task to another with light feet and shining eyes.

She said, "The brighter children don't need much rehearsing. The slower ones will get their lines in time. Mr. Colt of the variety store has offered a present to be put on the tree for every child who takes part in the program. Isn't that wonderful? Of course it's a sort of bribe. But some of them need it. You have to face facts."

She continued, "Honey did get the snakeskin bag for Madelene. I saw it in his drawer when I was putting away the laundry today. Poor baby. But I'm just going to believe that her reaction will help him to get a better perspective, one way or another. . . . And I saw the sweetest, sheer, scarlet wool scarf in Mr. Colt's window today. I think Pete will give it to Sue if he doesn't have to walk in and buy it himself. I'm going to talk to him about it tonight. After he goes to bed."

She said, "Pete was dear. He says he can't give anything to Sue. He wants me to understand. And in a way I do. But it would mean so much to her. There has to be some way out for both of them. . . . I'm going to give all the girls of Sue's age scarlet stocking caps. I want terribly to give her a checked wool shirt like so many of the others wear, but of course I can't give her more than I give the rest. At least the cap will match the scarf. If she gets the scarf."

Lorna said quietly, "I'll give her the shirt, Julie. I can do anything I want to. And I never bought a shirt in my life!"

Julie and I both realized that Lorna's annual income would hardly permit the buying of even one such expensive gift. She barely keeps up her running expenses. For years the house has needed repairs she could not afford.

But Julie said quickly, "Oh, Lorna! Bless you, bless you, and bless you!"

I knew Julie did not believe that anyone was ever the poorer for whatever he gave away, and also that she was beginning at once to figure how she could make this up to Lorna without seeming to.

One day Julie came home glowing from a rehearsal.

She said, "Mother! What do you think? Sue asked me if I'd like to have her do a dance on the program! She suggested it herself! I didn't know she could dance. Maybe she can't. I'm sure she never had a lesson. But I don't care whether she can or not. She wants to, and that's enough for me. She's going to. I said of course we'd love it. Mabel is shocked, but I can take care of Mabel. I told Sue we'd provide the costume. And Mother — could you make it? Something perfectly, utterly beautiful out of some of my old evening dresses? Something she'll probably never wear again, but something really frabjous she'll always have to keep?"

I had planned a good bit of Christmas knitting, sewing, and crocheting which was still undone but I knew that this would be a better gift to Julie than anything I could make or buy for her personal use; so I said yes, I would see what I could do, if she would bring me the material, and have the child come in from time to time to be measured and fitted.

It was in this way that I too fell victim to little Sue's curious enchantment. In fact, as time went on, I wondered how it was possible for anyone to hold out against her.

She came whenever I sent for her. She came often when I had not. She was in a state of complete delight about the look and feel of the rose-colored velvet from which I was cutting the bodice and of the crisp white taffeta which I was gathering into a brief, ballooning skirt. She was fascinated even by the thread, by the gleam of the needle and pins and the flash of the scissors. She would slip eagerly out of her faded cotton dress, or bunchy jumper and shrunken jersey, even out of her long, baggy woman's underwear, as often as I asked her, and stand stark naked in the smallest, most graceful and agile bones and the whitest skin — pearl-like — that I have ever seen or imagined, and step into the pink velvet shorts and then into the pinned or basted ballet dress with a hushed breathlessness that suggested to me a person of great faith lifting the Communion cup. She was never impatient, never grew tired, never twitched. And whenever I did not need her, she sat on the floor, near enough to watch my every motion, but never near enough to get in my way.

She could talk freely, or she could be happily silent.

When she talked she said things like: "You're my fairy godmother, aren't you? I always knew I had one. I love you, Mrs. Monroe. You don't mind my loving you, do you? I love all of you here. It's just like heaven here. You're so kind. You're just like an artist. And Mrs. Thompson is kind, too, and so beautiful. And Babe is adorable. And Pete is so handsome and smart. Pete's in my class, you know. I'm awfully proud to be in Pete's class. When I grow up, I'll bet I'll like to tell people I was in Pete Thompson's class. He's nice. He's sweet to Babe, isn't he? She's lucky to have a brother like Pete, isn't she? I'd like to have a brother like him. Any girl would. He's nice at school, too. Some people don't like it because he's smarter than they are. I think that's silly. Jeepers, even if I'm not smart, I'm glad somebody is. He never shows off a bit. He helps anybody that asks him. He even helps me if I ask him. I guess he doesn't like me, but maybe he will when he knows me better. Of course he's always so busy he doesn't notice people much. I try to get him to notice me, but he hasn't yet. Do you think he'll come to the Christmas party? If he does, he can't help noticing me in this dress, can he? Horace likes Madelene Augsburg, doesn't he? I see him walking with her most every morning. She's as pretty as a movie star. No wonder he likes her. I wonder how it feels to be pretty like that. Maybe I'll look better when I'm older. Horace looks like his father. Mr. Thompson is nice looking, isn't he? He looks like a governor. He looks stern, though. I'd never dare to speak to him. I'll bet Pete isn't afraid of him, though. Pete isn't afraid of anything, is he? I'll bet Pete will be governor when he grows up."

Sometimes she said, more slowly and thoughtfully, "It's lovely to be with you. I can just be myself. I don't have to try. You're just there and I'm near you. It's restful. It seems as if with everybody else I'm trying all the time. I don't know just what I'm trying to do, but I try awfully hard. Sometimes I think people would like me better if I didn't try so hard. But I can't help it, until something happens. I don't know what that something is, but I want it dreadfully. I have to keep on trying till I get it. Do you suppose I'll know I have it when I have it? It would be horrible if I didn't. I'd probably lose it. But I think I'll know; don't you, Mrs. Monroe?"

I said, "Yes, Sue. I'm sure you'll know."

"Why don't I know now?"

"Maybe because you're so young."

"Am I young? I know I act young. Maybe I look young. But I don't feel young. At least, not the way I think feeling young is . . . I don't know. I don't know much of anything. That's the trouble, I guess . . . It's dreadful not to know. It makes you cry at night . . . Mrs. Thompson always knew, didn't she?"

I said, "I believe she always thought she knew. Perhaps that is almost the same thing."

"I wish I could be just like Mrs. Thompson. Maybe I will be someday. After I find out what it is I'm trying to get. After I get it. I hope so . . . She lived on a farm, didn't she, when she was a girl? It must be wonderful to live on a farm."

"It isn't an easy life."

"Oh, nothing is ever easy, is it? I don't want anything that's easy. I just want a chance to work at something that I know what it is."

I said, "I think you'll get that chance, Sue. Just be patient. And I think you already know a great deal, for a child."

Christmas was on a Monday that year.

The Friday morning before, Babe left for school with a picnic basket on her arm. It held a white layer cake with coconut frosting which Ellen had made, and a popcorn ball and a card for each child in her room. Pete walked with her, carrying a carton of packages which Julie had wrapped and tied and Babe had labeled the afternoon and evening before. The contents were Titia's book, Molly's ribbons, Leslie's bracelet, Rupert's red plastic coin-holder with a quarter, a dime, and a nickel in the proper places, a chiffon handkerchief for Miss Atwood, and all the "some-things" for Jean and Simone and Eveline and Betty-May and others which Babe and Pete had carefully and happily chosen together, paying for them from Pete's summer savings.

Babe said, framed in the doorway, "Oh, Mummie! It's the day!" Her face was pink with excitement. Pete, outside on the step, looked down at her with a pleasure he for once felt no need to conceal.

I thought, "Jesus, if You had brought us nothing but Christmas, You would still have pointed the Way, the Truth and the Light."

But there was yet much to be done, many hurdles which human nature must be helped to clear.

Julie was to hold her final rehearsal of the Christmas program that night. She had felt that after the round of school parties, the children should go directly home in the afternoon. She wanted Babe to come directly home, and to be there when she came. She felt sure other mothers would feel as she did.

She had telephoned the church janitor the evening before and asked him if he would have the vestry warm at 6:00 P.M. on Friday.

He is a crotchety old character.

He said, "No, Mis' Thompson. I wun't. Now I don't want to be mean, but you've had me shovelin' coal down thar' every other day for three weeks, and sweepin' up arfter ye, too. Oh, I know you womenfolks struck up to do some sweepin' but 'twarn't to suit me, I'll tell ye straight out. I've been right over it agin arfter ye every time you been in thar'. Now I've got to heat up for the set-to thar' Sat'dy night and if anybody gits 'round to drag in a tree and such-like thar' tomorrer, it'll likely take me all day Sat'dy to dig out the place. I hain't a-goin' to be thar' a-tall tomorrer and you might's well make up yer mind so. I've got a mite o' business o' my own to tend to before Christmas — surprisin' as that may be to some folks — and I'm a-tendin' to it tomorrer. Git me?"

Julie said quietly, "Yes, Mr. Pease, I get you. But I had to attend to my personal business earlier this year. Between now and Saturday night I am giving all my time to the church. And the children and I must be at the vestry at 6:00 P.M. tomorrow, whether it is heated or not."

Mr. Pease said, "Well, 'twun't be heated, now I'm a-warnin' ye. And if you ask me, you hain't a-givin' your time to the church. You're a-givin' it to a shindig. Churches would be better off without shindigs, way I look at it. But I've larnt that folks like you don't take much stock in how I look at things."

Julie said, "Your opinion is your own, Mr. Pease. You've got as much right to it as any man. Often I agree with you, and you know it. This time I don't. Such shindigs are a very important part of my religion. Merry Christmas, Mr. Pease."

As she hung up the receiver, Horace called from the study, "Get wholehearted cooperation from the laboring class, I gather."

"Sometimes," Julie answered. "From some of them. Don't worry, Hon. I see Mr. Pease's point. I think he'll see mine. I think the vestry will be warm when we get there."

"Think the tree will be there, too?"

"Yes."

"Think Jake Pease will be prancing around decorating it?"

"No dear. I think you will. Not prancing, of course. I'm sure you'll be very dignified. But the tree should be at least ten feet tall with nice long, stout branches, and the base we always use is in the bottom of that closet where we keep Sunday-school supplies."

"Interesting information, Julie, but I'm obliged to say I can't spend tomorrow afternoon in the woods. I admit I had thought I could but I find I can't. Like Jake Pease, I have other business. Think of somebody else."

Julie stood still in the hall.

"Who, Hon?"

"Think."

"Honey?"

"Good thought."

"But Hon — I don't know. He's so strange lately. How'll I ask him?"

"With words, my dear. . . . I'll speak to him if you like."

"Oh, Hon, if you would!"

She came into my room, and repeated the telephone conversation.

I said, "What a pity, Julie!"

She was beginning to get circles under her eyes, and no wonder, on an eighteen-hour-a-day schedule. I wondered how Mr. Pease would like to follow her for one week, or would have even when he was her age, though he probably thinks of her as a lady sated with leisure. I hoped no one but me would notice the circles; at least, no one else in the family.

She said, "Oh, I think it will be all right. Mr. Pease just wants to assert his independence. He's a rugged individualist. That's part of New England. You have to respect him for it, really. . . . I am disappointed that Hon can't go for the tree. He always knows just where to get the loveliest ones for the bank. But if he tells Honey — and

Honey will do it — it'll be good for Honey, won't it? At least it will be something he can do about Christmas. Ever since he got that bag, while the rest of us have been so busy, he's seemed sort of shut out and cut off; it hurts me. . . . The more I think of it, the more I think it was meant that Honey should get the tree. I'll tell Hon to ask him to get ours for the house, too. It can be his present for us all. Oh, Mother, why didn't we think of that before? Why didn't he think of it?"

She ran out to the study and a few minutes after she came back, Horace called Young Horace downstairs. The study door closed behind him and stayed closed a long time, while Julie and I wrapped gifts in my room. When they went upstairs, they went together and we noticed that Young Horace had an arm across his father's shoulders.

Julie looked after them with quick tears in her eyes.

She said, "I knew it, Mother. I told you. Hon does understand the children — just at the times and in the ways I don't. It's such a good arrangement, giving every child two parents!"

Friday afternoon Sue was sitting by me while I sewed sequins on her dress, and Julie and Lorna were downstairs in the dining room tagging the gifts Mr. Colt had donated for the children of the parish who took part in the program, when Young Horace came in from school.

I heard Julie call, "That you, Honey? Come in!"

Young Horace answered briefly, "Can't stop, Mom. Got to change and go after your trees. Gets dark early in the woods."

But I thought there was a cheery, friendly note in his voice which I had not heard in all the weeks I had lived in Julie's house. I wondered if I imagined it.

No. As he passed my door he looked in, half-smiled, and swung his hand.

He said, "Hi, Gram! What do you know? Vacation's begun!" and went on, bounding.

He had not seen Sue at all.

I thought, "What has happened to him? Has Madelene given him some small encouragement at last? Could anything else affect him like this?"

I hardly knew whether to be pleased or not. But I was relieved. At least Julie's trees were to be delivered promptly and with good spirit.

I said to Sue, "There, child. I believe it's finished. Close the door and take off your clothes for the last try-on."

As she rose slowly from her crouching position on the floor, her face came into the light from the lamp I had turned on to sew by, because it was a cloudy day; and she seemed to me to have an expression of fear, mixed with her delight and incredulous wonder. With the tip of one finger, she touched one of the rose-colored sequins caught to the white taffeta, as if she thought it might be a dewdrop which would disappear. I suppose the sequins were to her the final proof of fairy-godmother magic.

There was no sound of her steps as she went to close the door. When her clothing was off and she reached for the velvet panties, I saw that she was trembling.

I asked, "Are you cold, Sue?"

She said, "No . . . I'm not cold."

Her voice was not a child's. Even to an old woman's ears it had the clear, true ring of early maturity.

She stopped trembling. She stood tall and very still while I hooked the tight bodice. Then suddenly she put up her hands and pulled off two wrinkled red ribbons which held the short braids on each side of her neck. Her hair fell heavy and raven black around her pixie face and she ran her thin fingers through it, fluffing it softly.

Just then Young Horace pushed open the door.

She said, "Hello, Horace."

She did not speak shrilly. Her tone was low, but not humble.

He stopped short. He stared for an instant. Then he grinned and whistled.

I was proud of Young Horace, I believe, for the first time since he said his first word at the age of eight months. And I thought better of teen-age boys than I had for a long time, because I saw what one of them could do for a teen-age girl.

He said, frankly admiring, "Well, Sue Halsey! Wouldn't have known you! Yumpin' Yimminy!"

I thought jealously, "Why couldn't Pete do that? Of course Pete is too young. But will he ever?"

Sue said easily, "It's the dress. Your grandmother made it for me. Isn't it lovely?"

Young Horace said, "Pretty sharp," and forgot Sue. But, with one stare and an exclamation, he had given her what she needed.

He looked over her head at me.

He said, eagerness running his words together, "Gram, I had an idea. Would you be willing for me to get our tree out of Grandpa's pasture? Pete says there aren't many spruces in there, but there are some. And I kind of thought Mom would like it better if that's where I got it; wouldn't she?"

I cleared my throat and told him, "Why, yes, Young Horace. I believe she would. It's where she and your Uncle Robbie always got theirs."

"You don't care?"

"Of course not. I'm glad you thought of it."

"You — wouldn't want me to get the one for the vestry — the big one — there, too, would you?"

"I don't know of any better use that could ever be made of one of the big ones. Yes, I'd like to see one of Grandpa's trees in the church vestry. It would — make me feel more at home."

"Okay," Young Horace said quickly. I think he was afraid I was getting emotional. "Here goes. Dad said I could take the station wagon."

He strode out with a nod and a grin at me which did not quite ignore Sue.

We heard him call to his mother, "I'm leaving, Mom. The tree'll be at the church before you are."

He did not wait for her answer. The door slammed on his last word, and we heard the engine of the station wagon turn over, catch, and roar away.

Sue said, quietly, "He's nice, isn't he?" And then, still quietly, "He noticed me, didn't he? He never noticed me before. It's the dress, isn't it?"

I told her, as casually as I could, "Not entirely. A pretty dress always helps, I suppose. But it was you in the dress. Do you think he would have noticed the dress if I had had it on a hanger?"

She laughed at that. We were both laughing when Julie and Lorna came in.

"Julie cried, "Sue, you darling! Why, you're a vision! Isn't she a vision, Lorna?"

She knelt and hugged the child.

Lorna said, "Somebody should paint the two of you just like that for a next year's Christmas card."

Julie said, "Let me see how it would look."

She drew Lorna down into her place, Lorna's hands on Sue's bare knees and Lorna's cheek against Sue's tiny waist, Lorna's eyes looking up and Sue's down. She stood off to study them.

She said, "It's too lovely."

Lorna said, "You aren't seeing what I saw, Julie. I'm the wrong complexion. Sue looks like you. Not as much as Babe does. But enough to be your daughter."

Sue whispered, "Do I really?"

Julie said, "I wish she were . . . Sue, darling, I got you a little Christmas present. It can't go on the tree. It's a sort of family Christmas present. And you have to have it before rehearsal tonight. I do hope they fit."

She brought out a pair of patent leather slippers.

Sue stepped into them. They fitted.

She said breathlessly, "I know they must be made of glass! But I'm not going to lose either of them off!"

She still felt like Cinderella, but a Cinderella permanently transformed. And so she was. Not so much by her two fairy godmothers, either, as by the spontaneous reaction of one gangling sixteen-year-old boy she hardly knew.

The front door opened.

Julie said, "It must be Babe — and Pete!"

She ran to the head of the stairs.

"Well, Baby! You're home from your first school party! Darling, was it fun?"

We could hear no sound from below.

My heartbeat quickened.

I thought, Didn't they like what she took? Didn't she get anything? Was there no ice cream? *Didn't a Santa Claus come?*

Anyone who thinks these eventualities would not have spelled tragedy to me does not know what it is to be a little girl's grandmother.

But Julie flashed me a smile.

She whispered, "She's standing down there getting something out of her basket. She hasn't even come in far enough so that Pete can shut the door. Her face is covered with chocolate. I can see it all the way from here. So she must have had a good time. I don't believe she even heard me!"

After a minute the door closed and Babe's solemn voice said:

"Mummie! Nothing else about Christmas can — possibly — be — as nice as this!"

Julie answered gently, catching her mood, "Come upstairs, Baby, and tell us all about it."

Babe climbed slowly, Pete following. Julie stood aside to let her pass and came into my room after her. She did not touch her. For this moment Babe was apart from us all. She was still in the world of school. Pete did not come in. He stood in the doorway, his eyes on Babe. He did not see Sue at all, though she still stood in the center of the room, swathed in her rosy glory and billowed, from the waist down, in sparkling foam.

Babe said, "They served our cake! And two kinds of ice cream! They liked everything I gave them. They said it was just what they wanted. I got my presents right out of Santa's hand. I got some pencils and a lollipop and a handkerchief with a Teddy bear on it and some caramels. I didn't eat any of the caramels. I just took one out of my basket. May I eat it, Mother? Before supper?"

"Yes, Baby," Julie said. "Eat it now. Now is just the time to eat it."

Babe showed no surprise, though ordinarily she is not allowed candy between meals.

She carefully took off the bit of paper and put the sweet into her chocolate-ringed mouth.

She said, "It's the best candy I ever tasted."

"Of course it is, Baby."

"There's more. You want a piece, Mummie? Gramma? Aunt Lorna?"

We all shook our heads, smiling, but saying nothing. We could not tell her that we were already eating hers with her.

She said, "Pete does."

She gave him one. He did not unwrap it. He held the small square in his big boy's hand and watched Babe.

She added quickly, with her mother's own smile, "Sue does, too. Here, Sue. I'll unwrap it for you and put it in your mouth. So you won't get your dress sticky. That's a dancing dress, isn't it? Can you dance, Sue?"

Sue said, "I'm going to try to. At the Christmas party at church. "You'll be there, won't you? You're going to speak a piece, aren't you? Thanks, Babe. Hello, Pete."

She did not trill it. Her voice was low and sweet. She did not even smile at him. Her glance was quiet, straightforward, and friendly. But it made no difference to Pete. He did not hear her nor see her as she was. The sound of her voice as it had been at other times still burned in his ears and the picture he already had of her in his mind stood like a screen between them.

The light went out of his eyes.

He said, "H'lo . . . Okay if I go upstairs, Mom? Got a radio program. Late now."

Julie said, "Yes. Okay, Pete."

She looked at Sue compassionately.

When he was beyond hearing she said, "I'm sorry Pete's like that, Sue. I don't know why. It isn't just with you. It's with — any girl."

Sue said calmly, "Pete's shy, that's all. I used to be, too. Almost — why, almost to this very minute!"

She glanced at me, confounded by the import of her own words.

She picked up the clothes she had flung on a chair.

She told Julie, "Pete's nice, though. He's smart, too. I like him. I always did. Maybe sometime he'll like me."

She went into my bathroom to dress.

A little later Ellen brought trays into my room for us all, and we ate around a card table set before the fire. Ellen was to serve dinner to the men of the family later when they were all at home.

As soon as we finished Julie left with Babe and Sue for the rehearsal, Sue carrying her dress in a wide box under one arm and the slippers in a narrow box under the other, Julie and Babe laden with presents for the vestry tree.

I could hear Julie telling the children as they went downstairs, "Daddy left the car for us today because he said he couldn't be back with it in time and Honey was taking the station wagon to get the trees. Wasn't that nice of Daddy? . . . You can't wear your ballet dress if the vestry is cold, Sue. It may be. Mr. Pease is very busy to-night — getting presents for his grandchildren, don't you imagine, Babe? Oh, look! It's snowing! We're going to have new snow for Christmas!"

Lorna stayed to fill the last of the red cheesecloth bags with popcorn, peanuts, and ribbon candy, working at the card table now that Ellen had taken the tea things away.

I offered to help her but she said there was no need of it, that she would have them all done in good season. So I took the welcome opportunity to get on with the knitting which had been delayed during the daylight hours by the work on Sue's costume.

All hands were flying swiftly and for a while we did not talk. I think the half-silence was pleasant to us both. We could hear the click of my needles, the crisp rustle of the corn, the shells, and the crystallized sugar sliding into the bright cheesecloth, the crackle of the fire, and the distant sound of music from Pete's radio.

I glanced across at Lorna from time to time, but she did not look up.

I thought, I have to admit Horace has been right on more points than I expected. Julie is getting tired, though I don't think she realizes it. Young Horace has begun to emerge from his doldrums — for some reason or other — without concessions on the part of either of his parents. Frederica hasn't "come round." Julie has had to depend heavily on Lorna . . . But on one score he was certainly wrong. Lorna hasn't "popped," and shows no signs whatever of a "pop" being imminent. As a matter of fact, I don't think I have ever seen her look so happy or so well in her life. She looks rested and refreshed. She is positively blooming. Yet she is obviously not in one of her merry moods. It seems more a matter of serenity. She is still the antithesis of Julie but not — somehow — any longer Julie's foil. She seems — all of a sudden — a lovely woman in her own right.

I wished I knew how to tell her so, but I was never very good at compliments. I hoped Julie had — it would be so easy for Julie — but I doubted if Julie had found time, this last week or two, to do more for Lorna than feel grateful to her.

I wondered what was keeping Horace so late, and whether Pete was getting hungry. I hoped Young Horace knew enough about Alvin's pasture to be able to find the spruce trees without losing his way. I wondered why he had not taken Pete with him; Pete could go about that pasture blindfold. I supposed Young Horace had not wanted to wait. . . . I thought of how Babe had looked in her blue snowsuit, her face smeared with chocolate, offering caramels, her eyes like two blue-white stars. I thought of Sue Halsey standing by unnoticed in her rose-colored velvet and twinkling white taffeta, but standing straight, not drooping, speaking only when she was spoken to and then naturally, not trillingly, because at last someone had noticed her, however briefly, not out of any kindness, but because he could not help it. I thought Sue was well on her way to finding that unknown wonder she longed for and could not name. But I thought she still had a long way to go, and that she would continue to need help.

I said, "Alvin! . . . How can I help that child?"

He said, "What she needs most is stuffing. Take her out home and fill her up. Let her pick up the eggs and go berrying and wade in the brook. Make her some clothes out of new cloth. Get her up with the robins and put her to bed when the whippoorwills come out."

He answered more quickly than usual.

I was glad he did, because almost before he had finished Lorna raised her head.

"What did you say, Mrs. Monroe?"

I chuckled.

"I forgot you were here, for a minute. I was speaking to Alvin."

She did not seem at all surprised.

She said, "Aren't you lucky you can? That you have someone you know so well, and love, to speak to?" She added, "I used to wonder if I could speak to Dad. Sometimes when I was very lonely. But I never tried. Because I couldn't think he would really be interested in anything I might say. He never was."

I chuckled again.

"Poor Alvin! I guess he thinks a lot I say is tommyrot. But it's a kind of tommyrot he's put up with so long he's probably used to it. Maybe it's a little pleasure to him, too, to hear it, just for that reason. I don't imagine what the angels say always interests him either, especially if it's high sounding. Alvin is a plain man . . . But I was pretty sure he would be interested in Sue Halsey."

"You were talking to him about Sue?"

"Yes. I was wondering how I could help her."

"Did he tell you? Or did I interrupt? I'm sorry —"

"It's all right. He can finish anytime. I guess likely he's had his say, for now. He thinks she needs feeding up. He never could bear to see a scrawny child. He says I ought to take her out home. Next summer, I suppose he means. But I don't see —"

"Of course it would be wonderful for Sue. I remember how I used to love to go out there, when I was her age. It seemed like heaven."

"To you, Lorna? Why, you seemed to have everything. All the things we didn't."

"Yes. But none of the things you did, Mrs. Monroe. And they're what a child needs most. Not just the country air and food, nor the open sky, the dew on the grass in the early mornings, the big barn and the berry woods and the brook —"

I thought she must have heard Alvin without knowing that she heard him.

" — but the smell of bread baking, the chance to make beds and help with the dishes, the singing on the porch at night, the feeling of comfort all through that house, the times when you sit sewing or knitting and a girl can talk to you and ask you questions without being embarrassed or hurried, without the fear that you will always remember it and bring it up later, when her mind has gone on to other things or along a different road entirely. You and Mr. Monroe did a great deal for Julie — and — Rob — and me. More than you realize. You made a home. A sort of home for the heart. A place for it to go whenever it is lonely, or afraid, or sad, or unbearably happy."

(*Does your heart ever go there, Robbie?*)

"I know I can never be grateful enough. And if you could take Sue out there for a summer, I should be grateful all over again. . . . You might put it on the basis that you need her, mightn't you? Then I think her foster parents would let her go."

"Yes, I might do that. I should like to do it. But fond as I am of Sue, I think much more of Pete, of course. And perhaps he needs to come as much as she does."

"Pete?"

"He spent last summer with me, you know . . . And — I'm afraid he wouldn't come if Sue were there. In fact, I'm sure he wouldn't."

"Oh-h," Lorna said. She nodded slowly. Her eyes saddened a little, but she smiled. "I see what you mean. And of course you're right. I just hadn't thought it all through. Pete is more important, even than Sue. You must never deny Pete anything you can give him; that's true. He is your own, and so full of promises which must be realized."

She finished filling the last cheesecloth bag and tied it. She said, "Isn't Pete very much like Rob, Mrs. Monroe?"

I answered, "I've always thought so."

"Have you heard much from Rob since the war?"

"Almost nothing. And little or nothing during the war, directly."

"You don't know exactly where he is, or what he is doing?"

"Only that he is in California. Or at least that the letters which we send to a post-office box in Berkeley are not returned."

"He doesn't answer?"

"No. We had one brief note after we wrote him about his father."

"Did that note sound like — Rob?"

"I don't know, Lorna. Since he first went to college he has hardly ever been home — never for more than one night at a time — and he has written so seldom that I have never grown acquainted with the man my son has become. Sometimes I have thought he was ashamed of us. More often I have suspected he was ashamed of himself. I hope it is the first. I cannot bear the second possibility. I push it away whenever it comes into my mind."

"I don't believe it is either. I used to feel I knew him — fairly well. I — admired him very much. A good deal as Sue does Pete. Do you remember?"

I said truthfully, "I had not thought of it for years. . . . I don't suppose he ever knew it. I wish he had, Lorna. But you were very different from Sue."

"Yes. And the difference is all to Sue's advantage, I hope — I feel sure — in the long run. I was proud, as people say — not of what I had, or of my family's position; neither ever seemed to belong to me — but of myself. I felt I was so much more of a person than anyone else thought I was —"

"You were, Lorna."

I could not help saying it, though in the next breath I sensed I might have offended her. I hadn't.

She said, gently, "No, dear Mrs. Monroe. No girl is really a person until someone else thinks she is."

As Young Horace, for an instant that afternoon, had thought Sue!

"I just wanted to be, so much that I convinced myself I was. And I hugged myself to me and hid in the folds of myself. Only someone like Julie could bring me out even a little way. Rob wasn't like Julie."

"No. Not at all. I used to wish, for his own sake —"

"Rob was himself. Like me. Too much like me, I'm

afraid. And he was two years younger, as Pete is two years younger than Sue. It is an almost unsurpassable age difference, in that direction, in the teens. Rob was as much aware of it as Pete is. And I was far more aware of it than Sue. Because I thought about myself, as separate from anyone else, far more than she does, and of the ways in which I was cut off from others. . . . I lost a great deal by it. . . . Perhaps I lost — the only chance for happiness I shall ever have."

"And perhaps he did, Lorna."

She shook her head.

"No. Because it is far more likely that a man of middle age will find a woman who knows he is a person, than that a middle-aged woman will be found by such a man. And, even if he doesn't — I feel quite sure that no man is as dependent on being valued highly by a woman or by any single human being as a woman is. Things can make a man into an integrated person. Experiences can. His own understanding of himself can. I don't believe any woman can understand herself until some man has understood her."

I said, "Then — things can unmake him, too."

Lorna nodded.

"That's true. So maybe the first things Rob saw after he left home and some of the experiences he had did more or less unmake him. As perhaps he would not have been unmade if he had had even one person who loved him at the time. As I think no woman could be unmade by anything that happened to her if she were with a man she loved and who loved her. . . . But what some things and experiences can unmake, others can make. Whatever Rob is doing now, the experiences he is having may be bringing him to terms with himself, wholly, as he never was, even when he lived at home and you were doing everything you could for him. You may be wonderfully surprised when you see him again."

I turned my head away.

I said, "I shall be wonderfully surprised if I ever see him again at all. If he couldn't come — or even say that he would soon — when he heard about his father —"

I could not go on. I was afraid that I was going to cry. I knew I should if she came and put her arm around me, as Julie would have done. It is very painful to me to cry. I can shed tears very easily late years, I find. But crying is something quite different. I did not do it, even when they told me Alvin would die, nor when they told me that he was dead; partly, I suppose, because I did not believe it. But I was very close to crying when I thought of Robbie, because I did not know what to believe nor what, if anything, I dared hope for.

Lorna did not leave her chair.

She said quietly, "Perhaps it was not time for him to come, or even to say that he would come. Even though it seemed to you it was . . . You wouldn't be too much surprised if he should come unexpectedly, would you, Mrs. Monroe?"

I could not answer.

She said, "Haven't you always known he might, at any time? . . . Haven't you sometimes even felt Christmas might be a more likely time than any other? So many people do go home at Christmas, who don't go often."

I said brokenly, "Yes. I have thought of it. Or just begun to think of it. But then I pushed it away. Like other thoughts . . . Lorna, what makes you think —"

"I don't really, of course. I only think you should always be prepared for his coming. Because, from what little I know of him, I feel sure he will come some day. And he must remember what Christmas means to you and Julie —"

"I don't think he does, Lorna." I straightened and went on with my knitting. "That's one thing. I don't think he ever knew what Christmas meant to us. Nor his father either. Nor Horace. I have become gradually convinced that men are incapable of feeling Christmas. And if you can't feel it, how can you know what it is, or what it means to those who do?"

"Many people," Lorna said, "feel much more than they are able or care to show. It is at least as hard for them as for the people who love them. Believe me, Mrs. Monroe. It is something I know a great deal about, from both angles."

I told her, "I know a good deal about that, too, child. But Christmas long ago melted any reserve I might have had toward it. So long ago that I cannot remember, nor even believe, I ever had it."

"Probably you never did," Lorna agreed. "But some people's emotional reserve is an infinitely higher and stouter wall than yours, dear Mrs. Monroe. The more's the pity."

She stood up and began putting on her coat. She looked taller than I had ever thought her. She was smiling faintly and there was a fresh, soft color in her face. Her eyes were bright.

I thought, "It has done her good to speak as freely as this. Much as she and Julie love each other, perhaps she has never appeared at her best when Julie was there. I have almost never seen her apart from Julie . . . And it has done me good to talk about Robbie, to know that someone else beside Julie and me ever thinks of him at all."

We kissed each other good night.

I had a few minutes to myself, and said:

"Now, Alvin. About little Sue Halsey. If I can't have her out at the farm, what can be done for her? Do you suppose Lorna might take her for a visit at her house? Do you suppose the Halseys would let Sue go there?"

Alvin said, "Doubt it. Folks ain't likely to go visiting for long in their own village. Besides, Lorna can't afford it, can she?"

"No," I admitted. " 'Tain't likely she could."

"Funny thing," Alvin commented drily, "how the West

money slipped away. Time was when we thought if we had a quarter part what they did we'd be on Easy Street for the rest of our lives, and leave the young ones well off. Now you can afford company if you want it, and Lorna can't. Guess we done all right, didn't we?"

"Don't brag," I told him. "Luck. That's all."

"Luck!" Alvin scoffed. " 'Twa'n't neither. Hard work, 'twas, and horse sense. . . . They always say 'tain't more'n three generations from shirt sleeves to shirt sleeves. I'd ruther stay in shirt sleeves myself, 'thout so many changes."

"All right for you," I said. "You was comfortable that way. Some men ain't. And much as Horace aggravates me, sometimes, I can't say I don't kind of like the looks of his business suits and starched white collars."

(*Do you wear white collars, Robbie?*)

Alvin chuckled.

"I grant you," he said, "Horace would be a cur'us sight in overhalls and a bandanna. Probably looked like a picked chicken in a hayfield. But give me a man that can make out with collars or without 'em. Them's the kind that can keep a-goin' whatever hits 'em. Don't do to car' all your eggs in one basket."

"Most folks have to," I returned smartly. "If they're lucky enough to have a basket. You car'ed yours in your overhalls' pocket. Horace car's his in a briefcase. Course, if anybody *had* plenty of baskets —"

That was what I had always wanted for Robbie. Plenty of baskets. But I didn't know that he had even one. Or a briefcase. Or a pocket.

I suppose I drowsed. I saw a little boy with gray eyes — was it Robbie or was it Pete? — sitting on a red milking stool in the middle of a big green world, round like a disk, and fenced in, at a great distance from him, with neat white pickets. All about his feet were baskets full of Easter eggs. Dozens of baskets.

Julie asked low, "Still asleep, Mother?"

I said, "No. Not asleep. Haven't been asleep. What time is it?"

She laughed.

"Ten o'clock . . . And if you haven't been asleep, I'm surprised you weren't polite enough to thank Babe and me for tucking this afghan over you and turning the light away when we came home from rehearsal. . . . You've had a beautiful sleep, darling, and I'm so glad. Now don't get up at the crack o' dawn in the morning, take an hour's rest tomorrow afternoon, and you'll be set for the Christmas party. We're all ready for it now and I know it's going to be the best ever."

The best ever, as she insists each Christmas is. Could this one be? With Horace only waiting for it to be over with? With no gifts from her older son? With nothing on the church tree for Sue from Pete? Without her father? Without Robbie? With her next door neighbor not speaking to her? With shadows under her eyes?

But now as I looked at her, I could not see the shadows. Her eyes were shining as Babe's had in the afternoon, lighting her whole face.

I asked, "Was the vestry cold?"

She shook her head and laughed again. I felt that she was laughing at me.

"Of course not, Mother. It was warm as toast. I knew it would be."

"Mr. Pease sacrificed his Christmas shopping?"

"No. I hope he's bought the stores out for those grandchildren of his, the ducky old procrastinator. I'll bet he's in the vestry by now, though. Sweeping and dusting like fury . . . No. Hon turned janitor."

I sat up very straight.

"Horace!"

"Mmm. That was what he was going to be so busy about. Why he couldn't get the Christmas trees. As soon as he could leave the office this noon he went down to the church and built the fire and kept the furnace humming all

the rest of the day. Mr. Pease talked about shoveling
coal! Wait till he sees how Horace diminished his pile in
one afternoon. Why, that vestry was like a greenhouse!
And was Horace proud of himself when we walked in. He
had on a pair of Honey's dungarees and was just peeling
off one of Honey's old sweaters —"

"Was Horace in shirt sleeves?" I asked loudly, to draw
Alvin's attention.

"He was. Rolled up, to prove how warm it was. Necktie loose and one-sided. A smudge of soot like a saber cut
across one cheek —"

"Was it becoming?"

Julie giggled.

"Well, I don't know how it would have seemed to his
directors. But he looked like Eisenhower and Laurence
Olivier and Ted Williams to me! Oh, Mother, it was just
like Hon!"

"Not," I ventured, "like the Horace Thompson I
know."

Julie patted my hand.

"Darling, you don't know anything about Horace yet,
really. But you will. . . . And Honey was there, too,
with the tree. They were decorating it together. Just the
two of them. Like a couple of kids. Like brothers, more
than father and son. Of course they pretended it was nonsense. They said they were hanging everything on it that
they could find and clearing out of there as fast as they
could. But I noticed the final effect was a perfect geometri-
cal pattern —"

"That sounds like Horace," I allowed.

"Yes, doesn't it? But it's right, for a public place. The
children and I were enchanted. It just inspired the children. If only they do as well tomorrow night! And I'm
sure they will. Mother, I hope you won't mind. Honey got
the tree from up home. From the pasture. I'm afraid he
didn't think to ask you —"

I always love to hear Julie say "up home."

I said, "He asked me. Of course I was pleased."

"Oh, I'm so glad. It smelled like home. I could hardly bear to leave it. But when we got here, we found he'd brought ours for the house from there too. It smells just the same. No other trees ever smelled quite that way. You'll see tomorrow. We're going to put it up in here. In your room. So you can enjoy it every minute. Honey says it's his Christmas present to us all. Just the way I hoped he would figure it out. I'm sure Hon suggested it to him. Mother, Honey seems so different tonight! So much more like himself!"

"I noticed he seemed different when he stopped in to ask about the trees."

Julie nodded.

"It's Christmas," she said. "Christmas does it. Even when you can't see how it can . . . I only hope it keeps a good grip — through the next few days!"

She folded the afghan and turned down my bed.

I asked, "Did Horace and the boys have their supper before you came home? I didn't hear them."

"You must have been already asleep. You knew when Lorna left?"

"Oh, yes. We had been having a good talk."

"I hoped you would. What about?"

"About — well, Robbie, mostly."

There was that instant of suspension that there always was when we mentioned Robbie's name. Suddenly I did not like it. It had not been there when Lorna and I spoke of him.

Julie said, "Really? . . . You know, I haven't thought of it for a long time. But Lorna used to like Robbie. Do you remember?"

I said, "I had forgotten."

"She did. I'm sure she did. She even argued for him against me sometimes."

"I'm sure she didn't have to argue very hard, Julie."

"No. I always wanted to see what he saw, as Babe does

with Pete. But I wanted him to see what I saw, too; or at least to try to. I was more insistent about that than Babe is. I suppose because I was older, instead of much younger. And I was awfully slow, somehow, to see that it isn't really necessary and that womenkind do it much more easily than men. . . . Lorna used to say she thought she could see what Robbie saw. She used to try to describe it to me. But I usually still couldn't see it. Maybe she really understood him. Did you ever think of that?"

I said I hadn't. I meant, "Not then. Not until tonight."

Julie said, "Maybe if Robbie hadn't gone away so soon . . . Maybe if he and Lorna could have known each other when they were older . . ."

She did not finish it. It was no use. It had not happened so. She set the fire screen in place.

She said, "Your bow window will be a beautiful place for the tree. I'll have the boys bring it in in the morning. You didn't see Pete tonight?"

"No."

"I didn't either. He was in bed when Babe and I got home, with his light out. I don't believe he was asleep. Pete seems to need so little sleep. But once in a while he does that — goes to bed early — when he has something to think out. . . . Hon said he was down in the dining room prowling around, claiming he was starved, when they came in, but still he didn't eat much dinner. That's probably another indication he's wrestling with some mighty problem. Do you suppose he may be reconsidering giving the scarf to Sue? I do hope so. I told him days ago that it was wrapped and tied and labeled, all ready for the tree — but that there was nothing written on the label, and wouldn't be until he wrote it. I left the package on his desk."

"Oh, Julie. Do you think it is wise to press him so hard?"

"I don't know, Mother. I only know Sue mustn't be disappointed tomorrow night. She mustn't have it spoiled for her. If you could have seen her dance at the rehearsal! She wouldn't do it for us before. But tonight — in that dress — well, I just can't tell you what she did to me!"

I thought, Julie is like Babe at school. She wants things right for Sue, but surely she wants them right for Pete, too. And can things be right at this Christmas party for them both?

I knew they would not be so without Julie's intervention, but I was certain she could not intervene successfully without aid from above and beyond herself. I tried to remember what she had said about the angels. . . .

As I was falling asleep in bed, a little later, I said to Alvin:

"We've got to admit that for once Horace Thompson done all right in shirt sleeves. And if you thought he looked like a picked chicken, I hope you didn't breathe a word of it in his ear, or the angels will have something to say to you!"

Alvin chuckled.

He said, "Angels don't bother me, Seleny, no more'n they ever did. I can hear 'em talkin' now, and it sounds real nice, but I can't get the sense of it yet. I was well aware, though, how you'd feel about it. So what I asked Horace was, 'Gee whillikins, how'd you get up all that muscle a-settin' to a desk?' "

I told him, "Alvin, I always said you had your faults, like everybody else, but still and all you was a dear good man."

Saturday morning, at breakfast (Julie is always telling me not to get up early, but an old woman can't sleep late, and she will find that out) I did not see Young Horace once cast sheep's-eyes toward the window, though he usually finds an errand to take him downtown at the time Madelene goes to the office on Saturdays, and also to be down there again Saturday noon, even though, Julie says,

Madelene nearly always has a date for lunch and a movie in a neighboring city and rides off laughing with some college boy or young local business tycoon, while Young Horace leans disconsolately against a granite hitching post (no more in demand than he) in front of the Light Office.

Julie asked, "You and Pete going to bring in the tree right after breakfast, Honey?"

He shook his head, wolfing his scrambled eggs.

"Got to go downtown. Sorry, Mom. But I guess Pete can manage the tree. Hey, Pete?"

Pete said, "Sure."

Their voices were friendly. Much more so than I had ever heard them when they were addressing each other.

Babe said, "I'll help, Pete. I'd love to help you."

Pete told her, "You can. Sure."

Julie said, with faint anxiety, "But I think Honey would like to help, too. It's his present to us. Wouldn't you, Honey? It can wait until you come back. You won't be gone long, will you?"

"All day, I guess," answered Young Horace. "It's okay, Mom. I had my fun getting the tree from the farm. Pete missed out on that. He can have what fun there is in setting it up."

Horace said gruffly, "Young Horace has agreed to help me at the shop today. Elevator boy went out sick yesterday. Hate to take anybody off a job to replace him. Got some big orders due to go out tonight — before the holiday weekend."

Round-eyed, Babe cried, "Hon-*ey!* You know how to run an elevator?"

His father answered for them.

"He can learn, can't he? He's got an idea of coming into the shop next summer, to fill in here and there while people are on vacations. Got to be versatile; got to be versatile to get on in this world, Babe. He'd better start practicing. He's sixteen, you know. Can't run up and down streets delivering newspapers all his life, the way he did last summer. Here's his chance to see how quick he is on the uptake."

Alvin had said, *Give me a man who can make out with collars or without 'em.*

I looked at both Horaces with rapidly growing respect.

Julie said softly, "Going into the shop next summer? How is it I never heard about this?"

"Oh," Young Horace shrugged, "just a little thing Dad and I cooked up last night."

But he knew she was pleased, as his father was pleased. She said, "Another Christmas present! Thanks — Young Horace!"

He gave her a quick grin and squeezed her shoulders between his hands as he passed her chair. He slid into his parka and reached the front door in his father's wake without overturning a single rug.

In the instant of silence which followed the closing of the door Julie turned to me.

She said, "Hear it?"

I said, "I'm not sure —"

She said, "I'm not either. But I think so."

"Hear what?" Pete asked.

Julie shook her head at him, fondly.

She said, "You'd never believe me, Petey."

"I would," Babe cried. "Hear what, Mummie? Hear what?"

Julie said, "Music, sugar pie. Voices singing."

Pete snorted.

"If I believed you, I'd be scared. That's a symptom of something terrible."

Julie said, smiling, "Not at this season, Petey. It's the angels. The Christmas angels."

Babe said, "Of course it isn't terrible, Pete. It's beautiful." Her little face took on a rapt look. "I hear them, Mummie. I hear them *just as plain!*"

Pete said, pushing back his chair, "Lemme out of here."

He went to the garage for the tree and the broad white base which fits over a white tub to be filled with water, and for the coils of what village people call running pine but Alvin and I always called evergreen. He spent most of the morning getting the tree firmly fixed and absolutely straight in the bow window. Babe and I draped the evergreen along the fireplace mantel, among the cards, over the doors and around the windows, until the whole room looked and smelled like nothing else in the world but Christmas. Julie ran in and out to help and advise and admire, but she was kept busy packing gifts and the bags of popcorn and candy to be carried to the vestry that night, and answering the telephone and putting in calls.

I don't intend to give the impression that all Julie had done in these weeks, or was doing even today, was by way of preparation for Christmas. She was at this time of the year, no less than any other, town chairman for the Red Cross drive, on the Library Committee, a member of the School Board, department secretary of the Woman's Club, and responsible for the needlework table at the bi-monthly sales which were expected to raise a large part of the minister's salary. She also had her usual duties of planning menus with Ellen, ordering groceries, preparing some of the family's favorite dishes, making and checking laundry lists, taking things to the cleaners, doing the up-stairs cleaning once a week, doing all the housework on Thursday, which is Ellen's day out; making minor repairs in electrical utensils, trying to find an electrician or a plumber when the needed repairs were major, keeping watch on the oil supply and the fireplace wood so that she could order more in time, but not too soon for the storage space available. And there were petitioners for cooked food, for used clothing, for secondhand furniture, for money, for cards to cheer the sick and flowers to comfort the bereaved, ringing her telephone or doorbell at all hours. . . .

If I were to tell all Julie did, there would be no time for anything else. And I am telling of her Christmas . . .

We did not sit down to lunch until nearly two o'clock and it was substantial because Julie said supper would be from the buffet so that we could serve ourselves when convenient, and it would be light because most of us would be too excited and too hurried to eat much and a simple meal would give Ellen time to get dressed for the party. Ellen is a strict Catholic, but her religious convictions will never keep her from any place where Babe is performing. Besides, sometimes Babe goes along when Ellen goes to her church to pray.

We were all hungry and the meat loaf smelled delicious. Ellen makes a tomato sauce for it and sprinkles grated cheese on it and serves it in a ring of tiny onions.

We had just picked up our forks — I am sure Julie had not taken one taste — when the telephone rang.

Ellen was serving Babe, and Julie said, "I'll get it, Ellie. I hope it isn't Hon to say Young Horace has put the elevator through the roof —"

I noticed that even in this moment of half-alarm, she called him Young Horace.

She ran upstairs. We heard her say:

"Yes? . . . Yes, this is Julie . . . Oh, you poor dear! But I really don't think you . . . Oh, I know, but she . . . Oh, of course I know how you feel, darling. But people . . . Why, of course I can, if you think . . . Well, maybe you're right . . . I certainly will; within five minutes. And don't worry!"

I thought, with a sinking sensation I could hardly understand, "Was Horace right, after all? Has Lorna —"

Julie appeared in the doorway in her mouton jacket, tying a scarf over her head.

I asked, "What's the matter? Was it Lorna?"

She shook her head. She looked a little anxious and at the same time amused, even oddly pleased.

She said, "Ellen, will you take Babe into the kitchen and give her a glass of orange juice? She didn't finish what I gave her this morning."

Babe protested, "Oh, Mummie! I *almost* did —"

But she let Ellen take her away.

Julie said quickly, "It was Freddy, Mother. I have to take her to Dalton City. I hope I won't be gone long. But I do want you to get your nap. So, Petey, I have to depend on you to see that Babe is all right. Couldn't you take her sliding, maybe?"

"Sure," Pete said agreeably. "But what's struck La Augsburg, for crying out loud? She sure was speaking to you plenty this time or there were some awful silences on the line."

"No silences, I assure you," Julie told him, dragging on her gloves, feeling for the car keys. "Anything but! It's supposed to be a secret but I know I can trust you two, and you should have an explanation. Just don't tell anyone else, except that I had to go out and will be back soon, I hope. It's a ghastly errand, really. Seems Madelene promised Freddy she would come straight home from the office at noon. When she hadn't come at one-thirty, Freddy was so nervous she walked downtown looking for her. You know Freddy doesn't drive. But Madelene wasn't there, and somebody told Freddy she drove away in a certain robin's-egg-blue, cut-down, 1938 Packard, and that she had her weekend case with her. Freddy knew she had the weekend case but she thought it was to bring home Christmas gifts in. Still thinks it was. But she knows who drives that car and has forbidden Madelene to have anything to do with him. So she's frantic. She called from a booth downtown and wants to be driven to Dalton to look for the child. Says if I don't take her, she can't wait for the bus, she's too nervous. Imagine Freddy hitchhiking to

Dalton and fine-combing the town for a robin's-egg-blue car! She'd die if anybody saw her! And somebody would be sure to! So goodbye all —"

"But why does she call on you, Julie? Why do you have to get mixed up in such disagreeable business? After the way she's treated you for weeks —"

If Julie heard me, she did not answer. I don't think she heard me. The door slammed behind her.

It was Pete who answered.

He growled, "Who else would she call? Who else *but* Mom?"

He succeeded in sounding disgusted, but he looked proud.

I said, "If only she had had her lunch!"

Pete said, "Mom doesn't seem to need food. Bet if it wasn't for the sake of the rest of us and the looks of the thing, she'd never stop to eat from one week's end to another!"

Babe was just coming back to the table.

She said, looking at Julie's untouched plate, "Why didn't Mummie have her lunch? Where's she gone?"

Pete cleared his throat.

"She and Aunt Freddy've gone to Dalton. Last minute shopping, maybe. Don't be so nosy, just before Christmas. Look, want to go sliding as soon as we've finished?"

"Oh, I'd love to! On the big hill, Pete? On the *big* hill?"

"If you eat a lot. Sure. On the big hill."

I lay down after lunch, but I did not sleep. In the first place a grandmother cannot be wholly unconcerned about a small child sliding on a big hill. I kept getting up and going into Horace's study to look out of the window, and they were always having such a good time and Pete was being so sweet with Babe and Babe was shouting so merrily that I was loath to turn away. I remember the bright winter days when I went coasting with my brothers and sisters in dishpans and on barrel staves; and others when

Robbie and Julie were flying down over the crust of the field and through the open barn onto the marsh ice of the pasture where they spun round and round together on the double-runner Robbie had made by nailing a board to their two little sleds.

I thought, The only thing we always have and that is always the same, generation after generation, is our children. Our young children. They talk a lot about security these days. Children are our only real security.

I wished that Robbie had a child. . . .

I went back after each little journey into childhood, into memory, and into my simple philosophy, and lay down in the room which was festooned for Christmas with greens from Alvin's pasture.

I said, "Smells fine, Alvin."

He said, "Out here it smells that way all the time."

I asked, "No flowers? No rare perfumes?"

He said, "Not for me, Seleny. Nothing could ever beat spruce and pine to my way o' thinking, Christmastime or any other time."

I lay thinking that when I was "out there," even though hand-in-hand with Alvin, I should smell spruce, probably, only at Christmas. Pine is at its best, I think, after a drenching shower on a hot summer day. But I like may-flowers, too, and lilac, and old-fashioned garden roses. I often long for them, in the cold months. Someday, some-where, I shall not have to wait . . . And I love the smell of new shingles, naphtha soap, fresh-cut grass, good food cooking, sea air, clothes just off the line, wild-strawberries, sweet fern, hickory-nut burs . . .

Pete came into my room and began doing something around the tree.

I sat up and smiled at him. His cheeks were very red.

I asked, "Where's Babe?"

"In the kitchen with Ellen. Having cocoa and cookies."

"Why aren't you having cocoa and cookies?"

"Kid stuff."

He grinned companionably.

"Besides, got something I better tell you. Okay to let 'er go?"

"Let 'er go," I told him.

He sat down cross-legged in front of the tree and worried the sole of his shoe. I knew this was not going to be easy for him to say, still he wanted very much to say it; and he was happy about it, on the whole.

"Look, Gram. . . . Think you could manage any way without me out at the farm next summer?"

For the minute it did not seem to me I could.

"Oh, Pete! Do I have to?"

"Well . . . No . . . I'll come if you really need me . . . But since you sold the cows, I didn't know —"

"I'm going to buy another one in the spring, Pete. I wouldn't feel at home without a cow in the barn."

"Well, but you wouldn't buy it just for the summer, would you? You'd want to get it in the spring and keep it 'til cold weather, wouldn't you? And I'd be in school, anyway, part of that time. So you'd have to get Buddy Austin to milk for you then, wouldn't you? Couldn't he do it through the summer too?"

"I suppose he could. But who will eat on the back porch with me, Pete? And sleep in the open chamber? And close the loft windows when it rains? And tame the squirrels? And fish for perch and pickerel for me to fry for breakfast?"

Pete said, "I don't know." He looked away and I thought his lip trembled. But when he looked back he was grinning, crookedly. "Like I said, if you do need me, I'll come, Gram. You know I like it out there. But, see, I'm going to be thirteen next summer, and I've never been away to camp. Dad talks about it, off and on. He says I don't have to go, but he'd like to have me. He says it was good for Horace and he thinks I need it more than Horace did. See, when I'm home and when I'm out at the farm, I read a lot, and collect things, and think. And I like that. It's what I like best. But Dad says it's what I'm going to do all my life, and if I'm ever going to spend eight weeks roughing it with a gang of boys, I've got to do it pretty soon, or I'll be too grown up in my mind to get any fun out of it. I don't know whether I'll like it or not, but I guess he's right I ought to try it; don't you?"

My heart ached, but I remembered Julie had said, "Hon knows the children in ways that I don't know them. It's a wonderful plan, giving every child two parents."

I said, "Maybe he is, Pete."

Pete nodded quickly and bent toward me. He looked relieved.

"I would like to go on a long canoe trip," he said. "They do that at camp, you know. I was looking at some folders last night. Dad gave them to me a long time ago, but I never happened to look at them before. They've got some swell pictures of overnight sites on islands and places. I never slept outdoors, you know. Except on the porch at the farm when it was hot. The sky must look nice. I think I'd like riding, too. And sailing. I guess I really wouldn't want to grow up without knowing how to handle a sail —"

"No, Pete. Of course you wouldn't. If you have the chance to learn —"

"Well, I do. And Dad says I could work around the bank Saturdays and afternoons and short vacations, to earn my next year's Christmas money. Sweeping up, you know, and polishing the brass and that kind of stuff. I guess it would be kind of a present to him if I said I'd go . . . Funny kinds of presents we're giving this year!"

"The best kind," I told him. "The kind that mean the most."

"Of course it's only for eight weeks. I could come out with you before I went to camp, and after I got back."

I knew Julie would not want to let him out of her sight at either end. I knew that even if he did come, it would be different. I knew that nothing about Pete would ever be quite the same again. He would be older and more confident. Why, he was already older and more confident! So — that was good. And Horace must be right. But I did not trust my voice to speak.

He said, "You wouldn't be alone, would you, Gram? Of course Mom and the rest are always out often. But you ought not to be alone, any of the time." He cleared his throat. "Can't you think of — somebody — you would like to have stay with you? I mean, whenever you want to be at the farm? Whenever — I'm not there?"

It was the clearing of his throat that gave me the key.

I said, "Pete Thompson! Were you in the hall when Lorna and I were talking here last night?"

He was still not very old. He flushed. He got to his feet before me. He stammered half angrily.

"What's that got to do with it? What if I did hear you? I wasn't trying to hear. I didn't hear much. I was just going downstairs to find out about supper. I was hungry. I made plenty of noise. You weren't whispering. You were both talking loud enough so you didn't hear me. I wasn't sneaking! What would I want —"

"Oh, I know, Pete. I know you didn't try to listen. I know you didn't want to hear . . . But I know, too, that though you say you were hungry, you didn't eat much after all; and you looked at those camp folders last night for the first time, and you went to bed early with your light out. Your mother says you do that when . . . Petey, you aren't going to camp just so that Sue can come out to the farm?"

"Lord, no!" Pete shouted, glaring at me. "Not by a long shot! What do you think I —"

But something hushed him.

I held out my hand and he took it.

I said, "Pete, you know I would a hundred times rather have you than Sue? You know I love you a thousand times more than I do, or ever could, love Sue?"

His whole manner altered.

He squeezed my hand awkwardly, unevenly, but until it hurt.

He said, "Sure I know, Gram. And I'd a hundred times rather go to the farm with you than go to camp. But just the same I'd better go to camp. And, long as I won't be there anyway, you might as well have her. I mean, I don't care if you have her, if you want her. It's up to you, I mean."

I said, "You're a good boy, Pete. I guess you're right, too. I'll ask her. In the spring."

He nodded again, like signing his name. I let him go. He wandered toward the door.

Just before he reached it he turned and growled:

"Don't get the idea I like her, though, any better than I ever did. 'Hello, Pete!' Ugh! I *don't* like her, and I'll never give her that scarf Mother got if it lies around my room *for six years* — and I wish you'd tell Mother so!"

I smiled at him.

I said, "I will, Pete. I'll tell her as soon as she comes home."

No. He would never give Sue the scarf. But he was giving his father the best he had to give him. And he was giving Sue, to have and to hold for a long time, his open chamber at the farm, his chair at the table on the back porch, the barnloft and the squirrels and the brook.

When Julie came in about four o'clock the first thing she said was:

"Mother! Didn't you take a nap?"

I said, "I lay down a long time. I couldn't sleep. I guess I'm too excited."

"Where are the children?"

"Up in Pete's room. They went sliding after lunch. Then Babe had cocoa and cookies with Ellen. Pete was in with me a while. A few minutes ago he took her upstairs. He said he was going to read to her."

"Pete is so good! Mother, how did I have the luck to get children like mine?"

" 'Luck,' " I quoted Alvin; adding quietly, "What isn't born into a child is bred into him, Julie. Good children never just happen."

Julie threw off her jacket and kerchief, kicked off her shoes, and sat on the floor with her feet close to the fire. Sometimes I think Horace and I are the only people in this house with any liking for chairs.

She said, "Poor Freddy!"

"Did you have a bad afternoon?"

"Awful. In a way. I never drove so fast in my life as I did going to Dalton. I am afraid Horace would be disgusted. But Freddy was in such a state! She had some notion Madelene might be taking the two-thirty train out of Dalton. I don't know why she was so sure the child had gone to Dalton at all. But we just had to get there before that train left. And whenever Freddy wasn't sobbing, she was talking a streak about this boy who drives the robin's-egg-blue car. If he is as Freddy describes him, any mother would be horrified, I suppose. I said once, 'There must be *something* good about him, Freddy!' But she just said, 'Nothing I ever heard. Not one single redeeming trait.' So I had to let it go at that — I don't know the boy — and drive as fast as I could. We did get to Dalton ahead of the train. We watched it come in and pull out."

"Madelene wasn't at the station?"

"No. And what a relief — for the moment! But then we looked for the car — around both theaters, in front of all the restaurants, even near the churches! By that time Freddy was imagining they had a marriage license, and I couldn't tell whether she thought it would be better if they had or hadn't. And she was beginning to say she wished they *had* been taking the train because at least we should have found them and she would not have let Madelene get on if she had had to hold her by main force. She was simply wracked, Mother. I was so sorry for her I could have cried, myself. And I admit I was bothered, personally, at the same time, by thinking how Horace

would feel if anything happened that attracted public notice and people knew I was involved in it. Because Freddy
was really beside herself. She wasn't responsible, and I
knew it. Most people would say she should have stayed at
home, but she couldn't, being Freddy. She was going to
ransack Dalton and she wanted me to take her. What else
could I do?"

"Nothing," I sighed. "Being Julie."

She made a mouth at me.

"Well. Anyway. We finally saw said car in the parking
lot at the rear of the hotel. I spied it first but, if my life
had depended on it, I don't think I could have pointed it
out to Freddy. The best I could do was to keep on cruis-
ing, pass it again from a different angle, and be very surprised but still hang onto the wheel and keep an eye on the
mirror when she said *'Stop,* Julie! They're *in the hotel!'*
The tone of her voice sent chills over me. But it was no
worse after that. As a matter of fact, it was better.
Freddy did an about-face. By the time I had the car at the
curb, she had composed herself admirably; she opened the
door and got out with great dignity. She asked me if I
would go inside with her and I said, 'I really don't think I
should, Freddy. You know Madelene wouldn't like it. It
might make everything much more difficult!' And she
agreed. She asked if I would wait until she came back. I
said of course I would. And I did. I waited three-quarters
of an hour. When she came, Madelene was with her."

"Unmarried?"

"I don't know. I judge so. Certainly she is not on her
honeymoon. She and Freddy got into my back seat and
I've just left them at their house."

"Did they talk?"

"Not a word to each other. Madelene did not speak at
all. Freddy and I talked politely about driving conditions.
Freddy thanked me for my Christmas card and said she
had sent very few this year, that she hadn't felt at all in
the mood. I could see Madelene staring out of the win-

dow. She looked very cold, very bored, and very stunning.
When she got out at the house she stalked straight up
the steps, without a glance at either her mother or me.
Freddy began to crack a little then. She stood on the sidewalk for a minute looking as if she did not dare to leave
me, as if she were trying to tell me that what I had seen
was a very small fraction, and only the beginning, and she
was at her wit's end already, with no confidence or courage
for going on. But all she said was, 'I don't know how to
thank you, Julie. I'll never forget that you did this for me.
Never. Nor that I didn't deserve it.' Her eyes filled up
with tears and when she followed Madelene her step was
almost — almost feeble. Ever her back looked sick,
Mother — and old! Not a bit like Freddy! . . . Oh, I'm
heartbroken for her. And for Madelene too. Even if they
have brought it on themselves, they didn't want to;
they didn't mean to; and it's just — just too much to
bear!"

I said, "No, it isn't, Julie. Nothing is. We can bear
whatever comes, if we think so, if we will. This is a crisis
for the Augsburgs. It may clear the air."

I was trying to be sympathetic, but I wanted her to forget the Augsburgs. I resented their filling her mind today
with their troubles which were the logical outgrowth of
their own bad relationships with themselves, with each
other, and with people whom they knew. Of course they
did not want trouble. Children do not want punishment.
But when they earn it, they usually get it, in one way or
another, and I agree with Nature that this is just and
proper. I did not think it was right that Julie should receive even the flick of the lash as it was raised to descend
upon the guilty. I wanted her to come back to Christmas. I
wished Lorna were there. Lorna would know what to say,
and would not hesitate to say it.

"I'll try to think so," Julie promised. "Since I don't
know of anything else to do about it at the moment."

She got up and walked about, tucking in a loop of evergreen here and there or spreading a fan of it softly against her hand.

She said, "I wonder if anything more about this little adventure will ever be known. I wonder, if it is, what it will mean to Honey. He hasn't given Madelene the bag yet. It was still in his drawer last night."

She was calling him Honey again.

I said, "Maybe he's forgotten all about it. He's running an elevator today, you know."

"So he is. My goodness! I hope neither you nor I will be stuck with a snakeskin bag! . . . No, I don't think he has forgotten. I'm afraid he will give it to her. . . . Mother, how can both he and Pete be so blind?"

I said, "They're not blind. Either of them. You know that as well as I do. They're just young. It takes a long time to grow up, and nobody can hurry it. . . . Sit down, won't you, Julie? I must tell you something about Pete."

She took a chair by the window. As I talked, gently, she turned her face more and more away. When I finished she said, "Oh, Mother —" and put her forehead down on the sill and cried.

I did not try to stop her. I thought it was good for her. I knew she was crying to quiet a tumult — a cacophony — of emotions — joy for Sue, sorrow for Pete and for all of us, pride in him, and a nagging sense of frustration that one who could do such big things was completely stopped by a small one; pity for Frederica, and fear for Madelene and Young Horace. She was tired, too. And sometimes there is no greater rest than comes with a woman's tears.

Finally she raised her head. She tried once to speak and could not. She shook her head, smiled waterily, blew her nose and said:

"You told that beautifully, Mother. I think the way you told it was one of the reasons why I . . . You know I don't want Pete to go to camp. I feel as if it were throwing him to the wolves. I may be wrong. I think Hon should know best. He wanted him to go last summer, but

you were my excuse — and Pete's. Now — because of Sue
— we don't have it. Of course it will be wonderful for
Sue. It will make all the difference, to her. By next fall you
will have her at least where I was at her age. From there
she can go on to — almost anything . . . But for Pete it
is the beginning of going away from us. And will that
mean what it did when — when Robbie went away?"

I said, "No. I don't think so, Julie. For one reason he is
still too young to go completely. He will be away eight
weeks, and then come back to us and have years in which
to think it over, and compare, and prepare . . . No, I
think now that if Robbie had gone earlier, for just a little
while, and then come home again, he might never have
gone — so far."

Julie said slowly, "I hope you're right. I know you're
very wise, Mother. And brave. You are much braver than
I am. I wish I were like you."

I said, "You seem to want everybody to get old too
fast, Julie. It wouldn't do to have us all old at once. The
world needs all ages."

She smiled a little.

She said, "I suppose so. But the younger you are the
more it hurts, I guess. I hope . . . I mean, I hope nothing that happens afterward ever hurts quite as much as
what happens when you are very young."

I wondered what had hurt her so much when she was
very young.

But she was not thinking of herself.

She asked, moving her finger along the windowsill,
"Did you know the reason why I cried, Mother? I almost
never do that."

"I know you don't," I told her. "But I could think of a
dozen reasons for it. Any one of them might have been
enough."

"Perhaps," she said. "But the one you couldn't have
thought of was the main one. . . . Just as I sat down

here, just as you were beginning to tell me about Pete, I saw Young Horace coming out of — Freddy's house."

Young Horace . . .

"Even if he was there only a short time, he must have rung the doorbell soon after I drove away. Almost as soon as Freddy and Madelene got into the house. Surely before they had time to settle anything; before Madelene got that icy cold, bored look off her beautiful face, if she ever does . . . I wonder if he saw her at all. . . . I think he did see her. . . . But nobody came to the door with him. He closed it behind himself, slowly. He had on the dungarees he wore to work, of course, and the parka, with the cap hanging between his shoulders. He looked — cute. Like any tall schoolboy, from the neck down. But his face looked like a man's, Mother. And his shoulders were a little stooped — like Hon's. His feet looked heavy. He seemed to have to remember to pick them up and put them down. And he went along the street without a backward glance toward Freddy's, and without looking once in this direction, or turning his head at all. He walked straight ahead, out of sight down the street. . . . Where was he going, Mother?"

It hurts to be old, too. And to have your children so old that you can no longer take them into your arms to comfort them.

Being old was hurting Julie now. And it was hurting me.

I said, "I don't know, dear. He was going — wherever he needed to be. He will come back."

"But will he be the same when he comes back?"

"Not the same. Nothing that is growing stays the same. But you know he has not been happy for a long time, Julie. Maybe, if he was ever to be happy again, he had to be more unhappy first."

She thought about this, gazing out of the window.

Suddenly she said very quietly, "Here comes Freddy."

She had opened the front door downstairs before Frederica could reach the bell. Their voices came, low but distinct, up the stairway to me.

"Freddy! . . . What's happened?"

"Julie. I had to see you —"

"Of course. Come into the living room —"

"No. I can't. I don't dare to leave this window. I don't know what Madelene will do. I just gave her the — the most awful dressing down. I completely lost my temper."

"Poor Freddy. You've had such a dreadful day!"

"But I was determined not to do that. I had it all planned how, if I once got her home again, I'd handle her so differently. And I did try. I spoke to her cheerfully as soon as I got into the house. I asked her to wait while I lit a fire and said then we'd talk. She didn't answer but she waited. Then I sat down on the sofa beside her. I've never let her smoke at home before, but I asked her if she wouldn't like a cigarette and she took one. I tried to tell her quietly and truthfully what I had been through, and why I was so frightened. I held onto myself. I didn't get excited. She didn't say anything but she was listening. And then — and then —"

"Young Horace came."

"Oh — you knew?"

"I saw him coming out. Later. I was afraid he had — interrupted you. It's too bad, Freddy. But of course he didn't know — he's been working at the factory all day."

"That's what he said. It wasn't his fault. It might have been anybody. I wish it had been anybody — but Horace! . . . He's a dear boy, Julie. Everything he said and did was quite perfect. You would have been very proud of him. . . . But I've got nothing to be proud of — everything to be ashamed of — including myself —"

"Freddy, you mustn't feel like that. I wish you would sit down and have a cup of tea —"

"No. I can't, possibly . . . Listen, Julie. We both know Horace has been attracted to Madelene for months, and probably you know as well as I do that — that the way she has treated him and talked about him was — abominable. Just because he was younger than she, and because he is still in school, and doesn't have a car of his own to drive and a lot of money to spend. I haven't wanted to admit it to anybody, but now I have to. My child has no sense of values. She doesn't appreciate anything for what it is. . . . I don't suppose Horace ever knew the things she said about him, though; and for my sake and yours, and maybe more because his devotion amused her, I think she had been nice enough to him when she was with him. Until today. Today she wanted to hurt somebody. And he was there . . . Is he at home now, Julie?"

Julie said carefully, "No. . . . No, he isn't here."

"Well, he came to bring her a Christmas present. He had it under his arm. He came in smiling. He said, 'Hi, Madelene. Missed you this noon. I was running the elevator for Dad today — accounts for these dress clothes. But I ran uptown in the lunch hour to give you this. Thought I'd catch you but they said you'd just left. Didn't have time to come up here then, so it had to wait till I got through work. Merry Christmas!' By then I was out in the kitchen, starting some hot chocolate and cutting cake. For a minute I thought this was going to be good for Madelene — give her a chance to let down — bring her back to something like normal! . . . But I was wrong. I seem to be wrong in everything I think about Madelene and almost everything I do for her . . . Though I'll never regret taking her out of that cocktail lounge this afternoon, leaving her drink untouched, and that greasy-haired no-good glaring into his own glass, plenty conspicuous in a public place. At least they will both think a long time before they take a chance on my seeing them together again. . . . But it's Horace you want to hear about."

Julie said steadily, "I want to hear whatever you want most to tell me, Freddy."

"I want most to tell you about him. Because you ought to know. If you think best, I want you to explain to him what happened before he came today. I know he wouldn't speak of it to anyone outside. But perhaps if he understood . . . if anyone could understand . . . I wouldn't expect him to forgive Madelene. I don't even think I want him to forgive her . . . but he might mind less what she said. I don't know, Julie. You'll have to decide about that. . . . This is what happened. After he said 'Merry Christmas,' there was a dreadful silence. Then I heard him say, 'Aren't you — going to open it, Madelene?' After a minute she said bitterly, 'Oh, sure, I'll open it.' There was the sound of paper tearing and a cover tossed off. Then she said, 'There. I've opened it. Satisfied?' He waited another minute and then he asked, very low, 'Don't you like it?' She laughed. I heard her strike a match. She said, 'I've already got a snakeskin bag. A better-looking one than this. I saw this in Old Colt's window. Everybody saw it lying there for weeks, drying up in the sun. What do I want of the damned thing? I wouldn't want it even if somebody I can stand had given it to me. And I wouldn't want anything *you* gave me, Horace Thompson. When are you going to wake up? For heaven's sake, please *keep out from under my feet!*' . . . I said, in the kitchen, '*Madelene!*' But neither of them seemed to hear me. I wanted to go in where they were, but I couldn't move. Everything went dark where I was. I heard Horace say, just as bitterly as she, 'I'll do that little thing.' Madelene laughed and said, 'Thanks, awfully.' Then the door closed behind him. Not loud, but slowly and firmly."

Julie said, "I saw him close the door."

"Then things began to get lighter around me. They brightened until I felt as if I were all afire. I felt strong and I walked into the living room and stood over Madelene. I told her everything I wanted her to know — about Horace and you and your whole family, and about her and me, and what the Thompson friendship ought to mean to us, and what return we had made you for all you offered, and how Horace compares with that boy she was with today, and how you compare with me — but I said it in a way I had not meant to say it. I said it as if it were a knife and I wanted to kill her with it! . . . Julie, am I losing my mind?"

"*No,* Freddy —"

"I'm either losing it or finding it. Madelene and I are both going to be much worse after this — or much better. I don't know which. I've got to go home and try to find out. . . . Julie, if Horace can't forgive us — can you?"

Julie said, "There's nothing to forgive, Freddy. Nothing. If Young Horace doesn't realize it yet, he will. There had to be a blow-off in this thing. It was — unstable equilibrium. I only wish I knew how to help you more — and Madelene too."

Freddy said, "You've done everything you could for us. The rest we have to do for ourselves. Pray for us, Julie. And heaven bless you."

The door opened, and closed.

Julie lingered a little in the hall and then came slowly up the stairs.

"Did you hear, Mother?"

"Yes, Julie. I heard."

She stood by the tree, pressing a thorny branch against her cheek.

She said, "Smells good. Clean and good."

A minute later she said, "Ellen has supper on the buffet. You'd better go down soon, Mother. I won't eat — just yet."

"You had no lunch, did you?"

"No. But I'm not hungry. I'll have something by and by. I must go up now and lay out Babe's dress and brush her hair. . . . Did Lorna call?"

"No."

"That's queer. She said this morning she would probably give me a ring about three o'clock to let me know whether I should pick her up. She wouldn't say positively that she would come tonight. I don't know why. I hope nothing is wrong. I'll try to reach her later."

She stooped and kissed me.

"One other little thing I have to do. I have to get Sue's scarf from Pete's room. I promise not to mention it to Pete. I'll get it when he isn't there. . . . But it's Sue's scarf. It has to go on the tree. And there won't be anything except her name written on the card . . ."

I held her close and let her go, as mothers are forever doing with their children.

From the doorway she said:

"Tonight is the Christmas party, you know! In spite of everything —"

In the glow of the streetlamps — which in our village are the same now that they shield electricity as they were when gaslight flickered in them — last night's snow glistened softly on the branches of the elm trees and on either side of the walls as we went from the car to the church door that evening.

The stars were out. I looked to see. You have to look for them in a town sky. In the country you see them without trying. The air was crisp and cold. I was grateful for the warmth of the black sealskin coat Julie made me buy last fall, and rubbed my chin against the luxurious softness of the collar.

Babe squeezed my hand.

I remembered a little girl squeezing my hand when I was another little girl and the two of us were climbing stone steps, set into a bank wall, to the unroofed platform which ran across the whole front of a country church. A door was ajar and through it I could see many other little girls in shawls and capes and little boys in tight jackets standing in awe around a big Christmas tree strung with popcorn and cranberries, lighted with candles, and wonderfully dotted, here and there, with dangling, unwrapped gifts. I could even see now, as I could not then — and indeed, at the moment I was remembering, it had not yet been hung there, for Lovice still had it clutched under her shawl — a gift for Selena Tabor. A blue glass basket with a fluted, frosted edge. For seventy years that blue glass basket has always been on mantel or windowsill in the room where I stay most. The first gift I ever had from a Christmas tree! . . . I remembered a little girl squeezing my hand when it was my own little girl and we were riding together along a snowy road, both our hands under a buffalo robe, the sleigh bells jingling, the horse's ears pricked high, and Julie leaning against me to peer past her father's driving arm for the first glimpse of the district schoolhouse. I seemed to see that schoolhouse in the distance, its small-paned windows rosy — that soft reflection of oil lamps on glass — and also, at one and the same time, I saw its interior from the chair where I sat with the edge of a desk pressing against my waist. The room was smaller than the church. The school tree was smaller than the church tree. Everything was smaller than when I was a child, except me; and all the more miraculous. The tree had tinsel instead of popcorn, bells and balls like fairyland fruit instead of candles. Even the children were smaller, it seemed; especially mine; my Robbie and Julie. Yet they were seated on the dais where the teacher's desk usually stood, and by and by they would speak and sing. Robbie had a brown wool blouse gathered into an elastic at the bottom, and a wide, plaid silk tie knotted under his round chin. Julie's dress was dark-blue serge with a red velvet yoke and cuffs and sash. I had made both the blouse and the dress, and I had sent by Alvin for a whistle to put in the blouse pocket, and for a bit of gilt braid to sew on the red velvet yoke like a necklace.

I remembered . . . I remembered . . . It is strange how much one can remember while walking up to a church door.

Julie said, with light but firm support at my elbow, "You probably hate this, Mother. But no sprained ankle for Christmas, please!"

I did not hate it. Her touch was a comforting clarification. I was here, and this was now.

She said, "Hon is locking the car. Not that he expects anyone to try to make off with it. Simply a matter of routine." She sang softly, nudging Pete, "Open the do-or, Richard!"

Strange about songs. Lovice and I used to breathe hymns in our throats on our way to Christmas parties. Julie and Robbie sang the popular music of the First World War at the top of their lungs, riding home in the sleigh. Tonight it was "Open the Door, Richard." But whatever you sing at Christmas becomes a Christmas song.

Still the strains of the old carols are always in our hearts and heads at this time of year, whether we realize it or not.

The door was heavy on its cold hinges. Pete had to use both hands. When it had opened an inch or two, the bottom struck a wedge of ice which he kicked at. Ellen, too, dragged at the door, but it did not loosen until Mr. Pease gave it a thrust from the inside.

He looked out at us grimly, the light from the ceiling of the vestibule making the short gray hairs on his old head stand out separate and stiff.

He said, "Awful early, ain't ye? 'Tain't hardly warmed up here yet. Didn't expect anybody to git round this soon. Can't have a hot fire goin' here twenty-four hours a day, y' know. What coal I got's s'posed to last the winter. Half gone now, and winter hain't hardly begun."

Julie said cheerily, "If we need more coal, we'll have to get more, Mr. Pease. Don't worry. I know we're early. I've got bags of popcorn and candy to put on the tree. We can keep our coats on. Wonderful evening, isn't it?"

Mr. Pease grunted. He stood back a very little, to let us in.

He said, "Now don't let none of the young ones go traipsin' upstairs anywheres. It's shut and dark, and cold as Greenland's icy mountains, and 'twas last year this time, too, but still some of them little varmints went up by the choir stairs and got hymn books out o' the racks and piled 'em up to set on and tried to play the organ and I don't know what all. You see't don't happen agin. Now we got them new covers on the pew cushions, I hain't a-goin' to have 'em all smooched up and tore."

Julie said, softly, "I know how you feel about the cushion covers. They are beautiful, aren't they? I'll see that the children stay in the vestry."

Mr. Pease stood like a guard before the white stairway winding upward from the vestibule, while we felt our way down dim, uncarpeted steps toward the barnlike room in the basement which is the vestry.

I thought, of course, of the innkeeper who barred Joseph and Mary from climbing a stairway to comfort, and sent them through the dark night into a stable. And for the first time I wondered whether it was true that all his rooms were filled; or were some of them closed because their furnishings were too beautiful for use by common people? Were the closed rooms cold "as Greenland's icy mountains" because he had no faggots with which to warm them, or because he was saving his faggots to make sure he would have some left over in the spring? Or had he glanced shrewdly at Mary and decided against running the risk of having a baby born in his house? Was there a rule even then, "No Children Allowed"? And we cannot consider it any excuse that he did not know this was to be a Baby. Though perhaps we should. For the people of the world seem to have had to wait until Jesus was grown up and could tell them that every baby is a Baby. And how many have not learned this from His teachings even yet!

Babe's hand was still in mine.

I wondered if, as Mary groped toward the stable door, she felt the hand of her Child leading her, encouraging her, though He was yet unborn . . . And if, a few years later, when His hand was small, warm, and snug in hers, she remembered that she had felt it before she had ever seen Him. . . .

But the barnlike vestry was neither dark nor cold that night, as we went into it.

Alvin's tree stood in the far corner, its pointed top brushing the ceiling, its broad, stout branches lit by a hundred twinkling, richly colored bulbs, dripping with silver icicles, and blossoming with books and toys bought from Sunday-school funds, packages wrapped in the poinsettia paper which is the Christmas hallmark of Colt's variety store, and many other packages, including those Julie and Babe had taken down the night before, tied up in blue and green and pink and gold papers, fastened with bright tape or bows of ribbon.

Around the tree in a semicircle Sunday-school chairs were arranged in rows, a book of Christmas carols at each place. Behind the chairs were long, narrow tables set with stacks of plates, bright paper napkins, paper cups, and covered trays of sandwiches and little cakes. Along the walls dove-colored curtains were drawn and candlelights in brackets shone softly.

This is what Ellen and I saw. But after one glance at Babe's face, we saw what she saw. And that is past describing.

Pete said, "Here's a higher chair for you, Gramma. It's Mother's, from the primary room."

I sank into it gratefully.

Ellen helped Babe out of her boots. Then while the child tiptoed reverently about the room, Pete and Julie tied the scarlet bags to the branches of the tree. I saw that he could already reach as high as his mother. Her children will outgrow her, physically, sooner than mine outgrew me, for Julie's build is smaller than mine, and her three have inherited Horace's height. . . . I saw Julie rescue the package for Sue from among the bags and tie it to a low branch, deep in against the trunk, her face lowered, not speaking. . . . I saw Horace come in, take off his overcoat, fold and lay it neatly across a chair back, and open the door of the furnace which stood in the opposite corner from the tree. The reflection from the bed of coals ruddied his long, thin face. I thought he was, as Sue had said, a very distinguished-looking man; and nothing he did could take away from the distinction of his manner or appearance.

I wondered where Young Horace was. I knew both his father and mother were anxious about him, though neither of them had mentioned him tonight before the other children or me. I wondered how much Julie had told Horace about the Augsburgs.

I wondered where Lorna was. I knew Julie was anxious about her, too. She had not been able to reach her by telephone, and when we stopped by, at the big house on lower Main Street, on our way to the church, there was no light visible from the street, Lorna did not answer the bell, and the door was locked.

Julie had said, "I'll just run around to the back for a look at the windows of her room."

A minute or two later she came slowly toward the car from among the prickly branches of the dark cedars which almost overgrow the broken bricks of the walk. She wore a look of alarm until she thought we could see her. Then she smiled, but her eyes were still grave as she got in beside Horace.

"Not there?" Horace asked.

"I — don't know, Hon," Julie answered. "If she is, she has gone to bed and didn't hear me. I threw some bits of ice against the bedroom window. There is no light but the window is closed. I don't think she would go to bed with her window closed. And I can't imagine that she would go out without calling to let me know. Do you suppose — I wonder what I ought to do — what I can do —"

I tried to think of something to say before Horace said the wrong thing. I felt that Julie could not bear much more anxiety now. But my old brain is slow sometimes, and I was worried, too. I should have remembered that Horace was not saying wrong things lately.

He said, setting the car in motion, "She probably called and nobody heard the telephone. Why should you do anything? Lorna is a perfectly capable woman. If she needed you, she certainly could have reached you before this. She may be like Jake Pease — have a little private business of her own. You're on your way to a party. She may be there ahead of you."

Julie burrowed her kerchiefed head against his shoulder for an instant.

Babe said, "My Daddy and Mummie love each other, don't they?"

I answered, "Yes. They do. And that makes you a very lucky little girl."

Babe countered, "Why? If they didn't, I wouldn't be here."

Pete said, "Sometimes after people do, they don't."

Babe repeated, "Why? That's silly."

Julie laughed a little.

She said, "How true. Out of the mouths of babes —"

She did not speak of Lorna again. But I knew she was disappointed not to find her at the church and that as she hung the bags she was thinking of both Young Horace and Lorna. I could not quite forgive them for giving her this concern tonight, but knowing that neither of them would have wished to do so added to my own concern and no doubt to hers. . . .

Sue came in, breathless from running.

She cried, "Hello, everybody! Oh, how beautiful it looks!"

She hurried up to the tree, her old black coat flying

open, her neck stretching long and slender above her collar. She had two packages in her hands. They were wrapped in white paper and stuck all over with little seals. She tossed them under the tree.

"Who're they for?" Babe whispered. "Who're they for, Sue?"

Sue cried, "One's for you, sweetie. I won't tell about the other one."

She hugged Babe and Julie.

Pete slunk behind the tree and crossed the room to stand by his father.

Sue came and sat with me.

She said, "My dress is all ready, Mrs. Monroe. On a hanger in the closet. I've got my slippers on. See?"

She took off her dull, worn rubbers and thrust out her feet.

I said, "My! How they shine. And so long and narrow! You've got a lady's foot, Sue."

She sighed blissfully.

"They feel just like dancing . . . Christmas is wonderful, isn't it, Mrs. Monroe? . . . I never was so happy in my life. . . . I'm so glad there was just you here when I came. You're all here but — say, where's Horace?"

I said, "He wasn't ready when we left. Probably he'll be along later."

"Did he say he would?"

"No," I admitted. "He didn't say."

"Horace is so grown-up. Kids his age don't always come to the parties. I wish he would, though. He worked at the factory today, didn't he?"

"How did you know?"

"He told me. I saw him on the street."

"When?"

"This afternoon."

"About what time, Sue?"

"Around four or five o'clock, I guess. Why?"

"I just wondered. Was he going toward — home?"

"No. He was at the bus stand. He said he was going to Dalton. But he couldn't have gone, could he? And got home before you left?"

She guessed nothing. Her eyes were only wide and interested. But something in her gaze reminded me of the summer that was coming and I felt suddenly that I could not risk deceiving her in any way.

I said low, "Sue, this is a secret between us. But Young Horace wasn't at home when we left. We don't know where he is. His mother is worried about him."

Sue looked puzzled.

She said, "That's funny. Funny he didn't tell her where he was going, I mean."

"We think he was upset about something. Nothing that happened at home. Something that has nothing to do with any of us. Maybe that's why he didn't tell her. Maybe he just — forgot."

She nodded, satisfied.

She said, "That must be it. He wouldn't mean to worry her. He's nice. I remember now he looked sober. But he looked all right. I mean, I wish she wouldn't worry. I asked him if he was going to Dalton, and he said yes. I asked him if it was last minute Christmas shopping, and he said yes; he was going to blow in what he earned today. He didn't hardly look at me when he said it, but then lots of people don't. . . . I told him to be sure to be back for the party. I didn't know then what time it was. I went along home, and after that I guess I forgot about him, I was so excited . . . But I hate to have Mrs. Thompson worried."

I said, "Remember you aren't supposed to know she is. But when you get a chance, tell her you saw him waiting for the Dalton bus and that he said he was going Christmas shopping with the money he earned today. It may relieve her mind a little."

It would not be complete reassurance, of course, but I thought it would be better than nothing. And when Julie came over, a few minutes later, to help me take off my coat, and told me in a whisper what Sue had told her, I knew that it was.

People were crowding in now, many of them with personal gifts to add to already laden branches, and filling the chairs, nodding and smiling, putting back their coats, taking off children's snowsuits. There was a hum of conversation. Mabel Saunders was setting to work in the kitchen. I could hear her heavy tramp and the clatter of stove lids. Julie left me to go about among the children, perking hair ribbons, touching the chins of little boys, showing them their names on typed programs, answering their questions. I saw them finger her bracelets, rub against the soft stuff of her plaid skirt; and a very small child reached up both arms to pull her head down to his. I thought of all teachers everywhere, and all children, some of whom are loved and know it, and others who have no one in their whole world to whom they can turn for tenderness. . . .

At my elbow Sue said, "If Mrs. Thompson should die, what would become of us?"

I said, "There would be someone else, Sue."

She shook her head.

"There never was anybody else here like her."

I said, "If that is so, perhaps it is because she is here. Perhaps there is not often more than one in a place. But there is always one."

Not that, in my heart, I believed it. If this old globe should ever fall apart, it would happen for no other reason than that we did not have enough love to hold it together. There is no synthetic substitute for love. Nothing else will do.

Mr. Ransome, with his fat little wife and tall, spare, spinster daughter (who does social service in Boston but was with her parents for the holiday weekend), made a bustling entrance. The women seated themselves hastily and I could hear Mrs. Ransome murmuring our names to

Miss Ransome. Mr. Ransome paused just inside the door to fish for his pocket handkerchief and wipe the steam from his glasses. He was smiling conscientiously but I thought he was mildly disturbed. As he eased the bows of the glasses over his ears, he was looking at Julie and had taken a step or two toward her when Horace spoke to him from beside the furnace. Then he turned quickly, as if with relief, and they talked together, Mr. Ransome at some length, tipping his head back to peer up at Horace, and Horace answering briefly. I could not hear anything they said. But when Mr. Ransome finally did go down to Julie, he was beaming all over as usual, and his pulpit voice boomed genially.

"Well, well, Mrs. Thompson! Are we all set and ready to go?"

She gave him the typed program from which he was to announce each number and he said, "Well, well! Looks like we have a real treat in store!"

Julie called, "Come, children," and those who stood close to her, those who had been gathered about the tree, their hands behind their backs, trying to decipher the names on labels, and others who had waited shyly by their parents' knees, all slid into the front rows of chairs.

Grace Dewey took her place at the piano and played the opening bars of "O Little Town of Bethlehem."

Mr. Ransome announced, "Number Twenty-three. Twenty-three. And everybody sing!"

The Christmas party was beginning.

Julie had promised it would be the best one ever, and it was. I realized suddenly why it always is. Christmas is cumulative. Every year which has passed since the birth of Christ, whatever else it has lost, has retained and added to the magic of light and color against a dark background, to the human capacity for appreciation of chords and bells and melodies, to the sweetness of children's voices, the brightness of children's eyes, the delight of giving, the comfort of receiving, and the ecstasy of renewed hope and faith.

A brown-eyed little boy with hands in the pockets of his brand-new, sharply creased gray wool shorts gave the recitation of welcome. Four eight-year-old girls dressed in white, holding red cardboard placards lettered in tinsel, spelled out SNOW. A tall boy with an engaging grin told of the night when he waited up for Santa Claus. Another song from the book; and a toddler, finger doubtfully touching her chin, lisped two lines which nobody understood but which everybody loved and applauded generously. A chubby older boy, broad-shouldered and straight-backed, recited in a big voice a page from Dickens's *A Christmas Carol*. He did not smile. This was a serious moment for him. He made me think of Robbie. And Pete. When he sat down the toddler jumped up, curls bounding, no longer doubtful, and squealed proudly, "He's my bruvver!" For this the applause was deafening.

Sue, beside me, said, "That's Paul and Mary Speare. Mr. Pease's grandchildren."

I said, "She is a darling child. And he seems a bright boy."

I was glad Mr. Pease had taken a day for Christmas shopping, however belated.

Two boys and three girls did a little play — we used to call them dialogues — about choosing proper gifts for their elders.

We sang again. It was like all the Christmas concerts I have ever heard, but better. Better because it was this year's.

Mr. Ransome announced:

" 'Why I Love Jesus'; by Selena Thompson."

It startled me. Who was Selena Thompson?

Babe slipped from her chair in the front row. Oh, of course. Babe was Selena.

No, she was Julie. A Julie-that-never-was.

She stood beside the Christmas tree, her eyes ashine, the narrow pleats of her red skirt still whirling from her motion as she turned, her blouse crisp and white as frost, her dark hair held behind her small pink ears by a white ribbon printed with holly leaves and berries.

She said in the clear, thoughtful voice of the intelligent and perfectly adjusted child:

> *I love Jesus because He was so little, and*
> *   Because He became so great;*
> *He never was too little*
> *   And He did not come too late!*
>
> *I love Him for His kindness, and*
> *   Because He's always near;*
> *Because He taught us there is nothing*
> *   That we need ever fear.*
>
> *I love Him for all the words He said*
> *   Which are so plain and true.*
> *He gave us churches, homes and schools*
> *   And gave us Christmas, too!*

It was such a thought as is printed in a thousand paper-covered books of "Recitations for Christmas," expressed with such simplicity, in such familiar words, and in such a broken, singsong meter that it could not be called a poem, hardly even a thought. It was only a "recitation for Christmas." Yet coming from a child's red lips, with a child's eyes shining above the words, against the background of a Christmas tree, it told that child's grandmother and parents, and all the other average parents and grandparents in that room and every other room in the land where it, or something very like it, was being repeated, what we most wanted and needed to know:

"The children know Him and love Him well."

Many clapped their hands. I could not do so. I felt very still. But I wanted to smile at someone. Julie was not in sight. I looked for Sue beside me but she was not there. I glanced about for Pete and saw him standing near the furnace, but his head was turned toward the wall; in the embarrassment of burning pride, I knew. Was it pride in what Babe had said and the way she had said it, or in her childish charm and the fact that she had not forgotten or faltered in her lines? Pete is still very young. I looked above his head and my eyes met Horace's, directly. I am not sure they ever did before. Certainly not at any time when it mattered. Now it did. And his eyes looked exactly as mine felt. Proud, misted, but, above all, mightily reassured. We smiled at each other.

I thought, He will take this into the factory and into the bank for the new year. As I shall take it back to the farm. I thought, After many years, I believe I am beginning to know my daughter's husband, and that if I get to know him much better, I shall love him.

Love was in the air. It sang all around us. Julie might have called it the angels. If it was, they were flying close now.

Someone else was speaking. I shall never know who.

For as I turned my eyes slowly from Horace's, I saw a third figure near the furnace. Young Horace was leaning against the wall, half in shadow. I could see only one side of his face. I thought it looked white and very grave. His cheek twitched slightly. I knew he had been home, for he was wearing his tan tweed coat, brown gabardine trousers, and a brilliant yellow tie. I thought he had put on the tie in a spirit of defiance, and perhaps it was the tie, in part, which took the color from his face. His hair was brushed very smoothly, with the deep wave which boys of his age affect nowadays softening the margin of his forehead on the side which I could see. He looked older, with indications of his father's distinction, and very much alone. My heart went out to him. And yet I suppose he preferred to be alone. I was shifting my gaze discreetly, wishing that I had some way to let Julie know he was

there, when he, too, as his father had, caught my eye. I
don't know what he saw in it; by then certainly neither of
us was thinking of Babe. But a minute later he stepped
over the back of the small chair which Sue had left vacant,
and sat down.

He said, "Hi, Gram."

I whispered, "Hello, dear. I'm glad you got here.
Handsome tree, isn't it?"

He glanced at it. I saw a glint of satisfaction. He nodded. But what he said was nothing I had expected of him.

"Sure. Gramp grew the best."

I thought, "Alvin! Did you hear? That's Julie's and
Horace's boy. Their first one. The one that used to cry to
go home whenever they brought him up."

Alvin said, "Don't you s'pose likely I know who 'tis?
Branched out a mite, ain't he? Learnt everything worth
lookin' at ain't right in his porridge dish. Healthy sign.
He'll make out."

There was no time for anything more.

Mr. Ransome was announcing Sue in a voice I thought
somewhat subdued.

" 'The Dance of the Christmas Fairy'; by Susan Halsey."

Grace Dewey's fingers touched the piano keys. Sue
came, spinning slowly from the coatroom, wearing the
tight, rose-velvet bodice, the full, brief, twinkling white
taffeta skirt. There was no sound of the black patent slippers. They might have been of satin or velvet.

I thought of a poem I had read many times:

> *Let us walk in the white snow*
> *In a soundless space;*
> *With footsteps quiet and slow*
> *At a tranquil pace.*
>
> *I shall go shod in silk. . . .*
> *We shall walk through the still town*

In a windless place;
  We shall step upon white down
  Upon silver fleece. . . .

We shall walk in velvet shoes:
  Wherever we go
Silence will fall like dews
  On white silence below,
  We shall walk in the snow.

I wondered if Sue had ever read it. I did not suppose
she had. I thought she should have worn sheer swirling
white; how unreal she would have looked in white! Or she
might have worn black; soft, clinging, unrelieved black;
how utterly beautiful she would have looked in black! I
knew the rose bodice and sequinned taffeta were wrong
for what she was going to do. I hoped no one else would
know it.

Then I saw that it was not wrong.

This was not the poem which the girl named Elinor had
written. This was a poem which a girl named Sue was
dancing. She had made it all her own, and the dress I had
made belonged to it, was part of it.

The steps were slow, the pace tranquil, the town still,
but there was no sadness in the world where Sue walked,
and the silence which fell was not of dew but of snowflakes. Flakes which drifted through the air like stars
come down to play; and Sue played with them, was one of
them. They lay on her upturned face, caught on her skirt,
filled her cupped hands. She and they were gleeful together, spun slowly together, more and more slowly,
rested together, and as they rested, they prayed. They
saw God, and God saw them and knew what He had created was good; and He was glad. And they were glad and
played again, and the older stars in the sky were the more
brilliant and everlasting for this merriment below. The
whole firmament which had been trembling faintly was

stabilized. In its place the earth stood fast, swung true in stately measure. The night was shortened. As the soft drifts piled up, the sky was brightening for dawn. There was a streak of rosy light across the east.

The music stopped. The dance was over. Sue had disappeared.

For a minute or more the room was as silent as when she left it. Then the applause came, but uncertainly, as if no one felt quite sure applause was suitable. I wondered what this dance had meant to Mr. Ransome, to Mabel Saunders who, through the sliding panel between the Sunday-school room and the kitchen, had seen dancing in her church for the first time . . . to Mr. Pease and his grandchildren . . . to Pete who is responsive to so many things to such a degree that he must hide it. I wondered what it had meant to Sue herself, and whether she would ever be able to tell me.

Young Horace said low, "Hey! Gram!"

I looked up, bewildered. I had completely forgotten him.

He said, "That was something, wasn't it?"

I said slowly, "Yes. It was. . . . I think it really was."

I had never approved of slang expressions. The more modern they were the less I approved. But now I realized for the first time how much meaning they have for those who understand them. They are phrases or single words with which the young express feelings they could not express in any other language, and which in any other language they would deny ever having had. I saw suddenly that Pete, for personal release and to be articulate with his own age group, now needed only to learn these few teen-age words and phrases and to become adept in using them.

Young Horace added an outdoing breath, "Mm-*mmh!* That kid's sure got something."

He could not say the dance was incredibly moving and beautiful. I could have said it, but still I should have been far short of saying what I felt. He could not say, "Sue may be a great dancer some day. She is a hauntingly lovely child. She will be an amazing woman." Only old people can risk thinking in such terms. Even if stated, they would have been only half-truths. No one in the church that night knew what Sue Halsey could or might become. She was only beginning to be.

He could say, and had, "That was something. She's got something."

With this he was satisfied and so, I found, was I. Just what these "somethings" were must be left by both of us to a future revelation which would unfold as slowly as the movements of her dance.

The program was going on. . . . It was concluding. . . . As the room hushed, it seemed to grow dim.

A small voice asked loudly, "Where's Santa Claus?"

Older people chuckled sympathetically, happily.

Mr. Ransome said "Well, well, now that's what we're all wondering! Where *is* Santa Claus? Of course he is a very busy man. But he gave his word he would be here sooner or later. Let's listen hard. We may hear the jingle of his sleigh bells."

We listened hard, but heard nothing.

Mr. Ransome said, "Well, well! Why don't we all sing 'Jingle Bells,' while we're waiting? We all know that, don't we? Everybody sing!"

Grace Dewey went back to the piano. The gay old notes tinkled. But not everybody sang. The children were still trying to listen for sounds outside, and the older people were beginning to talk among themselves.

I heard Mrs. Ransome murmur to Miss Ransome: "They must have found someone to do it. He wouldn't speak as he did if they hadn't. It was strange the Guyers didn't try to reach Mrs. Thompson before she left home. Mrs. Guyer said he had been feverish all day. But maybe they thought up to the last minute that he would be able to come. I don't know why it was put on your father, though. It wasn't his responsibility to get a Santa Claus. Quite a number of the church people weren't in favor of having one, and he shouldn't have to be mixed up in it, one way or another. But that's the way it always happens. I suppose maybe they drafted Mr. Pease, the janitor."

Drafted Mr. Pease? To be Santa Claus? Never, I was very sure.

I said to young Horace, "Maybe Santa Claus isn't coming. I understand Mr. Guyer is sick."

Poor Julie. Poor Babe. Poor . . . Why, short, stout jolly Mr. Guyer had been the Sunday-school Santa Claus every Christmas for ten years! Julie had said in the very beginning, "One thing I'm sure of . . ."

"Keep your chin up, Gram," grinned Young Horace. "He's coming. Never fails."

Sue tiptoed along the side aisle through the dimness and reached the end chair in our row before she saw that Young Horace was sitting by me.

She stopped, startled. He looked at her with smiling, shrewdly narrowed eyes for an instant, and then stood up.

"Got your seat, haven't I, Sue?"

"Oh, no," Sue gasped. "I mean — thanks but I don't want it. I — I forgot something I have to tell your mother."

She had taken a step or two away when he whispered, "Hey!"

She paused, half turning.

"When you've told her, come back, will you? Before I forget something I have to tell you."

She whispered, "Okay."

I remembered a song. An old woman's head is full of old poems and old songs.

> *Over the banister leans a face*
> *Tenderly sweet and beguiling . . .*
> *Timid and tired with downcast eyes,*
> *I wonder why she lingers*

Saying good night again soft and low —
Somebody's holding her fingers.

Holds her fingers and draws her down
Suddenly growing bolder . . .
A question asked . . .
She has fled like a bird from the stairway
But over the banister comes a "Yes"
That brightens the world for him alway.

There was no banister, no good night, probably no alway. But there was the sweet timidity, the tiredness, the downcast eyes, the grip of something other than fingers, the growing boldness, the question asked, the birdlike flight, the whispered "Okay," and at least a temporary brightening for them both in the dusky vestry.

The light burns dim in the hall below
Nobody sees her standing . . .
Nobody, only those eyes of brown
Tender and full of meaning,
Looks on the loveliest face in town . . .

Only those. And mine. Mine do not count because I am a grandmother with a reputation for never remembering what young people have chosen to leave behind. And a temporary brightening, to my mind, was all either of them needed now.

I knew of course what Sue had suddenly "remembered" she must tell Julie. Over bald heads and the crowns of velvet hats I saw Julie's face as she listened. I saw it clear of concern. I sighed with relief.

Now if only there would be a Santa Claus!

There was.

As the last verse of "Jingle Bells" died away, bells jingled merrily above our heads. There were heavy steps on the choir loft stairs. The stairway door opened, and the biggest Santa Claus I ever saw crowded through the narrow opening. He was tall, he was broad, and he stuck out in front quite as far as his bulging pack swung out behind.

He called in a furry Scotch voice through his thick beard,

"Mur-ree Christmas, everybody!"

Utter silence fell. The little ones shrank into their chairs and stared, wide-eyed. I expected Julie to lead a chorus of answers but she did not say a word. It was left for Mr. Ransome to boom genially, "Well, well, well! Merry Christmas to *you*, sir!"

Santa Claus was not taken aback by his reception.

He shouted, "Think I was never going to get here, kiddies? Well, I was stuck in the belfry. Started to swing down on the rope and it broke before I got my feet off the roof. Quite a heavy man I am, as you can see. So all the time you've been singing, I've been sitting up there in the belfry, splicing the rope. Lucky I'm a Jack-of-all-trades, hey? That's what my wife thinks, too. Mrs. Santa Claus, she says she couldn't get along without me nohow. Says life up at the North Pole would sure be tough if I wasn't a real handy feller in an emergency. Funny thing, too, you know, how often emergencies come up. Sometimes seems like life's just one long series of emergencies. Ever notice that? . . . Well, never mind. We're not having an emergency here tonight. We're having Christmas. And we're starting with oranges. These didn't come from the North Pole, you know. We don't have oranges at the North Pole. No, sir. A lot of other places, too, oranges are mighty hard to come by. But not for you. You're in luck. You've got two places in your country that grow the best oranges in the world, and stores right up here on your main street that'll sell 'em to anybody. Even sold me some as I was on my way down here. And never batted an eyelash, either. Who's a good catch?"

He set down his pack and began taking golden balls from it, one in each hand. They whirled through the air in smooth arcs, two at a time, until every child had one, and many adults too, and there was laughter again.

"So!" rumbled Santa Claus, slinging the empty sack over his shoulder. "You have your Christmas oranges. Now let's see what's on this handsome tree for you. There's something for everybody, I know that. Some of your Sunday-school teachers helped me to see to it. And there's something special for every one of you who took part in the program. I don't know what it is. Surprises from Mr. Colt of the variety store in your town. Say, you've got a pretty fine town here, ever think of that? Pretty fine town that has children like you and older people who do so many things for you children. If I ever leave the North Pole, I think I'll live in this town. That is, if you'll have me. What do you say? Think I'd be a good citizen?"

"Sure, Santa Claus . . . You bet! . . . Come on, Santa Claus . . . Would we have Christmas every day then?"

"Not a bit of it. We only have Christmas once a year at the North Pole. I don't make Christmas, you know. You make it. What would Christmas amount to without you folks to get ready for it? And Christmas sure takes a lot of getting ready, as I often tell Mrs. Santa Claus. I only do my part and I admit I'm kind of slow at starting on it sometimes. I'm getting old and lazy. But Mrs. Santa Claus gives me the nudge. And I s'pose you're the ones that give her the nudge. Christmas is a lot more than getting presents. But you'll know more about that when you're older. And presents are pretty important too, hey? Well, now, let's see what we've got here. I can't see very well. These whiskers kind of get in my way. Won't a couple of you young people take the presents off the tree for me? And a couple more read the labels? . . . That's fine. Now when I call your name, you come right up and get your present. So I'll know it didn't get to the wrong person. How's that? All right. Here we go —"

He called the first child's name, and the first child went down the aisle like a sleepwalker in the course of a blissful dream. . . .

I said to Young Horace, "Why, he's wonderful. Who in the world is he?"

Young Horace raised his eyebrows.

"Don't you know, Gram?"

"No. Do you? I didn't suppose there was such a big man in town."

"It's Dad."

I am sure I blinked.

"Horace? No! He isn't a big man!"

"Sure he is. Tall, isn't he? You never saw him stuffed before — and whiskered."

I still could hardly believe it.

"And the way he talks! He's usually so quiet. And that Scotch burr."

"Never heard it before? It's his specialty."

"Then — your mother must know!"

"Sure she does. Now. But she never heard Mr. Guyer was sick. Mr. Ransome told Dad when he came in. And Dad said he'd do it."

That was what they had been talking about when Mr. Ransome came in and Horace stopped him from going down to Julie.

"Well — he's a wonderful Santa Claus."

"Sure. You can't beat Dad when he gets started. He's a lollapaloozer."

I could hear Horace saying, weeks ago, "I am probably going to have to cut the Christmas tree and drag it to the vestry on my back, unless I'm willing to watch you do it." . . . He had not had to get the tree, as it happened, because he was too busy at the time serving as janitor. Had he even suspected that he — he, Horace Thompson, president of the bank and owner of the twine factory — would have to prance about in the role of

Santa Claus? I was inclined to think now that he had had a premonition.

Julie had told me, "Darling, you don't know anything about Horace, really. But you will . . ."

I watched the children getting their presents, as Babe had described the school party, "right out of Santa's hand."

Young Horace was stepping backward over his chair and pushing it beneath Sue.

I heard him say, "That dance of yours was super."

"Honestly, Horace?"

"You bet!"

"Gee. I'm glad you liked it."

I kept on watching the children. I wanted to speak to Sue about her dance, but I knew that all she needed to hear had been said. So I only reached for her hand, without looking at her, and from the pressure she gave back to me I knew we understood each other.

Now gifts were beginning to come off the tree for Sue. She went down for each one and slipped back into her chair hastily, opening each package eagerly. Young Horace still stood behind her. She found a framed picture from the Sunday school ("Look, Mrs. Monroe! Isn't it sweet? I know just the place —"); a gold-plated barrette from Colt's ("Jeepers! I'll never wear pigtails again!"); a pair of red wool socks from Babe (*"Babe! Thanks!"*); the plaid shirt from Lorna ("Hully Gee! Oh, she shouldn't've — where is Miss West? Didn't she come? I'll go over there first thing in the morning! Look, Mrs. Monroe! Can you 'magine!"); the stocking cap ("Horace! From your mother!").

The last package she got was almost the last on the tree. I wondered that Julie had not realized it might happen this way when she put it so deep into the branches. But even Julie cannot think of everything.

As Sue came up the aisle with her long, flat box, I felt

that the Christmas party was ending, like a piece of music, and I waited for the last note. I cannot say exactly why it still seemed so very important; only that this would complete Sue's Christmas, round out her fourteenth year. It might set the key for whatever lay ahead for her, or it might mean nothing. It could undo all that had been done.

She said happily, picking at the ribbon, "No name but mine outside. Must be a name inside. . . . Whee! It's a scarf! What a duck of a scarf! But no name here either." She shook the tissues. "From — you, Mrs. Monroe?"

I said no.

"Of course not. You gave me my dress. . . . Well — oh, I'll bet I know!" She whirled, radiant. "Did you give me this scrumptious scarf, Pete?"

Pete still stood by the furnace behind us. He had two or three packages under his arm — one of them from her; none of them opened. He was looking at the floor.

Poor Pete! . . .

He growled, "What? . . . Me? . . . No."

Sue turned from him slowly. Her shoulders sagged. She seemed to be making herself small. She touched the scarf shyly, and began to lay the tissues gently over it, as if it were not hers after all. . . .

Horace, behind her, said, "Fooled, weren't you?"

She did not lift her head. Her breathing was so light it hardly stirred the front of her dress; her unbecoming, light-blue rayon dress put together without care by unskilled hands. Until now I had not noticed what she wore.

He said, "You were getting warm. Guess again."

She turned her head without moving her shoulders, and stared up at him. Her face was toward me, but she no longer knew I was there. I saw her dark eyebrows lift, her eyes widen in the center and narrow at the corners, her lips begin to curve, color come into her cheek, the pulse quicken in her throat.

She whispered, "You?"

He said, "It sure is time I got a little appreciation around here."

She said incredulously, "Gee! I never s'posed *you'd* give me a present, Horace. I knew you were nice, but — gee-e-e-e!"

Suddenly she was pulling back the tissues again. Now the scarf was hers. Her first gift from a boy. She caught it up and put it against her cheek. She tucked it around her neck and looped one end over the other.

She said, "Mm-m-m! It's soft as a — as a kitten! Oh, Horace, I love it! Whee! Am I proud!"

Now she was reopening all the other packages, shrugging into the shirt, snapping the barrette into her hair, pulling on the cap at a saucy angle. Now the pale rayon dress was concealed. Sue looked like any other village girl on a winter evening, except that her eyes were brighter than most, her smile more ecstatic. Her fingers kept going to the ends of the scarf.

She said, "Horace, I never had anything so lovely in my life!"

He said easily, "Okay. So I'm appreciated."

He could not have known how much, how deeply; and neither could she know how much he needed a girl's thanks that night. Does anyone ever know how much what he gives is worth to the one who receives it?

Mabel Saunders was bustling in with steaming earthen pitchers of cocoa. Santa Claus rumbled his big "Mur-ree Christmas to you all, and a Ha-appy New Year!" and vanished up the choir loft stairs. Julie ran up the aisle and paused behind us on her way back with a stack of plates.

She said, "Sue, darling, will you follow me with the sandwiches? And would you lend us your brawn for the trays of cocoa cups, Young Horace? Mabel's pouring it now."

Sue said, "Thanks awfully for the cap, Mrs. Thompson. I'm crazy about it. And did you see the scarf Horace gave me? Isn't it bee-eautiful?"

Julie glanced at the scarf. Her eyes widened in the center and narrowed at the corners exactly as Sue's had.

"Young Horace gave it to you?" she exclaimed. "Is that what he went to Dalton City for? Oh, Sue, it's lovely! I saw one just like it in the variety store window weeks ago and when I noticed it was gone, I wished you had it! What luck!"

She went on with her plates.

At the front of the room she made a little announcement.

She said, "I have a surprise for you. After the sandwiches and cocoa, we're going to have cakes and ice cream! The ice cream is a surprise to all of us. The Sunday school couldn't quite afford it, but it was delivered while the program was going on. There was a card with it. It says, 'With regret that I was not able to help with the Christmas party this year, and with my love and best wishes to you all, Frederica Augsburg.' "

She was smiling. Her voice was not quite steady, but perhaps I was the only one who was aware of that. The children were still applauding the ice cream as she began passing out the plates.

The children ate mightily, their elders lightly, but with the very appearance of food an atmosphere of comfort and relaxation, of singular peace filtered through the whole building. It seemed to me that if I were upstairs, alone in the dark, cold auditorium, I should still feel it; the pews would be warmed by it and the organ pipes gleam. It was as if partitions had been taken down and the roof lifted off, but no cold came in, only the dark-blue, cloudless sky and the starlight.

People talked together.

Ellen contentedly dipped ice cream for Mabel to serve. She said, "The children done real good, didn't they?"

Mabel agreed, "Yes, they did. You'd never have expected it a week ago. Such a time as Mis' Thompson had with 'em one while there. But she was patience on a monument and it come out all right. Seems Mis' Augsburg's come down off her high horse, too."

"I thought's likely she had, this arfternoon. She'n Mis' Thompson went off somewheres together."

"Well, there. Another gale blowed out to sea. Always darkest before the dawn, they say. Don't know what she could a-had against Mr. Ransome, anyway. Real nice man, seems to me. Godly, too, for which I'm thankful to the bottom of my heart. Course I don't know's he could speak Latin like Father Clement. But there, I couldn't understand him if he did."

"Father's awful nice too. Kindly. Not hard, like some."

"Always said so. Father Clement's as nice a man to meet on the street as anybody'd ask for. Bespeaks a Protestant just as pleasant, just exactly, as he does a Catholic."

Mr. Pease was saying to Horace, "I wouldn't 'a' been in your shoes for a mint of money, but you sure made a good job of it, I'll say that. Guess you've put Bill Guyer's nose out of joint."

"I hope not," Horace said hastily. "Or else I hope he gets it right back in, before another Christmas rolls around. Never was so hot in my life. Thought I'd never make it back up the stairs. I'm too old for such carrying-on. We're too old for Christmas, Jake. They ought to pension us off."

They both laughed.

Mr. Pease said, "Young ones have sure had quite a time. Look at 'em stow away that ice cream. As my old daddy used to say at Thanksgiving, 'The doctors'll ride this road tonight.' Don't remember we ever got sick though, at that age, stuffin' ourselves with anything fit t' eat. Green apples, they was somethin' else again."

"Nothing ever tasted better than green apples, though, did it?" Horace asked. "Unless it was froze'n'thaw apples. How long since you ate a froze'n'thaw apple, Jake?"

"Gorry," Jake said, rubbing his chin, "Must be sixty years."

Horace laughed and dropped his hand on Jake's shoulder.

"Told you we're getting on," he said. "And the trouble is, getting on doesn't bring a man any advantages, does it? Womenfolks, for instance, boss us around as much as they ever did, don't they? Take you and me. Would we be hanging around here right now if it wasn't for women? No. We'd be home with our boots off, taking our ease."

"Women is cussed," Jake agreed. "But tarnation take 'em, I always say, what'd we do without 'em?"

"Well, you've got something there," Horace told him. "I suppose the world couldn't get on without these young rapscallions that are here tonight, and if we didn't have womenfolks to tend to them, mostly, we'd be worse off than we are. Shoveling coal and Santa Clausing may not be too tough after all. Could be worse. Eh, Jake?"

"Yes," Jake nodded. "Now take tomorrer. I'll have to be here bright and early to git cleaned up before church, but I'll have the place to myself. Won't be nobody botherin' of me. I'll know 'twun't be happenin' agin for another year. I can't beef too much. Besides, them young ones of my girl has had the time of their lives. Hear how that little Molly spoke right up about Bub? 'He's my brother,' she says. Bet that tickled her grandmother some."

"They're smart kids," Horace said. "I notice Bub is on the honor roll at school right along, and he's started an account at the bank lately. We're keeping an eye on that fella, Jake. Going to be a place waiting for him all right, when he's through school."

I saw how Horace had managed to keep up production through the war when other factories were closing down. Even while he was in the service, his foremen had been faithful and older men had worked longer hours because younger employees were away.

Miss Ransome said, "The people here are so congenial, aren't they? It's a real inspiration. They all seem so fond of one another, almost like the members of a big family. I should say that, as church groups go, this one is ideal."

Mrs. Ransome whispered, "You're seeing us at our best, of course, dear. It isn't always so. In fact, there was quite a decided split in the congregation when we first came. But your father has done well. Very well . . . Wasn't he in good voice tonight? Singing away with all his heart! I love to hear him. And I know he is very pleased that Mrs. Augsburg sent the ice cream. Not only because the little ones are enjoying it so, but because it was such a friendly gesture. She hasn't been to church since we came, and never happened to be home when he called, but people say she is a wonderful worker, and maybe this means she will be back with us soon. We did find out that neither she nor her daughter has been attending any other church."

Mrs. Pease complimented me on Babe's speaking and I spoke to her about her grandchildren. Grace Dewey asked me if I had ever seen anything more truly religious than Sue's dance and I said I hadn't.

Sue said, "I never could have done it with anybody else playing, Miss Dewey. You just made that piano say things to me!"

Tears came into Grace's eyes.

She said, "I wish your folks could have been here, dear. I wish my father had been alive to see you. Nobody was ever more interested to see a child do something — something really out of the ordinary! He would have talked about your dance for days."

Mr. Ransome, overhearing as he helped his ladies on with their coats, cleared his throat and said, "Is this a little Ruth St. Denis we have in our midst, Mrs. Monroe? I read somewhere just the other day that Ruth St. Denis is dancing now as a part of the worship service in some great church. She says she is dedicating the culmination of her life and art to this expression of her faith. It is unusual, but I imagine it is a very moving thing to see, a great inspiration."

I knew this reading had fortified him to face the criticism he had no doubt met in many homes in the parish when word went around that Sue would dance in the vestry.

I said, "I think Miss St. Denis has always had a great faith. Perhaps that is why even people like me, in little towns, know about her, though we have never seen her. Surely she is one of the few American dancers whose names will live, and perhaps her faith is the main reason why."

Sue said, "I never heard of her before. I never heard of much of anybody." She added wistfully, "But I would love to see her dance."

Grace said, "And she would like to see you dance, child. I am sure of that."

Now everybody was leaving, children clutching toys, parents clutching children, everybody saying it had been a fine party, one none of us would ever forget, and "Wish you Merry Christmas!" "Wish you the same!"

Julie came up, leading a sleepy, sticky Babe.

"Coming with us, Young Horace?" she asked. "Always room for one more. Besides the presents! Babe's going to be asleep in somebody's lap anyway, before your father has the car turned around."

Young Horace said, "Never mind about me. I'll be along."

"Aren't you tired, dear?" Julie asked.

He grinned at her indulgently.

He said, "What's tiring about riding all day? I'm glad of a chance to stretch my legs. Guess I'll walk Sue home first. Okay by you, Sue?"

I wondered what she would say. I did not know what girls said nowadays.

She said, "Gee, that'll be super."

They went out a little ahead of us and when we came down the church walk they were almost out of sight down the street. As they turned a corner, their hands caught and swung.

Julie, standing by the car while Horace unlocked it, said, "Well . . . of all things . . . I should never have thought of it! . . . But what a burden off my mind!"

From the shadows Pete growled, "Off *your* mind!"

We all laughed. Even Babe laughed. She always laughs when everyone else does. She snuggled sleepily against Pete in the car.

She said, "Pete, you slay me! . . . You're my boy-friend, Pete."

He took her on his knees.

He said, "Okay. Sit tight . . . And don't give up your seat; see? No matter what."

Julie said, "He means, until you're pushed off, Baby. Then yield gracefully."

But neither of them was listening.

The car moved smoothly across the light snow. The street was deserted except for church people going quietly home from Christmas parties. The sky lay on the tree-tops, the stars pricking through. The party was over. The night was hushed. We were a part of something much bigger than ourselves.

"Shall we drive by Lorna's?" Horace asked.

Julie shook her head.

She said, "She's asleep. Or else just come home. I'm sure she's all right. Everybody must be all right."

She dropped her head on Horace's shoulder.

He said, "Somebody should sing about the surrey. That part having to do with 'noddin', droopin'. . . . Whoa, you team! and just keep a-creepin' at a slow clip-clop.' "

Julie said, "Would be nice. But not necessary. Everybody's too tired. Lovely and tired . . . Wasn't it a lovely party? Didn't Babe do splendidly? Weren't we proud?"

Pete said, "You bet!"

Ellen said with a pat, "Bless her heart, God love her."

"Wasn't Sue beyond all words?"

"As usual," said Pete. "Hey, I forgot — sure. Very good."

"Weren't all the children wonderful?"

"Beyond whooping," misquoted Horace.

"Wasn't Mr. Ransome a dear about the whole thing? Wasn't Mabel simply a brick? Wasn't it perfectly marvelous what Frederica did —"

"Wasn't Jake Pease," inquired Horace, "out of this world?"

"At the end, yes. You buttered him up. I saw you doing it, and nobody can do it better, once he sets out . . . Hon, what were you stuffed with?"

"Stuffed with? Oh. Oh, yes. Had a pew cushion on front and a hymn book on each hip. Effective, wasn't it?"

"Ho-on!" Julie gasped.

"What's the matter now?"

"Oh — nothing . . . Only — did Mr. Pease know it?"

"Not yet. He will in the morning. Mean you think he won't like it? Oh, well. Knew there was some reason why I was buttering him up."

We had been in the house just long enough to get the snowsuit off the sleeping Babe when the telephone rang.

"Oh —" Julie exclaimed. "It may be Lorna!"

Horace said, "Take it. I'll roll the infant into bed."

Julie said, "Hello? . . . Oh, Lorna, where have you been? . . . Oh. Well, but couldn't you have let me know? Not that it's any of my business, of course, but I was worried, darling. You said you'd call . . . Oh. Hon said you might have . . . Well, that's all right, darling.

Perfectly all right. We missed you terribly at the party, that's all. See you tomorrow? . . . Oh, but you must. The children will be decorating the tree all afternoon and there'll be stockings to fill at night. You always help us fill the stockings, you know! And I've so much to tell you — you've no idea! More things have happened to-day! . . . No, I couldn't. And anyway I won't. I'm saving it as bait. I want you to come up. Come as soon as we're home from church. Come for dinner . . . All right, darling. Don't struggle with it any longer, whatever it is. But come as early as you can. Sue loved the shirt. She wore it home. It looked adorable on her. But she said she was coming over to tell you about that tomorrow. She'll probably tell you other things too. I'm afraid she'll scoop me. I wish you'd leave a note for her, telling her where you are, and come over here before church is out . . . Well, if you can't, you can't. But try. And do make it as early as possible. I'll be watching for you . . . Good night."

She came into my room, her forehead creased.

"What's up?" Pete asked.

She said, "I don't know." She looked at me. "Lorna's being awfully mysterious. She tries to explain it, but nothing she says makes any sense. She's been out somewhere this evening. She said a friend asked her to drive into the country, and it was such a fine night and all. She didn't say who the friend was, and of course I didn't ask. But it couldn't have been anyone from town. She doesn't have that kind of friends. I don't believe she was driving into the country at all. Lorna is such a poor liar. But I know she has been out. Not at home, ill or depressed, or anything like that. She sounds — well, excited."

"Then that's all right," I said. "That's fine."

I resented Julie's curiosity about anything which Lorna preferred to keep to herself. I saw that intimate friendship, even with Julie, had its drawbacks.

"I hope it is," said Julie. "I hope it isn't anything she is going to — to be disappointed in. She has been so happy for weeks. She was looking forward so much to Christmas — and now, all of a sudden, when it is almost here, she is tangled up with something else. She says she can't possibly come up in the morning. She won't even promise she will come at all tomorrow. It seems so strange —"

Horace, coming in, said, "Women are strange. But as Jake Pease always says, when properly inspired, tarnation take 'em, what'd we do without 'em?"

There was a new expansiveness, a released geniality about Horace. I tried to guess what had caused it. I thought it had to do with Christmas being so nearly here that it was already partly over. Whatever its basis, it was making us all much happier, including himself. I began to suspect that if Alvin had been forced, either by his own sense of duty or by a family which habitually cut its cloth by a pattern which could never be completed without his cooperation, to take a more active part in Christmas, he might have enjoyed it more if only because he would have had the satisfaction of knowing he earned the return to everyday life which follows. I remembered he had always valued highest what he had earned.

I did not think I said this.

But he whispered in my ear, "I'm still glad my woman never bit off more than she could chew!"

Young Horace came up the stairs and stopped in the doorway. I thought he was pleased to see us and that he knew we were pleased to see him. But he did not want to risk coming in, embarrassed not by what we might say but by what he might see in our faces if he came too close, or lingered. That age, I have learned, is painfully sensitive to approval by its elders.

"Hey, Pete! Come 'ere. Owe you something, don't I? How much?"

We heard Pete mutter, "Don't owe me anything."

"Sure I do. Price of one scarf. Get it off my conscience. And yours."

"Get it off yours some other way. 'Tisn't on mine. Pay Mother. She bought the blasted thing."

"I gave it to you, Pete," Julie said.

"Gave it to *me!*" Pete spluttered. "Heck of a thing to give to *me!*"

"Well, I certainly didn't give it to anybody else," his mother insisted.

"I did, though," Young Horace snapped. "So what are we going to do about it?"

"Nothing," Pete told him. "Just had a brainstorm. Here's the solution. Q.E.D. I gave *you* the scarf. For Christmas. Didn't know what else to get for you, so I gave you a nice fancy fire-red scarf. 'Soft as a — as a kitten,' " he mimicked. "Can't be a worse choice than a napkin clip anyway. And I hope like sixty it won't last you as long to talk about. If it does, it's the last thing I'll ever give you."

"Pete," Young Horace said solemnly, "it's a deal. Thanks a million. It was a perfectly swell scarf, and I'll never mention it or the napkin clip again. Roger?"

"Roger," Pete agreed.

He followed his brother upstairs. I could hear them still talking much later as I lay in bed. I never had heard them before, at night. I thought of Robbie. I wondered what difference it might have made in Robbie's life if Little Alvin had not died of scarlet fever.

The next morning, directly after breakfast, we all went to church. It was snowing hard, but while we were gone Ellen — whose service came much earlier — hung a wreath on every outside door, tucked bittersweet into all the window boxes, and wired the little blue spruce beside the porch with Christmas lights. The wreaths — of her own making, and her gift to the family — were not exactly a surprise, for she had urged Julie not to buy any this year. But we had not known when they would go up, and we had had no hint of the red-gold berries. She had switched on the current because it was such a dark day, and stormy; and as we came up the street the brick house was like a stout and merry ship, riding the crest of a giant swell with every porthole lighted, the crow's nest twinkling gaily, and the flags all flying "Merry Christmas."

As we opened the door, strains of "Come All Ye Faithful" came low and sweet, yet with its own majestic challenge, from the kitchen radio.

Julie stood still in the hall.

She said, "We're home. From here on, Christmas is all ours." She looked from one to another of us. She said, "For once, at last, I have you all together."

I thought of Robbie and did not want her to know I thought of him. We had not even had a card!

I said quickly, "I'm going to leave my hat and coat right here and ask Ellen to lend me an apron. I hope she hasn't got everything done. It won't be Christmas for me if I don't get near to a stove."

Julie cried, "Oh, Mother, I hoped you'd say that! Will you make some biscuits? I soured some milk just in hopes!"

Soured some milk indeed, I thought. Such nonsense! There was never any lack of sour milk at the farm. But it is true that, with other mixing, biscuits are not so moist and soft. People so fortunate as to have everything fresh must perhaps sometimes go to the trouble of deliberate souring, or life will become dry and without flavor.

She, too, came into the kitchen, and whipped the potatoes, made sauce for the pudding. Babe picked out nutmeats from English walnut shells which Pete cracked. Ellen stood by undismayed, half-laughing at us but happy to have us with her, handing us things, but still lifting covers, sniffing at the oven door, and keeping an eye on the clock.

I thought, If I were to set out to save the world, I should begin by having the whole first floor of every house one grand big kitchen.

After dinner, boxes of Christmas decorations were brought from the blanket chest in the storeroom, and the boys and Babe spent the afternoon in my room wiring the tree with strings of colored bulbs, and dotting every space between with glittering balls, bells, cones, and tiny trumpets, some of which had been cherished from the days when Julie and Robbie had their trees at home; others Julie and Horace had brought back years ago from England and Germany; still others Pete and Babe had bought this week at the five-and-ten.

I thought, It is like every wedding. Always something old and something new . . .

Julie was in and out, admiring, between the last-minute wrappings of gifts for the family. When the tree was finished and prodigally tied up with strands of tinsel, there were still bells and balls left over which she tucked in among the evergreen on the mantel or attached to the swinging strands around the doors, and little snowmen and silver ships for the windowsills, and clear green glass medallions to place along the upper sash, against the panes, so that what light there was outside came through them and was reflected in green blots like wavy-edged clouds on the walls and ceiling.

Horace, lounging for a moment against the door frame, said, "The halls may now consider themselves decked."

Julie asked, "Isn't it beautiful, Hon?"

He said, "Looks as if you were ready to give a show. Nothing heavy, of course. Some sentimental operetta. Very pretty; yes. And may I say the lead has improved in appearance since the dress rehearsal last night? Looks to me much less like a retired diva and rather more like an ingenue. Agree with me there, Mrs. Monroe?"

I heard him but did not answer. I should hardly have known what it would be tactful to say. Certainly there was truth in his observation. But I had another matter on my mind.

I had just lifted the blue glass basket which Lovice Cheney gave me so long ago, to place it where it would make a better balance in Julie's decorative design, and noticed that it was empty.

Empty! I stared into it foolishly.

Julie asked, "What's the matter, Mother?"

I said, "My key! The key to the door up home. I have always kept it in this basket. But it isn't here."

Julie said, "The key? Why, it must be — maybe when we put up the evergreen — "

She took off the evergreen from the sill where the basket had been, and shook it. She ran a finger into the corners, took down the green glass medallions and raised the inside window, peering into the space between that and the storm sash.

She said, "It's very strange. Nobody has dusted or vacuumed here but you or me."

She looked along the edge of the carpet below the window.

She said, "Babe, did you ever take the big brass key out of the blue glass basket? To look at or to play with?"

Babe, who had been pivoting in the center of the room, casting airy glances this way and that, as children will, as if expecting any lost object to float by on a gentle breeze, suddenly stood still and put her hands together.

She said, "Oh, no. I never did. I know I shouldn't play with Gramma's things unless she says I can. And 'specially a key! I never touched it, Mummie. Honest and truly, Gramma. I never, never did —"

I knew this was an opportunity for play-acting eagerly seized upon, but I knew too that it was sincerely felt and that the concept grew out of only a few months in a village school where there were little people who did wrong and denied it, and therefore where even those who had done no wrong felt themselves forever suspect.

Pete burst out angrily, "If she says she didn't, she didn't. You all ought to know that!"

I said, "Of course we do, Pete. Nobody thinks —"

Julie said quietly, "We only asked you, Baby. 'No' was all you needed to answer."

But Babe avoided her mother's eyes. She sidled toward Pete and leaned against him. Nobody suspected anyone else of anything worse than carelessness, if that; yet suspicion had come into the room and darkened it.

Horace said, "It isn't hard to see how a thing as small as even a big brass key could be misplaced here in the last few days. Very likely it will turn up by the time the — forgive me — the debris is cleared away, if not before. If it doesn't, I'll run out to the farm and take an impression of the lock and have a new key made. You won't have any need of it right away, will you, Mrs. Monroe?"

I said of course I shouldn't, that we had made altogether too much of this, that no doubt I should find it soon; I might have taken it from the basket myself (though I knew I hadn't); it might have slipped in among the papers on the desk, or be behind the Christmas cards on the mantel. I said they must not give it another thought; that I appreciated Horace's offer to get another one made, if this did not come to light before spring.

But Julie knew that a new key would not be the same at all, however well it fitted the lock. That key had gone to market in Alvin's pants pocket whenever I had gone with him, or wherever else we had gone together, from the day we were married until the children were old enough to go separate ways from ours. After that, whenever the door was locked from the outside, the key had been left on the porch railing under the conch shell Alvin's Uncle Joe had brought back from the Gulf of Mexico long ago. We had all lifted that shell, hundreds of times, to put the house key under it, where it lay ready and waiting until the first one to come home picked it up again. Both Julie and I could see it plainly, shining in the sun or spattered with rain, as we lifted the shell. We felt it warm or cool against our palms. Our fingers inserted it swiftly, confidently, into the worn hole in the front door and turned it to break the last barrier between us and all we had known longest, loved best, needed most to be sure of.

When Horace and the children had gone out, we two closed the door and almost guiltily began as thorough a search as was possible in a room so crowded. We were still about it when Sue came in and as soon as we had told her what we were doing, she helped us, crawling behind my sofa, looking into the corners of the closet floor with a flashlight, even turning out the pockets of my dresses.

Julie said at last, "Unless it's under the tree, it isn't here."

I said as cheerfully as I could, "Then it's under the tree. Because of course it's here. Nobody could have taken it away."

Sue looked from one to the other of us. She twisted her hands in her lap.

She said, "I've been here a lot. I hope you don't think I might have taken it. It wouldn't have been any use to me, would it? Of course I've wanted terrifically to see your house, Mrs. Monroe. But I'd want you to be there to show it to me. I wouldn't want to go out there alone. I've never been out there. I'm not sure I even know the way —"

Julie exchanged a glance with me.

She said, with spurious brightness, "Oh, dear, Sue! You sound like Babe! She nearly broke our hearts, just because I asked her if she might have picked it up to play with. Of course you didn't take it. Nobody took it. We just can't find it, that's all. And it's nothing but a key."

But she avoided my eyes as Babe had hers. Because it was more than a key.

She said, "Come now. Let's forget about it. Did you go over to Lorna's after church?"

"Yes. But she wasn't there."

"Wasn't there?"

"She'd left a note for me. She said you told her I was

coming and she was sorry she couldn't wait but she had to go out. She shouldn't've bothered, but it was awfully sweet of her, wasn't it? I certainly love my shirt. And all the things. I wouldn't — why, I wouldn't feel dressed without them now."

Julie said, "They're more than becoming, darling."

I added significantly, "Especially the scarf."

Sue flushed and we all laughed.

But I kept glancing about the room. I tried to keep from doing it, but I could not help it. I knew I should never rest properly until I knew where that key was. And now Julie was distracted, not only by the loss of the key, but by the fact that Lorna was continuing her mysterious adventure.

Sue soon gave Christmas carol singing in the Square after supper as an excuse for going home early, and we accepted it. As she went out into the hall, Young Horace came downstairs, and both Julie and I were relieved when we saw, from the window, that he was going down the street with her.

She said, almost irritably, "Now, Mother! We must pull out of this! It's absurd. After all, nothing has happened but that we have misplaced a key. Anybody would think, from the way we're acting, that we had lost the whole farm."

I agreed with her. We made a creditable effort to "pull out of it." At supper — which I made a point of having with the others in the dining room — we silently complimented ourselves and each other on giving every appearance of having done so. But apparently we were mistaken.

We did succeed with the children. Babe was so given over to excitement about the ceremony of hanging stockings that she completely forgot the key, and since she felt no further concern about it, Pete had none. Young Horace had never been more than politely interested, and as soon as the stockings were hung (only two this year, for the first time), and Babe had gone to bed, he slipped off to the carol singing.

When Julie came downstairs she said, "I take it Sue and Honey have a date."

I said, "They both seem to be set on a fair course, just now."

I was thinking of Alvin's Uncle Joe. She was determined not to.

She said, "The first date in the family! How soon Babe will be making one! Though tonight she won't even use a pillow for fear it will stop up her ears to the blend of carols and mythical sleigh bells."

"And angel singing," I smiled.

"The carols must drown that out," Julie said. "At least, I can't hear it."

I said, "It isn't the carols. Julie, something is wrong."

She said, "Maybe it's right. Maybe we only think it's wrong."

We sat silent, not even seeing the Christmas tree, except as an object which might be perversely concealing an old brass key Alvin used to carry in his pocket. I opened the evening paper. She held a cigarette.

Horace came in quietly.

He sat down by the fireplace.

He said, "Ladies of the jury, I have a confession to make."

We stared at him.

"You're both still worrying about that key, aren't you? It's going to spoil your Christmas if you don't know where it is, isn't it? As I have suggested before, you are a very sentimental pair. But sentimentality is no crime. Stealing is. I stole your key, Mrs. Monroe."

Julie exclaimed, "Horace! What are you talking about?"

"About the key. You know. *The* key. It's no excuse that I didn't know it was *the* key. But perhaps — I hope — you may consider it a sort of extenuating circumstance that it is perfectly safe, that it will probably be returned to you tomorrow, certainly no later than the day after, and that I had no idea you would miss it, considering all aspects of the seasonal whirl."

"But where is it, Hon?" asked Julie, bewildered. "And why on earth did you take it?"

Horace sighed and put the tips of his fingers together, but his eyes twinkled.

"It goes against the grain to tell you that. Or rather against all the Christmas tradition which I have been so carefully taught. But if I must, I must. I — ah — I was trying to make, with all proper seasonal secrecy, arrangements for — ah — a Christmas gift. As you may know, Mrs. Monroe, I have never quite been able to bring myself to do Christmas shopping. I don't expect you to understand this idiosyncrasy. I am sure Julie never has. She thinks I am just stubborn. Well, I have to be stubborn about something, don't I? Anyhow, Julie has always bought our gifts which came from the stores. And she has even — I realize I should be blushing — bought her own gift from me. With a special check, I will say."

I did not look at Julie. We were both suddenly keenly aware of the beautiful things she had brought out to show to her father and me, caught up in the lovely mist of their gift wrappings. "— and this is what Hon gave me!" The copper samovar, the pearls, the watch set with tiny diamonds, the linen sheets and pillow slips, the books in tooled leather bindings and, just last Christmas, the mouton jacket . . .

"This year, however — ah — the two of you have to some extent overcome my resistance. Only to some extent, because Julie did our Christmas shopping and mine for herself. I am utterly incapable of that. But to this extent — that I — ah — sought to surprise you by a little scheme all my own —"

Julie cried joyfully, "Stop, Hon! You don't need to tell us any more —"

He sighed again.

He said, "Oh, but I do. Now that I've primed myself for the revelation, do let me get it over with. That, to be frank with you, is the part I dreaded most. If I don't make it now, it will hang over me all night."

How piteous men are!

"All right, darling," Julie said gently. "Go ahead."

I knew she wished she could take his hand, as if he were a child in the dentist's chair, but that he did not wish it any more than the child to whom helpless sympathy is cold comfort.

He continued, with wryly emphasized embarrassment, "I got the impression, Mrs. Monroe, that you enjoyed the convenience of electricity here and would find it a help at the farm; also that Julie would feel more at ease about you if you had it there when you go home, as she says you insist upon doing. So I have had the power company figure the guarantee required to run a line out there; and I took the key to — to give to a man whom I asked to make an estimate as to what the wiring of the buildings would cost, how many outlets there should be, and so on. My intention is to write you a check for the amount as soon as I know approximately what it will be. I hope to hear some time tonight or tomorrow. The key will positively be returned at that time."

He stood up quickly.

"So that is how it is. The check will be among your gifts, Mrs. Monroe. I shall appreciate it if you will regard it simply as another Christmas card. If I am wrong, and electricity at the farm is not anything you particularly want, no harm has been done. Put my card to whatever use you see fit. Now, if you ladies will excuse me — for some reason I seem to be exhausted — I am going up to bed. But fast, as our young would say."

He was gone.

I said, "Julie! It is the finest present anybody could

give me. I'd never dreamed of such a thing. Or rather I had dreamed, but knew positively that it was only a dream. How am I ever going to tell him — "

Julie said, "You can't, darling. That was the one thing he was afraid of, you know. That, and that I might kiss him."

"Can't you — kiss him, Julie?"

She laughed unsteadily.

"Oh, yes, Mother. But only when we are alone. And preferably in the dark. You see — I wish you could see — that Horace is like Oliver in *The Last Puritan* only in public. And everybody is public but me, and sometimes I am if the light is on. It isn't Horace other people see. It's just his position, and his manner and his defensive habits of thought, which make him appear absolutely different from what he really is. Actually he is more warmhearted and understanding — yes, even more sentimental — than we are, but he would be thrown for a complete loss if anybody knew it, except me. It even embarrasses him sometimes that I know it and that the children suspect it. You see, anyone who sees through tends to expect him to act as he is, and that he doesn't know how to do, doesn't even want to do because theoretically he disapproves of it. So, now that you know, you must still behave as if you didn't."

"That will not be difficult," I said. "I am a more naturally restrained person than perhaps he imagines. And I am not at all likely ever to be alone with him in the dark. All the less so now that he is having the farm wired for electricity. . . . That will be a great expense for him, Julie."

"Don't think of that. He can afford it."

"I wonder what your father would say. He never wanted electric power. He liked what he was used to."

"But you like improvements. And I am sure he would be glad for you to have what you want."

I chuckled.

I said, under my breath, "Now that it won't bother you, Alvin!"

She was laughing softly, too.

I asked, "What are *you* laughing at?"

"I was trying to picture Horace coming in here and taking that key from your basket. He must have been so gingerly about it!"

I laughed with her, and then sobered.

I said, "Julie, pleased as I am with Horace's present, I am more pleased by what you've told me tonight, even though I must try to forget it. I can at least remember that — he is not gingerly with you!"

This was delicate ground, between a New England mother and her married daughter.

We were both relieved — though startled — when the doorbell rang.

Julie exclaimed, "It may be Lorna! I hope it's Lorna! It seems late, somehow, but by the clock it's just past nine."

Ellen opened the front door. Julie ran to the top of the stairs.

"Lorna! I've been waiting for you all day! Close the door quick, Ellen; I can feel the cold blast all the way up here; the wind must have sprung up. Darling, how wonderful you look, all blown about!"

I did not hear the door close. I heard the rustle of sleeves and skirts touching, and then Lorna said, "Is Horace in the study, Julie?"

"No. He's gone to bed. At least he said — why?"

"Never mind. I know I'm going to astonish you. But will you please go wherever he is — or in the study by yourself? Just for a minute? I'll call you as soon as —"

"Oh, all right, darling; all right! Of course I will. But don't act so excited. I know crazy things happen on Christmas Eve. Just don't make me wait too long. I'll die of suspense. Besides, there's so much I want to tell you.

Mother and I both. We've just had such a surprise —"

"Well, you're going to have another one," Lorna told her. "If you'll go somewhere out of sight."

"I guess I'll find Horace," Julie laughed. "I might have a heart attack. I don't believe he's really gone to bed. But for goodness' sake, don't be long — and Ellen, close that door!"

She flew up the stairs.

I heard the front door close.

Lorna was coming into my room. She wore the familiar gray-green coat with the silver-fox collar, middle-aged both in style and in length of service, and the same old pearl-gray velvet toque which I sometimes thought might have been her mother's; but what Julie said was perfectly true. She did look wonderful, wind-blown. Her short fair hair was tangled around the toque, her slender face whipped to a high color by the driven snow, her eyes strangely alive and alert; and I felt that a stronger wind had sprung up within her than that which had stung her cheeks and disarranged her hair.

She said, "Dear Mrs. Monroe —"

She knelt before me with her hands on my knees and looked up into my face, searchingly.

She said, "I know I seem excited. But you aren't excitable, are you? You could bear a surprise, couldn't you?"

I heard myself say in a deep, strong voice, "Life has been a continual surprise to me, Lorna. What has happened, child?"

"I have had a letter from Robbie."

"A letter?"

"In fact — I have had a good many letters from him. I hope you and Julie will forgive me for not telling you so. He asked me not to. They were not letters I could share. They began when I wrote to him, at Julie's suggestion, early in the war. They said very little of what I am sure you and Julie most wanted to know about him. All along they were almost entirely about what he was thinking. He was working out terrifically difficult problems. The first was what to do with his life. And after a while he got another added to that. It was — what to do about me."

I said carefully, "When he has solved the first, the second will be solved for him."

Her lips curved.

She said softly, "They are both solved, Mrs. Monroe. He —"

But I had waited as long as I could. I gripped the arms of my chair.

I said, "Is Robbie downstairs?"

She asked, "*How did you know?*"

I said, "I heard him shut the door. Tell him to come up *here*. This minute."

I heard a strange step on the stairs. I saw a strange man in the doorway, his overcoat over his arm, his hat in his hand.

It was ten years since I had seen my son, and then only briefly. It was twenty-five years since he went away to college in New York State; over twenty since he had stayed as long as a week with us. In all that time I had not known him. Perhaps I had never known him.

Ten years ago he had not changed much, outwardly, from what he had been before he went to college. He was still a boy like Pete grown taller; square-built, solemn-eyed, reserved to the point of grimness. A boy nobody understood — or if anyone did, he did not know it. A boy few ever seemed to try to understand. Always thinking and never divulging his thoughts. A boy who did not belong on a farm and made no place for himself in school or city. A boy always seeking something he had not found and did not expect to find. A boy without a home. A man without a country.

No, I had never known him. I had only loved him.

Now he was — forty-three. A lean man with a big frame, holding an overcoat and a hat.

I did not know what to do about him.

Then he smiled. That one-sided grin. Alvin's and Pete's and — Robbie's.

He said, "Hi, Ma."

Then I knew what to do.

I said, "Robert Monroe, you come right over here and account for yourself! *Why* didn't you let us know? Haven't you grown up yet? Why can't you do things the way anybody else would?"

I hugged him. I kissed him. Tears ran down my face. I kept right on scolding all the time.

"Do you know it's been ten years since I laid eyes on you? What on earth have you been doing since you got out of the Army? Lock that door. I don't want Julie bouncing in here till I've had my say. She's just as bouncy as she ever was. I don't know where she got it from. How did you know I was here? Did you get my letters? We never know whether you get letters or not. You don't do anything about it. What have you been doing in California? Are you going back? Why don't you come out to the farm with me? I wasn't going until spring, but I could go any time. You're thin, Robbie. You need stuffing, as your father would say. It makes you look taller. Are you well?"

As I talked, I was thinking, He's looking at me. He's looking straight at me. He always used to be — looking another way.

Not only looking at me, but watching me closely with an attention, an interest, an affection, an *appreciation* that I . . . that I had never seen before in Robbie.

He said, "I'm fine, Ma. Want to scold me some more? I deserve it. I can take it. Dish it out."

He was still grinning.

"I'm wasting my breath," I complained. "You don't look as if you felt guilty. You're — pleased with yourself. And I want to know why."

He sobered a little, not too much. He had dropped his

coat and hat on the bed and drawn up a chair. His knee touched mine. He bent forward and began talking. I noticed how easy his position was, how easily his words came. This, too, was new.

Neither of us glanced toward the door. We heard no sound beyond it. If there had been one, I doubt that we should have heard it.

He said, "There is so much to explain that I hardly know where to begin. I've been a long distance away. Farther than California. Farther than the Pacific islands. Far from you. Almost beyond reach of myself." He smiled. "It took longer to come back than it took to go. I should have come sooner and faster if I could have. It wasn't my fault, Mother. Honest. I had to work my way back, alone. But I realize I did a good job. That's why I'm pleased with myself."

I understood only vaguely what he meant. I am afraid I did not want to know too much.

I asked, "Why couldn't you write more about it?"

He said, "I wrote it to Lorna. On the road back. I couldn't write it to anybody on the way out. I couldn't even tell it to myself. I began writing it to Lorna because of something she wrote to me. It opened a door. Just a crack. Can you imagine what that meant? No, of course you can't, except in a general way. I wouldn't want you to. But it made all the difference. . . . Another reason I was able to write it was because I had begun to see, in the service, what it did for men to talk about what bothered them. Some of them talked to chaplains. But it was Lorna who had opened the door for me, so I wrote to Lorna . . . It was not easy. I had been shut in and miserable too long. Almost as long as I could remember. You must have known that. I must have been very hard to live with."

I said, "You have been harder to live without, Robbie."

He nodded, and touched my hand.

"I'm sorry for that."

"Did we fail you at home, Robbie? Your father and I?"

"No. I used to think so. Now I know better. You did everything for me that you could. The troubles I had I made for myself. After I left home they were worse. After I left college, they were worse still."

He was still looking directly at me. I saw a shadow on his face of how bad they had been.

He said, "I studied electrical engineering at college, you remember. I thought I wanted a way of life which had as little as possible to do with people. You see, people were more or less like me, so I wanted to steer clear of them, because I was trying to get away from myself. And no wonder!" He smiled. "Engineering wasn't the answer. So I left college. I went as far away as I could get without a passport, in fairly long hops. I always thought everything would be better somewhere else. It never was. Because I was there all the time, you see. Do you see, Mother?"

I said, "I think I see, Robbie."

He did not want me to see too much.

He said, almost lightly, "I went into the Army as soon as war was declared, you know. Not because I was braver or more patriotic than the average. Just because it would take me still farther away. I didn't care how far away. The farther the better, I guess . . . But the war did for me the reverse of what it did for some. It showed me that I wasn't the only miserable man on earth. It showed me ways that a man could come back. It got me in touch with Lorna again. It gave me a degree of success I'd never had before. It made me realize how much many men want to live, and I tried to find out why, and what I wanted to live for."

"What is that, son?"

"A lot of things. I don't know how to list them in order of importance. I'll have to tell them to you in the order that they came to me. First, I wanted more time to find out about myself, why I had felt as I had, and how it would seem to feel differently. Then I began to want to learn more about other people, why they felt bad — or good — and what could be done to make us all feel better. They told me there was a name for this kind of study. It is psychology. I wanted to live to get back to where there were books about it, and men who would talk about what was in the books . . . And I did. I got back to California in June, and on the first of July I registered as a special student in psychology under the G.I. Bill. An auditor. That means that for twelve weeks I just sat and listened."

"Why didn't you write us that?"

He hunched one shoulder. There was a twinkle in the corner of his eye.

"Now I could be mistaken. But think a minute. How would it have looked in a letter? Unless I could have explained it all. And I didn't know the why of it myself, yet. I still wasn't sure of anything. Perhaps this was just one more of the hundred-and-one things I had tried and given up. Maybe it wouldn't be what I'd thought at all, and I'd be rushing off again. . . . Only there was this difference. It was Custer's Last Stand for me."

He smiled, to take the edge off his words.

"You see? If this wasn't right, nothing was right. I couldn't write letters in the midst of it. I didn't even write much to Lorna, those twelve weeks. I just sat down in chairs and held on and read and listened. . . . By September I knew it was right. I signed on as a regular. The three years I'd had in college counted as two for a major in psychology. So old Pop Monroe was a junior . . . But I still had one last hurdle to jump. I not only had to read and listen now; I had to begin to talk and write. I didn't know whether I had the stuff —"

"Robbie! *You?* Why, you could always learn anything. You were just like Pete —"

"Pete?"

"Julie's second boy. He's — he's you all over again."

Robbie raised his eyebrows.

"That," he said, "is a lad I want to meet. He was the baby, I guess, when I was here last. . . . Yes, I know I used to be able to learn, but that was a long time ago. And in this field I had to start from scratch. I never was like Julie, remember."

"No —"

"She was born with something in her bones that I've only begun to get from stones and blood and pain and sleepless nights, and what I'll be a long time getting the rest of from books and observation. But I'm going to get it, Mother. I know that now."

He looked at me for the first time with embarrassment. Like Pete bringing home a report card.

He said shyly, "I'm — I'm doing all right."

"Doing all right!" I scoffed. "I'll bet you're the best student they've got."

He laughed and shook his head.

"You don't know these G.I.'s. There's stiff competition in college these days . . . But I found out that I could do it, after about the first month. Then I began to realize how long it will take. Two more years for an A.B. Three more for graduate work. I'll be an old man for sure by then. Forty-eight!"

"Forty-eight isn't old," I assured him, from the height of seventy-five.

He said, "It's old to be getting a job. But I have a chance, they say, of getting one. I'll be ready for a graduate assistantship while the colleges are still jammed with students and understaffed. If I handle that, I may be kept on as a member of the faculty. Just may. It's a chance. But it's enough for me that I have the chance. Only, then I began to wonder about Lorna."

"What about Lorna?"

That one-sided grin, and, "I want to marry her, you see I had an idea that if I asked her she would."

"By then you must have been pretty happy."

"Not exactly. Not me. I wrestled with it for a long time. What did I have to offer her? Would it be fair to her? I'd gathered she no longer had much money of her own. I'll have mighty little for the next five years. I'll never have much —"

I said, "Robert Monroe, do you still think money is that important?"

He shook his head.

"No. Not now . . . But I'm only just completely over thinking so . . . I'm trying to tell you that this has been a long, slow process. I could change only one thing at a time. When I left California ten days ago, I knew I was going to be with you for Christmas, but I didn't write for two reasons. First, because I wanted to walk in, just as I have, without any advance excitement. And second, because I didn't know just when I would get here, nor what might happen in between to give me a different story to tell than I had when I left out there. . . ., Specifically, I still didn't know whether I ought to ask Lorna to marry me or not. I was so uncertain that at the last minute I almost didn't come. You see — the way she and I have been writing — it was going to be very difficult to account for our relationship to each other, or to you and Julie's family, if I came here and didn't ask her. But I still wasn't sure I should ask her."

I sighed.

"You make everything so hard for yourself, Robbie!"

He took my hand again.

He said, "Not any more, Mother. My main trouble always was that I expected perfection of and for myself and of and for other people. At last I have figured out that nobody is wholly happy in this world. Some people are happier than others. The unhappiest are people who feel they ought to be wholly happy and who fight within themselves and against other people to find what is not here and was not meant to be, except in flashes. I was one of them. The happiest people are those who do not question

God's purpose in creating an imperfect world because they realize it is as far beyond our understanding as how and why the world was created at all. They accept the world, filling as best they can their own place in it, doing what they can for themselves and others, taking gratefully what happiness comes, and bearing disappointments, failures, even what appears to be the opposite of progress in human relations, without loss of faith or of respect for humankind. I think I can claim this now as my philosophy. When I had nailed that, there was just one more thing I wanted. I asked Lorna to marry me, and she said she would."

I said, "Well, thank the dear, good Lord! . . . *How* did He bring you to ask her?"

I am not sure whether Robbie thought it was the Lord who had done it . . . whether he gave Him that name.

But he said, "By devious ways, suited to a queer duck like me. I did a lot of thinking on the train between California and Boston. Then I rented a car and drove down the Turnpike. Not fast. I took my time. When I got to the village — though of course I knew you were with Julie — I didn't stop here. I drove right on past this house and out to the farm. I hope you can forgive me for that. You see, I was caught up in a mood. A very pleasant one. I had a feeling that I was getting really back to the fork in the road where I took the wrong turn. I also had the feeling that when I saw the right road I should recognize it, and on the way out again I'd come to you. . . . I stayed there a night and part of a day before I knew what I was going to do about Lorna. Then I drove down and took her to the farm with me. We had supper there last night, and I drove her home quite late. Everything was settled between us then, but I wasn't quite ready to leave the farm. I slept there another night, and today — while you were at church — I came down for her again and we got a kind of Christmas dinner out there together. She brought the fixings — we baked a chicken in the oven, cooked vegetables in your old blue enamel kettles, stewed cranberries sweetened with some molasses left in the bottom of the earthen jug in the sinkroom cupboard. Had the house smelling like it used to at Thanksgiving. Then I found the freezer in the cellar and cleaned it up and we made ice cream with snow for packing . . . and talked a long time . . . and — well, that seemed to be where the road out began. So here I am — the bad penny. Only I feel as if I'd just been minted, except when I stop to think —"

"Then don't think," I said. "For goodness' sake, stop thinking for Christmas. *How did you get into the house?*"

He laughed.

He said, "I'm not surprised you ask. The way you had everything braced, barred, and bolted! But I knew you of old. I knew better than to expect you had left the key under the conch shell all winter . . . So I stopped at the bank as I came through the village Friday morning."

"At the bank?"

"I have to admit I knocked my hat over my eyes. It was probably pretty unnecessary. I doubt if anyone in town would recognize me now without a dog tag. Horace said afterward he didn't know but what it was a holdup. But I guess he was kidding. Anyhow, he took me into his office, and when I told him what I wanted, he said he didn't have the key but thought he knew how he could get it without attracting any attention. I waited there, and within an hour he brought it to me and I was on my way. . . . Horace is quite a guy, isn't he? He never turned a hair. Never asked me a personal question. Didn't act as if there was anything extraordinary at all about what I was doing. Businesslike as if I'd been cashing a check or opening an account. I was relieved. Still I didn't know whether I quite liked it or not. I never felt at all acquainted with him. But when I turned away from his desk with the key in my pocket, he stood up and said, 'Good luck, Rob. Take your time. Come and see us as soon as you feel like it. If you can make it by Christmas, your mother and Julie will be very pleased, as you must know. They've walked through a lot of Christmases without you.' For a minute I could have kissed the guy." Robbie chuckled. "Only I doubt if he would have bent down! Anyway, I said, 'I'll make it!' And I did. Easy."

I let out a long, slow breath.

I said, "Now I think you'd better open that door."

He nodded. He stood up. But then he hesitated, looking down at me.

He said, "So it's all right, Mother?"

I said, "It's all right, Robbie. Only — only we sent your presents to Berkeley, and there isn't a thing for you on — on the tree!"

He bent over me.

He said, "Don't mind that. I don't mind that. There won't be any presents *from* me on the tree either. I spent all I had on this trip — and on a ring for Lorna that I still wasn't sure I ought to give her. Now she's wearing it. And — this is all I have for you."

He reached into his pocket and dropped a handful of bright ribbon, buttons, stars, bars, and oak-leaf clusters in my lap.

He said, "That's the end of a long war."

He opened the door. The hall was full of silent people. Julie spoke first.

She said, "Well, it's *about time!*" And threw herself into Robbie's arms.

Then they were all in my room, all talking at once, asking and answering questions.

Lorna and Horace had already told Julie most of what Robbie had told me, but Julie was more incredulous than I, and more curious about details.

"Wasn't the house impossibly damp and cold, Rob?"

"Nothing like so cold as Attu. Fires in three stoves soon warmed it up. No. It was fine."

"I *don't* see how Hon ever kept it from me *three days!*

All that about checking the cost of wiring and outlets —"

"It was true. I've got the estimate right here —" Horace said, waving a casual hand, "Good reliable fellow, I thought. Expert."

Young Horace said, "Friday? I was out at the farm Friday afternoon. You didn't have any fire going then!"

"That was the coldest time," Rob grinned. "Your father told me you were coming. I waited until you'd come and gone. Not that I didn't want to know you, young fella. But I wanted a while to get my feet, first. Been a long time, you know —"

I felt that all the men understood and accepted this more easily than any of us women. Unless, perhaps, Lorna, who knew more than we would ever know.

Pete said, "I bet he watched you from the window, Horace."

Rob grinned, "I did, that."

Young Horace struck his brow.

"Haunted!" he said. "And never knew it!"

"Where did you sleep, Robbie?"

"In the alcove off the folks' room. Where I always did. It hailed in the night. I heard it bouncing off that sloping roof just like it used to. When I woke up in the morning I knew it had stopped hailing. I didn't know whether it had cleared off or not. You never do in that room. But it had."

Pete said, "That's where I sleep when I'm out there."

Rob looked at him.

He said, "I know. I found your rock collection. It had some of mine in it."

"Gramma said you wouldn't mind. You had good garnets."

"Of course I don't mind."

"That was summer before last. Last summer I collected insects."

"I collected insects once, too. But the moths got into them. Moths are cannibals, aren't they? How many kinds did you get?"

"Five hundred and thirty-one."

Rob whistled.

Julie was exclaiming over Lorna's ring.

"Did you know he was coming, Lorna?"

Lorna shook her head, smiling at Robbie.

He said, "How could she? I didn't know it myself. I almost took the next train back, in Boston."

Lorna said in her soft voice. "I didn't *know* he was, Julie. But I felt quite sure —"

Horace chuckled.

He said, "You'll find it's no use, Rob. You can't fool them, even when you fool yourself."

They talked about the wedding. Rob and Lorna wanted to be married at the farm Thursday night.

Horace said, "Now they'll want to paint and paper the house throughout."

I thought he sounded discouraged.

Rob said firmly, "Nothing like that. There'll be nobody there but we who are here now."

"And Mr. Ransome," said Lorna. "And Babe. And Sue."

"Ellen and I'll clean it," Julie promised.

"I'll get greens from the pasture," Rob said. "The boys will help me. We'll make the house warm and dry and Mother can come out with me by Wednesday. We'll have ourselves a time." He smiled at Lorna. "Sorry I won't be seeing much of you, dear. More later."

She said she had a few things to keep her occupied. She wanted to have her house ready for sale before she left. Horace said he thought the bank would be very glad to buy it. He would take it up with the directors Tuesday morning.

Lorna said, "Horace, you're a darling."

She kissed Julie and me. Julie made her promise she would come for dinner the next day. Robbie took her home. I watched his hands as he held her coat. I knew he loved her.

As soon as they had gone, Horace said, "Quick now. What's for Babe's stocking?"

I think he sensed that it was time for Julie to be active and for me to be left with my thoughts which run so freely between the past and the future. Once I should have assumed he was only in a hurry to have the day over and get to bed.

Julie and Young Horace dropped an orange, a candy bar, some nuts, several little toys, and a picture book in a bunny-fur jacket into the big red flannel sock with Babe's name embroidered on a green band at the top. They left a monkey-on-a-stick and small doll in a Russian dance costume looking out engagingly above the name. I remembered Julie's long black stocking, which I had knit for her to wear to school, hanging behind the kitchen stove just as she had taken it off when she went to bed, the shape of her small foot and sturdy leg still in it.

Young Horace said, "Okay. That'll make her eyes stick out. Now off with you, Pete. Your Santa Claus in on his way."

I sensed that Young Horace was at last enjoying his own experience at being Santa Claus.

Pete said, "Okay." He looked at his mother. "Gee, I'm glad Uncle Rob's coming back. Want to talk to him tomorrow. He's swell, isn't he?"

"Yes," Julie said. "He's — swell. And isn't it nice Aunt Lorna thinks so, too? Sleep well, Petey."

As he went out she blew a kiss after him. He did not see it, and she had not intended that he should. She smiled at me as she came back into the room.

Young Horace had already tossed an orange, candy and nuts into the red sock labeled "Pete." Now he was dumping a boxful of trinkets in on top. He took a big safety pin from his pocket and fastened a scout knife by its chain to the toe.

He said, "There! That's what he's getting from me.

Only let him think it's from the old guy with the stomach and the beard. Less embarrassin' all around."

Horace stood in the corner looking into his pipe as he pressed the tobacco down with his thumb. I remembered Alvin with his paper spread wide on Christmas Eve. But now there was no anger in me for either of them, and no sorrow for them either. They asked only the privilege of celebrating Christmas in a man's way. Surely their women, in making out their Christmas lists, could include this gift for them.

Young Horace said, "I'm turning in now. . . . Kind of nice I had a chance to earn a little money yesterday, hey, Mom? Got a few things — like the knife — at the last minute. Not much."

He looked sheepish, and yet he looked proud. He looked very young, and yet it was plain that he was growing up and that one of the most painful incidents in his growing was behind him.

Julie said, "A little is quite enough, dear, for this year. And you've given us many intangibles already —"

Horace said, "Get your grades up by midyears, son, and you can earn a day's pay at the shop any Saturday you want to." He let his hand drop on Young Horace's shoulder. He said to Julie and me, "Maybe there'll be a new horse to get into my harness before I fall out of it. Maybe he won't be a horse. Maybe he'll have rocket power."

He steered Young Horace into the hall. They went upstairs together.

Julie went quietly about the room, tying small bright boxes to the branches of the tree, bringing larger packages to add to those already heaped beneath it.

Finally she stood back and surveyed it.

She said, "Oh, Mother — it is the loveliest one we ever had!"

Robbie, behind her, said, "It is, Julie, isn't it? And in your own home, Sis. Some time — a long time from now

— maybe we'll all have Christmas at my house. Some little old kind of house on some comfortable, frugal Faculty Row."

Julie turned swiftly and locked her fingers behind his neck.

"Robbie, darling! Mother and I've got you to ourselves at last. Are you really all right, Robbie? Is everything all right?"

His eyes smiled over her head at me.

He said, "Of course it is, Julie. I know I've kept you waiting a long time to hear me say so. But you've always known it, haven't you?"

"It was for me, Robbie. Not for you."

"It was for me, too, if I'd realized it. It took me a long time."

"Do you love Lorna very much?"

"Of course I do."

"How long have you?"

"If you mean how long have I loved her, I suppose it's over twenty years — since she first came out home. If you mean, how long have I known I loved her, only a few months. I had to find out other things before I could find that out."

"You've found out a great deal, haven't you, Robbie? When you were talking to Pete, I watched his face, and yours. What do you think of Pete, Robbie? Is he going to have to learn — your way?"

"Maybe. Partly. Maybe a man always has to get it through logic, through experience — through his mind. And for a long time every mind is a mass of conflict and confusion shut inside a tough shell. . . . But Pete will be all right. He's learned a lot already. If he ever needs help, I'll help him if I can."

"If anybody can, you can. . . . Robbie, are you going to mind if it is too late for you and Lorna to have children?"

"We're going to have children. Big children. Hundreds of 'em."

"But that isn't the same as having one — or more — all your own."

"I don't suppose it is. Quite . . ."

"Robbie . . . if you ever need Pete — or he needs you — very much, I'll send him to you. Wherever you are."

"I believe you would. But what would Horace say about it?"

"If it came to that, Hon would let him go." She turned to me. "Wouldn't he, Mother?"

I said, "A week ago I shouldn't have known. But now I can agree with you, Julie."

A little later she went out with him to show him where he would sleep.

I got up and moved about the room in a daze, folding the homespun spread, laying back the blankets, slowly getting my clothes off in the bathroom, opening the window. I stretched myself out on the bed.

Julie came back as I had known she would.

I tried to shake myself alert.

She asked, "Awfully tired, darling?"

I said, "I don't know. It's like the time the dentist down here gave me gas. I was still there with him, but I didn't seem to be me and he didn't seem to be him. I wanted very much to talk, but I kept quiet for fear anything I might say would be silly."

"It will all be straightened out when you wake up. It'll be Christmas morning, and Babe will be running in here in her pink sleeper with the bunny feet and Pete right behind her with his striped pajamas half unbuttoned and his hair on end —"

"Julie, how are you going to bear having Lorna go away? You've been so much together so long; you depend on each other so. If you had known what it would mean, could you have suggested that she write to Robbie? Are you sorry now you did?"

She laughed a little.

"Mother, darling, why do you think I suggested it?"

"You hoped this would happen?"

"Of course I did. Not that I thought there was a chance in one million it would. And when she never mentioned it again, of course I stopped thinking of it. . . ."

I said, "It will be fine —"

My voice faded.

She touched my hand.

"Good night, Mother."

"Wait a minute. . . . I was going to say it will be fine for Robbie to have Lorna. It will be fine for Lorna to have Robbie. Robbie hasn't had anything but himself for so long. Lorna hasn't even had herself. She just had you. That wasn't enough. No woman is enough for another woman. But you . . . I probably sound just as I would have if I hadn't kept quiet that day at the dentist's . . . I've forgotten now what I was going to say. . . ."

"Were you going to ask me how I'm going to manage without Lorna?"

"Yes. That's it. She — her companionship — her very dependency, I see now, was built into your life. Won't she leave — a place that will always be empty?"

"If you weren't so sleepy, you'd know better, darling. I'm not losing Lorna. She'll be our link with Robbie. Don't imagine he's going to write to us much more than he ever has. If he writes, it will be to Pete. Lorna will tell us what he — and she — are doing. All the things women like you and me want to know. The things Robbie — and Pete — don't consider very important or at all interesting. . . . And with Lorna away, and happy, I'll have more time for other people. The village is full of other people. Freddy and Madelene to begin with."

"Frederica will never be the — comfort to you Lorna has been, Julie."

"Oh, no. But I suspect she'll be even more absorbing."

I thought of what Robbie had said about Julie.

"She was born with something in her bones that I've only begun to get from stones and blood and pain and sleepless nights . . ."

I thought of Robbie.

I saw him, a little boy, astraddle a high limb of an oak tree in the yard at home. It was dusk and the whippoorwills were chirping. He looked down through the branches at us — Alvin and me — and said, "I wish every leaf up here was a gold piece. I'd have a million dollars, wouldn't I?"

Alvin chuckled and answered; no, it was Robbie speaking beside me in his shabby, ill-fitting tweed coat. The lamplight from the kitchen shone on his upturned face and smiling eyes.

He said, "Someday, boy, you'll be mighty glad to find they're still God's good green leaves!"

Alvin was not exactly with us, but not far away. It was he who had chuckled. And now he spoke.

He said, "Merry Christmas, one and all!"

I opened my eyes and sat up in bed. I don't know how long I had been sleeping. It may have been exactly midnight.

And beside my window, in the starry dark, the angels, who had been singing softly all the time, let their voices out in full, jubilant chorus.

CHAPTER X

Christmas 1947

Tim was Essie's darling. Tim was short and stocky, with long arms and big hands, a bush of sandy hair, eyes as blue as the heavens above on a pretty day, and a smile that always touched the heart for one of two reasons — because it was so gay, or because it was so sad.

Tim had been Essie's darling for six years and her husband for five, the father of Sharon for four, and of Doody (baby talk for "Junior") for two.

Tim was Irish. Born in this country of parents born in this country, but still as essentially Irish as shamrocks, pink pigs, Northern potatoes, colleens, leprechauns, and the lovely, winding, tortured, enchanted streets of the Dublin which he had never seen.

You will understand from this that Tim was moody. He had high moods and low moods, never a medium mood. He either loved Essie so that it tore him apart, said she was perfect, that nothing and nobody was good enough for her; or he was very, very angry with her for working too hard, for not loving him tumultuously, for not spending enough money on herself, for spending too much money on other people, for getting up so early, for going to bed so late, and above all for not answering him back when he scolded her. He either spoiled his children deliciously, or declared they were so noisy he could not make his voice heard in his own house and he was being driven to a tavern.

You will understand that Tim liked to make his voice heard in his own house.

That was all right with Essie. Everything Tim did was fine with Essie. Tim was Essie's darling, and Essie was always in a a medium mood and naturally quiet.

This month he was moody about money. He always was, early in December, but this time it was worse than usual. Or perhaps it only seemed so to Essie because she wanted so many things for him and the children for Christmas, and food cost so much, and with the two of them so small she had not been able to earn a penny herself all the year.

"Essie," he had growled on December second, fixing her with a gimlet gaze from beneath his heavy eyebrows, "Christmas is coming on."

"Yes, darlin'," sighed Essie, smiling at him across the heaped mending basket. "And there isn't much money to spare, is there, Tim?"

"Essie," he said, "I have made up my mind."

He filled his pipe. Poor, darling Tim. He allowed himself only one pipeful of tobacco to an evening.

"There is *no* money to spare, this year. You won't believe that. You never have believed it. But this year there is *no money* for Christmas. We've got to keep up our savings. We never know when there will be doctor's bills. Maybe hospital bills. The world is in bad shape, Essie. It may get worse. The children will get more expensive every year. There may be more of them. They've got to be educated. And then we'll be old. But we don't want to be dependent on them. We've got to be ready for old age, Essie. We may live a long while before we die —"

"And whenever we do, there'll be funeral expenses," said Essie thoughtfully.

Tim shot her a suspicious glance. She might be laughing at him, inside. So much of what Essie did was done inside. He did not like that. He wanted to know Essie through and through, as no doubt she knew him. Nothing he did was done inside. He was open as a book.

But why should she be laughing? Nothing was ever truer than that there were funeral expenses to be met when anybody died. And how would he feel, with all the rest he would have to bear, if he did not have enough money to give Essie a grand funeral when she left him? And how would she feel if he went first and left her no money to take care of everything with dignity and enough over to tide her through? Even a woman must be able to look ahead that far!

"There will," Tim growled. "Before long we ought to be thinking of buying us a lot and setting a decent stone. . . . So the savings must be kept up, Essie. And as things are with us now, all the rest goes for necessities. Now there will be something for the children for Christmas. Don't think there won't. But *I* will buy it. I will walk to work the rest of the month and take my dinner with me. I've figured that that way I can save ten dollars. Ten dollars is a good deal of money for one day's celebration, if it is well spent. And I shall spend it well; you can depend on that. One toy apiece, and mittens and caps and sweaters."

"What about Christmas dinner?" asked Essie faintly. Tim leaned forward.

"That," he said largely, "will be your contribution, Essie. Fix your mind on that. Whatever you can save on what we eat between now and then, you can add to what is spent for food on Christmas day. I know it won't be much. But you will be wanting to do something to get ready for Christmas, and that is what you can do."

He will save by taking his dinner from home, thought Essie. I will have that much more to buy out of the grocery money. And what else can I save —

Tim sprang up.

"You're not satisfied," he shouted. "That doesn't suit you. You want me to tell you to order a turkey. You want me to hand over twenty-dollar bills for you to spend on a new doll and a silk dress and a drum to blast the eardrums with and maybe a tricycle or an electric train. Well, you didn't marry a rich man, Essie. When will you face it that you didn't marry a rich man? I have all I can do to keep a roof over my family and nourishment in their stomachs and stout shoes on their feet. I work hard all day and stay awake nights, figuring and worrying, and what thanks do I get? What help do I get? Whose fault is it you married a man like me? Did I force you into it? Did I hide what I was? Did I tell you I was rich or ever would be rich? What have you got to complain of but your own bad judgment? Why don't you say something, girl? Are you going to sit there all night with your breath coming in and going out and not carrying a word or even a sound?"

Essie looked at him helplessly and sighed. Nothing he had said was so. Where should she begin to deny so much which was not so? Especially since he knew it was not so.

"I was only wondering," she murmured, "how I would get a Christmas present for you."

"I take that," said Tim with elaborate coldness, "to mean, as well, that you were wondering if I didn't think of getting one for you. Well, as a matter of fact, I have thought about it. But I have decided that we are grown up at least, or ought to be. I don't want you to get me *any* present. And I am not going to get you any present. We have spent too much on Christmas presents for each other in years past. Look at that watch you gave me the first year we were married. I could have done without a watch. A gold watch, anyway. Look at that green velvet kimono-thing I gave you. When did you ever wear it? You haven't worn it for a year. I don't suppose you liked it, anyway. It probably was the wrong color. I guess you knew it wasn't practical. Well, it wasn't. We'd both be better off now if I'd got you a good blanket bathrobe to keep off the chill when we're trying to stretch that coal. Because we've been foolish so far, is it any reason for us to keep on being foolish? . . . But what's the use of talking? You've always spent money like water at Christmas, and I don't doubt you're making up your mind to do it again. But I will say this: If you squander money this year, you'll have to steal it first!"

He strode off to bed.

Essie cried a little, mostly because she was tired. It had stormed all that day and she hadn't been able to put the children out into the yard.

About the time she finished mending she finished crying, and sat and thought for a while, with her chin on her hand, until the room began to grow cold.

Tim was asleep when she undressed in the dark, but he always roused up when she crept into bed, however carefully she did it.

"What is it, Essie?" he muttered thickly, "You all right?"

"Yes, darlin'," she whispered. "Don't wake up."

He flung out his arm, she cuddled her head into his shoulder, and the next either of them knew the alarm was going off.

The evening of December twelfth, Tim was very late home to supper. He had warned Essie he might be. The children were already in bed when he opened the door and stepped into the kitchen.

He stopped short just inside.

The room was very quiet. It was shining neat and spotless. The checked sash curtains had just been done up; they stood off from the windows like ballet skirts. The table was set with the gold-banded china and the tall etched goblets. Essie sat by the radio, wearing the green velvet kimono-thing, and snapping two of Sharon's white plastic barrettes into her heavy dark hair to hold it back from her temples. She looked up and smiled and said, "Hi, Timmy!"

She was the grandest-looking girl Tim had ever seen. She looked like a queen. And yet that green velvet put a pixie light into her gray eyes. The barrettes were like snowflakes on her hair.

Tim smiled back — his heartbreakingly sad smile.

He put down his packages among the gold-banded china and picked her out of her chair, held her against his snowy coat, and put his cold cheek against her warm one.

He said. "Essie, you're beautiful as the early dawn and the midnight star. What are you doing in this place? What are you doing here with me? I don't treat you right. I don't give you what you ought to have. I don't let you do what you want to do. I talk to you sometimes in tones and words you never ought to hear. Why don't you go away? Why don't you find a man who would be good to you?"

More silly, unanswerable questions. Essie pulled his hair.

"I thought you'd be pleased I'm all dressed up tonight," she pouted. "You said I never wore my housecoat anymore. I can't wear velvet when I'm spreading jelly on the children's bread or scraping it out of their hair, can I? I can't wear it when I'm frying doughnuts, or when the sink is piled up with dirty dishes. It has to be a Big Night when I wear velvet. And I thought this would be a Big Night."

Tim said, mournfully, "You should wear velvet every night."

Essie said, "Tim, darlin', if you turn my Big Night into a wake, I *will* leave you!"

He laughed a little at that, and they had their supper — a meat stew with carrots and feathery dumplings, a salad bowl with cottage cheese, and upside-down cake.

Afterward, he showed her what he had bought: A blue sweater for Sharon and a red one for Doody; a big book of paper dolls and a small red fire truck.

"But I see now," he confessed gloomily, "the way I figured wasn't right. It wasn't fair. You like to buy presents as well as I do. Better than I do. I'm sorry I got them, Essie. The rest of the money I save I'll bring home to you, and you can spend it. I know you wouldn't squander it. I don't know why I ever said such a thing. I don't know what gets into me. Essie, you can take these back to the store and change them, if you want to."

"Change them?" Essie repeated. "Why should I want to change them? What better could I get? They're fine. But I know what I can do, if you don't care. I'll get some yarn from the basket and embroider something on the sweaters. That can be my part."

While she wove a vine and flowers up and down the front of the blue sweater, and little green bats and balls across the shoulders of the red one, she told Tim of another idea she had had. She could take orders along the street for boxes of homemade Christmas cookies, and what she cleared, after the cost of the ingredients was taken out, would be hers to spend for her own Christmas shopping.

Tim said it would be too hard for her to do all that, but

if she wanted to, it was her right. He would not try to stop her. Only she must not spend it on anything for him, because he could not buy anything for her.

"Essie," he cried out, "why am I the kind of man that can't buy anything for his wife for Christmas? The wife I love more than my own soul!"

Essie put her hand over his.

"Sh-h-h, darlin'," she said. "Maybe you'll get a little bonus from the office before Christmas. You have sometimes, you know."

"But not always. It's nothing we can count on. That's our trouble, Essie. Nothing to count on."

"Sh-h-h, darlin'," Essie said again. "Don't talk so. We've got each other. . . . And if we can't buy each other anything big this year, some way we'll manage to get something small. Some powder for me, maybe, and tobacco for you. And we've got the things we've given each other before, Timmy. That's what you keep forgetting. Anything we've ever had we always have. Even — even when it's worn out or — gone where we can't see it anymore. Won't I still have this housecoat even when there isn't a shred of it left? Wouldn't you still have that watch if it had stopped ticking — even if you had sold or pawned it?"

Tim took out the watch, held it for a minute in the palm of his hand, and then rubbed it gently, round and round, against the green velvet covering Essie's knee.

"Essie," he said, "if I ever tell you you're anything else but the most wonderful woman a man ever had, promise not to believe me?"

Essie looked at him helplessly. What if she should make this promise, and he should remember it when he was telling her differently?

She pushed him away and stood up.

"I've talked too much now," she said. "I'm not used to it. My throat is dry. Let's have some milk and finish the cake before we go to bed."

By the twentieth of December, Essie had made five dollars and fifty cents from the sale of Christmas cookies packed in tin coffee cans which had been accumulating for years in the basement. She had gift-wrapped them and delivered them ready for mailing. She had an oven burn on the back of her hand and her fingers were sore from the can covers, paper, and string; but she was medium happy in her Essie way. Her work was done, for outsiders, and now she could begin her work for the family, which, to Essie, was play.

That afternoon she took Sharon and Doody upstreet to see the Santa Claus at the store and tell him what they wanted. Doody sat on his lap and pulled his whiskers and laughed heartily when Santa roared.

"Wanna cart!" Doody shouted gleefully. "Wanna cart can ride in! Wanna cart big as *me!*"

Of course he could not have a big red wagon like Pete Wainwright's, next door. But he could have a little one — one easy for him to pull. It would look big when he got it. Essie nodded and smiled at Santa Claus.

"Right-ho!" Santa Claus roared jovially. "A cart big as you. I won't forget. I never forget, sonny. Now what does sister want? Hey?"

Sharon was shy. She was like Essie. She would not so much as touch Santa Claus. But she drew her mother's head down.

"You tell him," she whispered. "You tell him, a doll I can wash. A doll with hair I can wash."

"What does she say?" Santa asked. "What does sister say?"

"A doll," smiled Essie, over Sharon's clinging arms.

"A doll, hey? Well, you're going to get a doll, sister. Wait and see if you don't."

"With hair — hair that I can wash," whispered Sharon. "You didn't say it. Say it, Mommie."

But Essie explained that another little girl was talking to Santa now. She led the children out of the crowd. They stopped at a counter and had ice cream. It was a kind of party. It was the real beginning of Christmas.

That night Essie took the next step.

She told Tim she had five dollars to spend for the children's Christmas gifts, that she had fifty cents beside, and that Caroline Michaud down the block would sit with the children for two hours for fifty cents, if the children were in bed. She asked Tim to go upstreet with her.

"Just to look in the windows, Timmy. I won't buy a thing. I only want to look and maybe ask some prices. I know just what I want to get. A cart for Doody and a doll for Sharon. But I want to — stretch it out. Will you, Tim?"

Tim was feeling fine that night. He said they would, too, buy something. They would buy the caps and mittens. And Essie should price whatever she wanted to, all the way up to mink coats if she said the word. Pricing never cost anybody anything. Looking never cost anybody anything. Who knew? Maybe they wouldn't always be poor. This wasn't Ireland, was it? Maybe Tim had a ship coming in some day. Maybe it was already heading out of some foreign harbor. . . .

Essie thought, "He has an idea he's going to get a bonus check. If he does, he's going to spend it for me. I wish he wouldn't. He needs so many things. There are so many things I want him to have. . . . But — that's the way he feels about me! I mustn't say a word. I mustn't spoil it for him, if he gets it. . . . It's usually ten dollars. Twice it was five. If it's ten, I ought to have half of it, to buy a present for him. But, whatever it is, it's his — and he'll want it all — for me. . . . Oh, dear, being in love is such funny business!"

They had a wonderful two hours, a magical two hours. Snow was falling silently in big soft white blobs. Street lights glowed through it like yellow balloons. Beyond the plate glass of the store windows were scenes of incredible beauty such as one is forever expecting to find in miniature within an icy grotto. Tim and Essie stood and stared with their hands clasped inside Tim's greatcoat pocket, and pointed and nodded and laughed.

Mostly they pointed at toys. Such toys as no child needs or would wish for if he never saw them. Rocking horses as big as collie dogs, panda bears the size of a six-year-old boy, dolls dressed for a wedding — the bride and the groom and all the bridesmaids, the flower girl and the ringbearer. Surely these were not meant to be played with. Only for adults to marvel at. And Tim and Essie marveled. . . .

They bought the caps and mittens. Sharon's cap was plaid, with scarf ends. Doody's cap was brown, with furry earmuffs. One pair of mittens had Donald Duck on the backs, and the other had Mickey Mouse.

They priced carts and found quite a good one for two dollars and ninety-five cents. It was big enough for Doody's Teddy bear. There were gaily dressed dolls for two dollars and though their hair was only painted, Sharon could imagine it was real. She had a nice little imagination.

Essie said, clutching her pocketbook, "I won't buy them tonight, Tim. On Christmas Eve, right after supper, I'll run up and buy them. I always like to have something left to buy on Christmas Eve."

Suddenly Tim said, "Essie!"

"What, Tim?"

"Let's do a make-believe!"

She had been hoping he would say that. They had not done a make-believe since Sharon was a baby. Essie had been afraid Tim was getting too grown-up ever to do another make-believe. But it was he who had suggested the first one, and they had done so many in the first years. A make-believe was pretending you were buying — had bought — a gift you could not possibly buy. It was not wishing. It was having — just for a minute.

"Oh — let's!" Essie cried, like a child.

They were both children — tall children. They ran from window to window with the wealth of the world in their hands.

They did not so much as glance at suits or shirts or housedresses, nor at double boilers, toasters, or snow shovels. They looked long, ardently, critically at framed pictures, at Numdah rugs, at bed-jackets and at smoking-jackets, and at jewelry.

And finally each made a purchase.

Of course he did not tell what it was he had bought. It was a great secret. A precious secret. But sometime before Christmas Tim would draw a picture of what he had bought for Essie — in his heart — and Essie would draw one of what she had chosen for Tim. On Christmas Eve or Christmas morning they would exchange them.

Essie would cry, "Oh, Tim! It's — it's beautiful!"

And Tim would say, "Essie, how did you think of it? It's too grand for me. But — how do I look?"

And he would march proudly up and down the room.

It is a fine thing for a girl to be married to an Irish boy. When he is in a high mood, it is so wondrous high the whole world is ablaze with light. And when he is in a low mood — well, you have only to wait until it passes. . . .

The evening of December twenty-third, Tim was in the lowest mood Essie had ever seen. It was so low that Essie was really frightened, and medium-Essie did not frighten easily.

He would not touch his supper. He did not answer the children when they spoke to him. He would not even put match to his pipe. He sat by himself in the dark living room and stared out of the window.

When Essie went in to him, he said roughly, "Go away, will you?"

About nine o'clock he put on his coat and hat and left the house, still without a word.

Essie thought, "At last he has gone to a tavern. We have driven him to a tavern. Because we are here, and tomorrow night is Christmas Eve, and he did not get a bonus, and knows he is not going to get a bonus. Poor Tim — poor darling Tim. Whatever tavern he is in, it is a lonely place. A noisy, crowded, desperately lonely place."

She cried more than a little. When he came back, she was still crying, and he did not look at her nor speak to her. He went to bed.

When she could get up courage to follow him, he seemed to be asleep. But she knew he was not asleep because he did not rouse up when she crept in beside him. He did not move at all. He lay like a log in the bed. And all the comfort she had was the sure knowledge that he had not been in any tavern. It was poor comfort.

Christmas Eve, he did not come to supper.

But when he did come, about eight o'clock, she knew by his step, even before he opened the door, that he was in a high mood again.

She left the dishpan and ran to meet him with dripping hands.

"Oh, Timmy! Timmy, darlin'! Where have you been so long? Have you eaten? I've kept things warm in the oven. The children have hung their stockings and gone to bed —"

He hugged her so hard he cut her breath off. He set her off from him, gazed at her hungrily, and then kissed her. He sat down, his hat and coat still on, and took her on his knee.

"Essie," he said huskily, "I know why you did it. It was because you felt as if you had to have a present for me, and I'd fixed it so you couldn't, any other way. It was no fault of yours. But — but it 'most killed me, Essie. I couldn't stand it. Now I've done what I had to do, too. Maybe it was selfish. I don't know. But I had to do it,

Essie. I couldn't — I must be a funny guy — but I couldn't stand it, even if you could."

Essie took off his hat and stroked his hair.

"What have you done, Tim?" she asked gently, blissfully.

She did not care what he had done.

He reached down with one big hand and broke the string on a box he had dropped on the floor. He tossed off the cover and pulled back tissue paper.

There lay a green velvet housecoat. This one wasn't brilliant green. It was a grayish-green. It didn't have buttons with sparkling red jewels set in. It had a zipper and a red crepe sash. The shoulders looked broad. Too broad for Essie.

Essie stared at it. She stared at Tim in complete mystification.

"Is it," she heard herself asking, "for — me, Timmy?"

"It is," he said. His eyes were shiny with tears, his voice hoarse with love and joy and sorrow. "It's not so grand as the other one, but it's the grandest that was anything like it that I could find, Essie. It may be a mite big, but you can grow to it, my darlin'. And it will look beautiful when you are in it. It was you always made the other one look so beautiful. It didn't look like anything on that other girl. It looked draggy and — and homesick!"

"Oh! Tim! . . .."

"Maybe you didn't think I'd ever miss it — ever know it was gone. I guess you didn't know what it meant to me to — to see you in velvet I'd bought for you, Essie."

He sighed, beginning to relax.

"Oh, Essie, when I went into that apartment down the street yesterday afternoon to fix the electric stove, and that strange woman came to that strange door in your kimono-thing, everything went all of a blur. I don't know what I said to her. I don't know what I did to her stove. I don't know how I got back to the office. I didn't begin to think until I was on my way home. Then it came to me what it was all about. What you had done. You'd sold your velvet kimono-thing for money to buy me a Christmas present, because you wanted a Christmas present for me so bad. Bad as I wanted one for you.

"I walked miles last night. I don't know where I walked —"

"Oh, poor Timmy," Essie whispered in horror. "Poor darlin' Timmy —"

He stopped her with a hug.

"But tonight I could do something about it. And I did what I had to do. Maybe I shouldn't have. Maybe it was selfish. Maybe I got a present for myself more than for you. If I did, you'll have to forgive me, Essie. But they gave me a bonus check. For twenty-five dollars! And I spent it all on — on a green kimono-thing for you to wear tomorrow morning just like you have every Christmas morning since we were married!"

"Tim —"

"Don't scold me, Essie."

"I wasn't going to scold you. But darlin' —"

"Next year, if I get a bonus check, you can have it all. To spend any way you want to. Every cent. But this year, Essie —"

It was no use for her to try to talk.

She pushed away his hands and stood up and went into the bedroom. When she came back she had her own velvet housecoat held up against her, the green of it making pixies dance in her eyes, the red buttons sparkling, the whole brilliant lustrous, heavenly soft, familiar folds of it flowing about her like a brook in Ireland.

Tim stared at it as stupidly as she had at the new one in the box.

"I never thought you'd see it on the other girl, Tim," she whispered. "She was nobody either of us had ever seen — until I went around taking orders for the cookies. She gave me an order and told me about a little party she was going to give last night. A man in the shop where she works had asked her out a few times, and then he stopped asking her out. So the best she could think of to do was to invite him and two other couples to her apartment for an evening. But she couldn't afford to buy a new dress and she was afraid she wouldn't look nice enough to — nice enough — well, nice enough. So I thought of my velvet housecoat. I didn't sell it to her, Timmy. Is that what you thought? I only lent it to her. And she brought it back this morning —"

All that time Tim had not interrupted.

But now he said, surprisingly, "She wore that to a party? A kimono-thing?"

"Timmy, darlin', I've told you over and over: It isn't a kimono-thing. It's a housecoat. It's a — a hostess gown. It's fine enough for any woman to wear anytime — in her own home."

"Hm," Tim said. "I wouldn't want you to wear it when any other man was around but me."

Essie's eyes widened.

"I wouldn't want to wear it when any other man was around but you. Besides, no man ever is, silly. . . . But *she* wore it for another man. And — and he didn't think she looked — draggy. He stayed after the others went — and asked her to marry him. Because — because that's the kind of housecoat it is! Of course I'm sure he meant to ask her, all the time. But she isn't. And she's so happy —"

Tim stood up. Light began to break all over his face. It twinkled in his eyes and shot off in little sparks from his hair.

He said softly, *"She's* happy!" After a minute he said loudly, "I'm happy! You're happy! Essie, call up Caroline! We're going straight down to the store and return this gray-green rag, this bulky bag with a red string around it! We're going to get that twenty-five dollars — and buy each other some Christmas presents! Hurry up, Essie! It's Christmas Eve."

Later, wandering up the street in the moonshine, the starshine, the lampshine, the Tim-shine, Essie asked casually:

"What do you want for Christmas, darlin'? A snow shovel that's like a scoop and runs on little wheels?"

"What would I want of such a thing as that?" demanded Tim. "Haven't I still got a good pair of arms and stout shoulders? Do you think I am an old man so soon? It would be a waste of money. . . . What do you want for Christmas, Essie? A piece of navy-blue velvet to make you a decent dress that I would let you wear when another man was around?"

"Why should I?" inquired Essie. "I only want to wear velvet for you. And I've got velvet to wear for you. We can't afford to be extravagant, Timmy."

She waited demurely to hear what he would say to that.

"Can't we, Essie?" he asked coaxingly, at last. "Just this once? For Christmas? When we've had such a stroke of luck?"

Essie did not laugh.

She asked very gravely, "Well — what are you thinking of, Tim?"

He did not know whether to be embarrassed or delighted.

He took a slip of paper from his pocket and showed it to her where the white light laid a rug for them before the revolving doors.

He said, "I was thinking — we might make our make-believe come true."

She looked at a picture, drawn in pencil and colored with a child's wax crayons, of a pair of earrings with dangling, ruby-red stones.

She smiled.

She took another picture from her purse. A picture in red ink, of a flannel shirt, a scarlet shirt of wool made satin-fine with interwoven rayon. Such a shirt as a man would wear as he sat smoking his pipe in his own house of an evening, its full, soft sleeves covering richly his long arms, its collar unbuttoned at his strong, handsome neck. A shirt for a man to wear opposite a girl in a green velvet kimono-thing, with ruby-red jewels on her breast, and ruby-red jewels swinging from her small white ears.

"I think," said Essie, "it wouldn't be at all extravagant to make make-believe come true. Just once. Not always. But just once, Tim — I think it would be really practical."

Tim looked at her helplessly. There was not a word for him to say.

"Especially," continued Essie in her cheerful, medium voice, "since both together they won't use up all our bonus money. We'll have enough over to go with what I have so that Sharon can have her doll with real hair and Doody can have his cart big enough for him to ride in."

She took Tim's hand and drew him toward the whirling doors.

Just before they were swept in, Tim found his voice.

"Essie," he said huskily. "I never was so happy in all my born days."

Over her shoulder, Essie smiled at him.

It is a fine thing for a girl to be married to an Irish boy. . . .

hristmas 1948

My small daughter says:

"I don't know which season I like the best. Spring is a prince, a lively, noisy, happy boy in a land where sound is music in your ears. Summer is a queen with flowers in her hair, busy with her children and her garden. Fall is her beautiful daughter running in the leaves which have come down to play with her because their work is done. Winter is the king, roaring his orders from the rooftops while we are snug and cosy by the fire."

If winter is the king, Christmas is the priceless jewel which slips from his crown or studded belt or giant scepter and rolls down the chimney and across the hearth to us, unscarred by time, untarnished by storms, unaltered by heat, and made only more precious by all the diversity of the history of human experience.

The Christmas jewel is not the same gem nor of the same size, color, or shape in every land, or every town, or every household. It tends to reflect whatever beauty it finds where it falls. Yours may be a smooth ruby, a delicately cut emerald, a many faceted diamond, or a clear turquoise. There are opals, too, with hearts of flame, pearls as pure as mountain snow, and amethysts.

I think ours is a block of amber.

The room where we sit "snug and cosy by the fire" has old pine walls on which long ago some boy with the sea in his blood cut a picture of a ship in full sail. The setting sunlight comes in through nine-over-six windows and when darkness falls we draw the inside shutters and see the yellow and red-orange of the burning applewood flickering on the pine and melting into its burnished surface. The old chests and settle, the tavern table, the Welsh dresser with its luster cups and plates, the pink stepdown Windsor chairs, and the big braided rugs my mother made all come alive too, with past, present, and promise for the future.

At our left hangs the deep-brown gourd which two hundred years ago was a blossom on a vine creeping through a chink in a wall and lying across a basket-bottomed rocker in a room which was part of the garrison house standing then where ours stands now. It served generations as a vessel to hang on a saddle for carrying molasses or rum. Now it is an ornament, shining with memories.

Before us, beside the fireplace, is a modern painting done by an artist whose exhibit I once visited in Fall River. I could not have left the exhibit without the promise that this picture would be sent to me. It is of popcorn being poured from the popper and a big salt shaker is ready on the table.

At our right is the portrait of our daughter at the age of five. Her blue eyes are turned up, seeing visions faintly and delicately suggested by the artist — an old, suspendered spinner of folktales, a child in a plaid pelisse, a jointed wooden doll.

Behind us, as we sit watching the fire, shelves my grandfather made when he was young hold our favorite books. Robert Frost's poems and Robert P. Tristram Coffin's, *Precious Bane, Maria Chapdelaine, Kristin Lavransdatter*, the *Journal of Katherine Mansfield, Jane Eyre*, and *Wuthering Heights*. There is a full shelf of Sarah Orne Jewett — *The Country of the Pointed Firs, Deephaven, The Country Doctor, The Tory Lover*, her letters, her poems, her biography, *Betty Leicester, Betty Leicester's English Christmas* — everything she ever had published between hard covers except *The Story of the Normans*.

There is much more, and all is more golden than gold, more liquid brown than the richest maple syrup, more glowing than live coals.

Without, the countryside surrounds us and we feel it throbbing. The pitch of the evergreens hanging in pale globules, the warm hides of the deer asleep in the snowy woods; the ruddy, lamplit windows of our neighbors; the stained glass behind the meetinghouse pulpit; the folds of the velvet curtains of the community hall which is the scene of our Christmas programs and parties; the cows in the barns and the fowl on the roosts. There are the field walls and cellar holes too, their stones veined with iron, glinting with flecks of mica in the moonlight, and holding fast their stories of the men who laid them up, the women who trod so many kitchen miles between or above them, the children who touched them with gentle, inquiring hands.

Beyond this second circle is Berwick Town. Here Sarah Orne Jewett's father cared for his patients; here Miss Sarah learned and wrote of herbs and people; here is the house where she was born, here where she lived and died, and was and is beloved. Here is the Hamilton House, where John Paul Jones danced away the night before setting sail from Portsmouth, the scene and the incident which inspired *The Tory Lover*. Here are the Lower Landing and the river where gundalows plied up and down and my grandfather learned to make plum duff. Here are the General Ichabod Goodwin mansion, the old Latin Academy which still gives superior training to young people, the public and parochial schools, the church spires, the shoe factory, the brick-fronted stores, the old cemeteries on the riverbank, the newer ones out Portland Street way.

Perhaps ours is a typical New England town. Certainly ours is a traditional New England country home. Yet with all our respect for the past, the present and the future are even more important to us, as to all New Englanders.

We are a man and a woman who trace our American family history from the first settlers, through our country's periods of trial and its steady progress to its present position of world responsibility. The man, in his daily work, seeks to develop emotional stability and maturity in as many American young people as he can reach. The woman writes as well as she can of what Americans have been and what she trusts they will become.

We have a son who is this year a freshman at a Maine college. He is majoring in history because he feels that it is there he will find guidance for times in which he will take his part.

We have a daughter with honey-colored hair who often plays with the doll she holds in the portrait, a doll given to me when I was seven by the aunt to whom it was given when she was seven. Kate Greenaway frocks are becoming to Sally. But she rides to and from the village school by bus, and this is her third year of ballet.

It is winter and the king's jewel rolls across the hearth to the father and the mother, and son home from college for the holidays, and the little girl sitting on the rug with an old doll in sprigged calico gown, kid gloves, and bead bracelet.

The past is the rich brown in our Christmas amber, the present is the snared gold, the future is the fiery dancing light.

CHAPTER XII

Christmas 1949

A novelette developed from a short story, both of which were published under the title Christmas Without Johnny.

Friday:

"How long is it till Christmas?" Johnny asked in a low voice.

His mother turned from the stove to look at him, sitting alone at the kitchen table.

He was too small for a nine-year-old, she thought as she had a thousand times. The baby, Deirdre, took after Jack; Deir had long legs, broad shoulders and stout hands already; but Johnny was small-boned like herself. What a pity it should be that way! He was thin, too, as Marge had never been. She knew that was because he did not eat enough. His eyes were enormous. Where did he get such big eyes? Perhaps they only seemed so because his face was small.

She put a steaming bowl before him and stuck a spoon into it.

"Goodness, I don't know," she said. "I've been too busy to think. Now eat that up, son. Every bit. And keep your eye out for the bus. I've got to run upstairs and strip the beds before Deir wakes up. Your lunch is on the chair by the door."

On her way she glanced at the calendar and paused.

Christmas . . . When she was nine, she had counted the days. Once she had crossed off each one before she went to bed, beginning at Thanksgiving. That was the last year she had wanted a doll. A doll with real hair which she could wash and curl. She had that doll still, and was keeping her for Deir.

"Why, it's only ten days," she said. "That isn't long, is it, Johnny? What you wishing for this year? Nothing big, are you? Like — a bicycle?"

He looked up, startled, as if he had not thought she was still there.

"Can't we wait, Mum?"

Can't we wait? What did he mean by that? Did any other child ever bring people up so short when they tried to talk to him?

" 'Can't we wait?' " she repeated, frowning. "I guess there'll be plenty of waiting. For anything as expensive as a bicycle."

"Can't we wait here till after Christmas?"

"Wait here? Oh, you mean stay here till after Christmas? Goodness, no. We'll be lucky if we get our stuff out before this lane is blocked full of snow. I don't like the looks of that sky a bit, right now." She glanced anxiously out of the window. "Moving is a terrible job, and when anybody's got it to do, the sooner it's done, the better. Think what fun it'll be getting up Christmas morning in a brand-new house. It won't be chilly upstairs there like it is here."

She smiled and shivered as she opened the stairway door.

Her voice and the tap of her quick steps echoed in the narrow passage.

"Hurry up," she was saying. "Eat your cereal before the bus comes. It's almost time for it to go over the lane."

Johnny sat as he was until there was no sound in the room.

Then he reached with a jerky motion for the milk pitcher. It was full and heavy and, as he poured, some of the milk spilled over onto the cracked oilcloth which covered the table. He watched a narrow white river flow out of the pool. As the river slowly broadened, brooks ran from it like twigs from the branches of a tree. One brook trickled close to the edge of the table. He took his handkerchief from his pocket and carefully, yet reluctantly, mopped up what had been spilled. He spread his left hand and looked at it, before he dropped the handkerchief over it as on a drying rack.

He was holding it there, looking at it, when his mother called, "Are you through, Johnny? The bus is going over!"

With his free right hand he dipped deep into the sugar bowl and sprinkled the gray island before him until it was white as the waters which surrounded it.

There. It was all white. Perfectly white. Like the Arctic. Like the pearly gates. Like the coffin in which he had seen his infant brother lying. Like any far cold place where no one has ever been and returned.

He pushed back his chair and stood up, stuffing the handkerchief into his pocket.

He looked at the walls. The smudged last sheet of the

calendar hung loosely on worn-out clips which once had pinioned a clean, full year. The rack, usually bulging with old newspapers, hung empty now that the best dishes had been wrapped and put in the barrel which stood in the sink room. The lounge his grandfather had made in his youth and lain on during the last weeks of his life was bare of cover and cushions. The braided mat was gone from before the stove. The knots in the pine floor looked up at Johnny like eyes with wrinkled lids; and the worn places where his mother's feet had pressed, and his grandmother's before her, were like hollows below cheekbones in a brown old face.

"Johnny!" his mother called. "The bus is coming up the hill. Did you eat all your cereal?"

He raised his head and turned it sharply from left to right.

He ran to the stairway door and pulled it open.

"Mum!" he called loudly.

"What? Your lunch is — "

"Mum — could I stay home today?"

His voice trembled.

She came to the head of the stairs and stood there, her hands on her hips.

"Johnny Lee," she said, "you may not stay home. You are not sick. You are never to play that game again. You know as well as I do what the principal said two months ago. He said it's the law that you have to go to school, and that feeling you get mornings is just trying to get out of going to school, and nothing else in this world. The doctor said so too. You don't have that feeling Saturday mornings. Now do you?"

Johnny shook his head, but the paleness of his face and the size of his eyes frightened his mother. She sighed and let her hands fall.

"Oh, dear," she said. "Don't you feel good, honest?"

"Sure," Johnny said. He tried to smile at her. "I feel pretty good. I just thought — you got so much to do —

can't I stay and — and help? I could take care of Deedy, couldn't I?"

The bus horn blew. The principal had given instructions to the bus driver as well as to Marge.

Johnny and his mother both jumped at the sound.

"No," his mother said with renewed determination. "Not on your tintype, young man. You do your job at school and I'll do mine here. When you get home I'll have a load ready for you and your father to take into town on the truck. Now grab your lunch and scoot!"

The horn blew again.

"Well, — 'bye," Johnny said.

"Quick!" his mother urged him.

She saw him close the door, heard him open others which he did not close, heard his running feet.

Then, from the yard: "Mum! Mum!"

"What is it, Johnny?"

" 'Bye, Mum!"

"Good-bye, sonny! Hurry!"

"Yup . . . 'Bye, Mum — " faintly.

"Good-bye, Johnny!" she shouted.

Then she sank down on the top step, warming her arms against her breast. She was afraid again. She felt empty.

"Good-bye, darling," she whispered. "Good-bye, my baby. My precious, are you all right? What makes you look at me the way you do? Why can't you tell me what's the matter? I don't want to make you do anything you don't want to. I want you with me every minute just like Deedy is, and like you used to be. But that isn't right. Your father says if I don't look out you'll grow up a sissy; and the principal says you're smart and the reason you've got low marks is I've let you stay out of school so much. He says you might be on the honor roll if you went every day. I used to be on the honor roll sometimes. I loved going to school. You'd like it if you got on the honor roll, wouldn't you, Johnny? I guess you'd be pretty proud. I guess we would too. You're never going to be big and strong to do hard work like Daddy. He won't give in to that yet, but I have, Johnny. You're going to do a different kind of work. Maybe if you get good marks in school we'll manage to send you to college, and you'll learn to be an expert accountant, or sell insurance, or be a teacher — even a principal, like Mr. Sturtevant. Think of that, Johnny! Someday you'll be glad we made you go to school. Some day we'll all be glad . . ."

She felt better. She thought of all she had to do and ran downstairs.

The sight of Johnny's untouched cereal moved her to healthy irritation.

"Johnny Lee!" she said aloud, sternly. "I could shake you! I know what this means — you'll eat your lunch at recess and won't have anything at noontime and come home hungry as a bear, wanting cake or bread with apple-sauce and brown sugar. Well, there won't be any cake in this house tonight, nor any applesauce; and the brown sugar is packed already. So if you eat this afternoon, you'll eat just exactly what you left this morning!"

She set the white island in the white sea into the cellar cupboard.

She was a sensible woman and she loved her son very much. Too much to spoil him.

The baby woke and called, and Johnny's mother ran upstairs again, snatched up the warm, chubby creature, covered with kisses the damp curls, pink cheeks, soft neck, and lively fingers, and carried Deirdre to the warm kitchen on her shoulders, both of them laughing.

"Now, pet," Marge said, "we'll have our breakfast. You'll eat a nice big one, I know. You always do. And then you'll help me all day long. You and I've got heaps and piles to do, sweetie-pie. I'm going to bring in lots of boxes from the shed, and we'll fill them up. Because we're going tonight to live in a new house. A beautiful brand-new house. When we look out of the windows there, we won't see just old fields and trees. We'll see cars coming

and going, and people walking by. You can wave to them
and they'll wave back to you. It'll be just like it was where
I lived when I was a little girl. Wave to Mummie, Deir."

Deirdre waved her spoon, ducking her head and looking merrily through her eyelashes.

"That's it," Marge cried in delight. "Oh, you darling.
You adorable. You know what you are? You're what they
write all the songs about. What would Mummie ever do
without you?"

Marge went singing across the kitchen, her round face
gentle, her blue eyes bright with love and eagerness, her
step young and light, her voice clear and sweet. The room
was no longer bare. It was not even the same room where
Johnny had sat and stared around him. It was the room
where he had once been as Deirdre was now, but so long
ago that the memory was like one of the dreams he had
over and over, most of them bad but this one breathtak-
ingly good. Bad or good, they were a part only of the
nights. This was the room from which time had ejected
him.

Johnny had gone to school.

His father came home about one o'clock, having asked
for the afternoon off from the shipyard for the moving.
Marge had cleared out the cupboards and warmed up the
leftovers. Deirdre was having her nap. Marge met her big
husband at the door with a hug, stood by the sink while he
washed, telling him what she had done, and sat opposite
him at the crowded table, her feet curled over the chair
rung.

"As soon as these dishes are dry, I'll pack them," she
said. "They're the last. All the bedding is into boxes, except Deir's. The clothes are in the trunks in the parlor.
You can load this stuff anytime and then I'll help you take
the beds apart. They ought to be loaded last, so they'll
come off first, and I can make them up while you come
back for another load. I had a pie left, and I've just made

a batch of biscuits, so with cheese and some bananas we can have a quick supper whenever you want to stop for it. I must remember to keep the milk and coffee and coffeepot where I can put my hand on them. If we're sure of a bite to eat and beds to sleep in, we'll be all right until tomorrow. Then I can start fixing up . . . I don't know how you're going to get our big bedstead and mattress downstairs alone, Jack. I don't suppose it's ever been taken out since it was put up there."

"Whatever goes up must come down, they say," Jack grinned, over his coffee cup. "All you've done, I guess I can handle my end of it."

Jack did not often smile. He was a sober man, of few words. Marge knew he was proud of her and what she had done since morning. He was eating hugely. The flavor of good food, she thought, is even better the second day. She looked back at her husband radiantly and took another helping for herself. It was good to work hard and eat well, with a man like Jack. It would be fine when he did not have a farm to take care of, beside his job on the yard. They would keep just as busy. They liked to be busy. But they would go out together sometimes, to church and to meetings at Johnny's school and to the playground where there were sandboxes for Deir to dig in. She thought of how Jack would look, walking down the street beside her. He was very handsome. Town wives of pasty-faced store clerks and lily-handed bank cashiers would envy her. Her admiration shone in her eyes and colored her voice.

"Lucky for me," she said, "I married a guy with muscle. But don't you dare hurt your back or anything."

She began picking up the dishes.

"Oh, Jack, you don't know how I'm going to enjoy my stainless steel sink!"

As he went out to the truck with the first of the boxes, she was singing again.

But as the afternoon wore on, the strain of the long day

began to be felt. They had both been up since daybreak. It started to snow and the truck skidded against the pump as Jack tried to turn it. He was some time getting it free, and a fender was bent until it cracked. Marge ran out to push and got her feet wet and had nothing dry into which to change unless she opened a trunk. A stock dealer came for the two cows and the hens, and though he paid the price he had offered, he grumbled about it, saying the hens were moulting and one of the cows did not look to him as if she would give as much milk as Jack claimed.

"You can take my word about the cow or you can get off my place," Jack said between his teeth.

He stood with his legs apart and his weight on his heels. His hands were thrust into his two back pockets as if he kept them there with difficulty. His plaid wool shirt flapped boldly in the icy wind.

Marge, in her wet shoes, shivered with cold and terror.

"As for the hens, what you expectin' to buy this time of year, — six weeks' old chickens? These hens have laid good and they'll lay again. You goin' to sell hens to people that want eggs, or feather pillers? You come here last Tuesday night and we made a deal. These are the same hens and the same cows. Take 'em or leave 'em. But you hold your tongue; see?"

The fat little dealer pawed at the snow.

"Come now, Jack," he mumbled. "I didn't mean nuthin'. Only —"

"I've got no time for talk that don't mean nuthin'. You takin' this stock or bringin' it back to the barn?"

"Oh, I'm takin' it, Jack. Sure, I'm takin' it."

The dealer climbed hastily into his truck. As he turned out into the lane, he waved his hand.

"Good luck to ye in town, boy. If you ever want to come back to the farm and stock it again, let me know."

"He'll burn before I do," Jack muttered.

"Dear God, I thought you was going to fight," Marge said, in awe. "If you had, you'd have killed him."

"If he hadn't took it back, I would have," Jack said, throwing boxes and barrels into his truck. "Nobody's goin' to tell me —"

"Look out!" Marge cried. "That's the best dishes!"

Jack stopped. He stood over her.

"Get into the house," he told her. "Out of this snow. Haven't you got anything to do to keep out of my way? You want to get down sick in the middle of moving? You want to drive me crazy?"

"Jack Lee —"

"You heard me, Marge."

She ran away from him, stumbling. In the kitchen she cried a little.

"Why does he have to take it out on me," she whimpered, "what the dealer said?"

But then Deirdre woke up again and the sound of her small untroubled voice, the smoothness of her cheek, the very warmth of her blankets were a comfort to her mother.

"Well, honey lamb! . . . Well, honey lamb, you all ready to come to town to live? Go ride? Go bye-bye?"

In the yard Jack's fury was passing. The cows were gone. He had raised them from calves and milked them morning after morning, night after night, his forehead against their flanks. They would never have as good a home again as they had had with him. And he might never milk a cow again as long as he lived. If it had not been for Marge this would never have happened, either to him or to the cows. But he had made them cringe, the dealer and Marge too. Now the dealer had the cows and Marge had her way. Maybe it was a good way. Two jobs were too much for any man. Life would be easier with no barn to tend and no wood and water to carry. Johnny had never seemed to be much help on the farm. He wasn't stout and he wasn't handy. Marge thought it would be better for him, living in town; she thought he needed boys of his own age. Maybe he did; his father did not know what it was Johnny needed. Anyway, it would be nice for Marge, living where she had neighbors. No wonder she talked too much when he was around; the rest of the time, out here, she had nobody to talk to; she had never grown used to being alone. Probably it had been too much to ask.

He sighed.

He thought, I'm gosh-darned tired. I wish the kid would get home. He ought to be able to take one corner of the mattress if his mother held one and I went ahead to carry the weight of it.

He went into the house, and when he saw that Marge had been crying, he touched her hair. It was pretty hair. The color of maple syrup.

"Did you change your shoes?" he asked her.

She shook her head, close to tears again.

"You go change 'em," he said gently. "Only take a minute. I'll watch Deedy. Then we'll take the beds apart. The rest of the first load is on."

It was as near to an apology as he ever made. It was near enough for Marge. She rubbed her chin against his arm as she passed him.

Before they had the beds apart, the school bus came but it went by the Lee place without stopping.

"For goodness' sake," Marge exclaimed in dismay. "Where on earth is Johnny? Jack, you don't suppose Miss Besse would keep him after school so he'd have to walk home in the storm? Johnny says she's threatened to, but I never thought she would."

"I'll find out," Jack said grimly. "If she did, I'll have a piece of her hide."

He rammed Johnny's folding bed into the space he had saved for it on the truck and stood by the lane as the bus came back. He held up his hand and the bus stopped.

"What you done with my boy?" he asked. "I need him."

Johnny would have liked to hear that.

"Why, he got off down the road apiece," the driver said. "With the Morris girl. Guess that's a love match, Jack. Guess you Lees start young."

He winked over his shoulder and several girls tittered. As the bus coughed and the driver shifted gears, a boy with dirty teeth leered at Jack, through the window, and make an obscene gesture.

Jack thought, That Young Bill Sudbury. If I was Bill, I'd thrash him within an inch of his life.

But Jack was not Bill, and the bus was bearing Young Bill safely beyond Jack's reach.

Jack tramped back through the drifts and told Marge:

"The kid got off at Morris's road. Didn't you tell him there'd be work to do here tonight?"

She brushed her hair out of her eyes.

"I thought I did. I'm almost sure I did. He must know we're moving today!"

"I don't know what he knows," Jack growled. "His head's always in the clouds. Sometime he's going to bump into something and bump hard . . . Well, maybe he'll be here when I'm ready for the mattress."

He wasn't, and Jack would not wait. He started down the stairs with the mattress on his back and lost his grip on it as he tried to go through the door. Marge ran, got her knee under one end, and somehow held it up off the snow until Jack could drag in onto the roof of the truck. She had not stopped for overshoes, and now her feet were wet again.

"What did you do that for?" Jack demanded when it was done. "Nobody asked you to. I could have carried it if you'd left me alone."

He could not tell her to change her shoes for she had no dry ones to change into. He could not tell her to dry her feet in the oven for they had let the fire go out, not daring to leave it burning when they closed the house.

They looked at each other in despair.

Then Johnny came into the yard. They heard his shuffling step, and turned their attention from each other to him.

They did not know how he had spent his day, except that he had been at school, that he had not been here while the work was being done, when the dealer had insulted his father and hauled Old Moll and Sparked away like so many cans of milk or so many pounds of beef, when his mother wept from hurt and fear and wet her feet doing what he might have done if he had been there and could give a hand where needed like most boys of his age. They only knew that he was coming back, late, now the work was done, shuffling slowly through the new snow.

He did not know how they had spent their day, except that they had had it — they and Deedy — here at home where a woodfire crackled and a teakettle sang; that the whole last day was gone and he had lost it.

He was coming into the yard as he had so many other nights, but it was no longer his yard. It was filled with a load of furniture which did not look familiar. It did not look alive. The yard belonged now to someone else. The house belonged to someone else. The barn belonged to someone else. And the pump, the apple trees, the stone walls, even the snow and the sky. He was a stranger here and belonged nowhere. All he had to belong to, to lean against, were his mother and his father.

He said, "Hi . . ."

"Where in tunket have you been?" his father demanded. "The last hour?"

"I — was in the woods. By Morris's —"

"With that Morris kid? All this time? What for? It's a good thing you're going to get away from her. You've hung onto her skirt ever since you could walk. Don't you know it's got everybody laughing at you? Why don't you try holding your own with some boys for a change? How you've ever rode two years on that bus with Bill Sudbury and never come home with a black eye or a bloody nose I'll never figure out. What do you do when he's around, anyway? Crawl?"

Johnny stood blinking.

His mother was sorry for him. She knew he could not fight Bill Sudbury. But why didn't he do what he could do?

"You said this morning you wanted to help," she reminded him reproachfully. "It doesn't look like it. Your father and I've done every single thing alone. After he'd worked half the day, too; and driven twenty miles. I don't know what you were thinking of, Johnny, not to get here as soon as you could. Seems as if even Deir's helped more than you have." She sighed. "Well, we're all ready. I'll go get my coat and bundle up Deir, and we may get there before dark."

She went wearily toward the house.

Johnny looked at his father.

"We — we going to stay down there when we go?"

"Stay? What do you think we're going for? The ride?"

"You — have you fed Old Moll and Sparked?"

"Old Moll and Sparked are gone."

"Gone!"

Where had they gone?

"A lot you care," his father said. "You never even learned to milk 'em!"

He gave a sharp pull at the rope, trying to stretch it far enough to make a knot which would hold the mattress in place over the rough road.

"If I only had a few inches more," he grunted.

"Maybe," Johnny said in stifled voice, "maybe I could find another piece — you could tie on —"

But Jack made what he had do, as he had learned he often could. He went into the house for his gloves, beating his bare hands against his sides. Marge was trying to pick up her handbag and the box which held their supper, while she held the baby on her arm.

"Daddy take," Deirdre said, holding out her hands. "Bye-bye now. Bye-bye now. Daddy take."

Jack laughed and took her. She gurgled.

"You know where you're well off, don't you?" he said.

"Now have we forgot," Marge asked, "anything we'll need tonight?"

"Don't worry," Jack told her. "I can come back if I have to. So far so good. Let's go."

"There's the lamps," Marge said. "You can get them tomorrow. We won't need them. Maybe we can sell them. Some people — oh, Jack, am I really going to have electricity at last?"

"You bet you are. Within an hour. Come on."

"I haven't left anything mice can get into — oh, there's a bowl of cereal I thought Johnny might eat. Well, I'll dump it out for the birds and take the bowl along. If he's hungry, I'll give him a biscuit out of the box . . . I've got your teddy, Deir. All right; I'm coming."

She turned the key in the lock and dropped it into her handbag.

She climbed to the seat of the truck and Jack handed up the baby to her. He came around and slid in behind the wheel and started the engine.

Marge thought, Now this is kind of cosy, all of us and our supper and our beds going to ride together. Those poor women who used to start off in covered wagons, worrying about Indians and not knowing when they would ever sleep in a house again! They weren't like us, with a new house waiting for us, a cement walk leading up to it, and electric lights and an electric stove and a bathroom in it. Goodness, I feel rested already just thinking about that house, in spite of all I've got ahead of me yet before I lay down!

"Where've they got you tucked away, Johnny boy?" she asked cheerfully, peering into the back.

"Johnny!" his father exclaimed. "He went looking for a piece of rope as much as fifteen minutes ago. What is he, growing hemp to make it?"

He shouted, "Johnny! . . . JOHNNY!"

There was no answer.

Jack sprang down and strode back to the barn. The low rumble of the big door opening was a hollow sound.

"Johnny! You in here?"

From the dusky, dusty silence Johnny's eyes looked out. He was sitting on a barnacled, three-legged stool. Behind him was the mow of hay which had been sold with the farm. Beside him were the empty stanchions.

"What on earth are you doing, Johnny?"

Did he really miss those cows?

"I stopped . . . I just stopped to think . . ."

"What about?"

Jack rested his hand on his son's shoulder.

"About . . . oh, Dad, I never had my pony!"

Johnny began to cry. It was not that he wanted a pony now. He cried because he was too big even to want the pony which had once been promised him and which in imagination he had fed and watered in this barn so many nights and mornings and ridden so madly over fields and pastures and led so carefully when Linda sat astride the shaggy brown back; but which in actuality had never been his and now would never be. He cried for all the other joys and comforts he had longed for and which he was now too big ever to have, and yet too small for joys and comforts which come to those of size and power and experience and wisdom. He cried because he had been desolate, and because of his father's hand on his shoulder.

Jack looked down at him with mingled sympathy and exasperation.

He, too, had once wanted a pony, and he had never had one. But he had not really expected to have. He had known better. A child of six should know that a pony cost

money and was of little use and that after a few years a
boy's feet would drag on the ground if he tried to ride a
pony. What kind of a nine-year-old was Johnny that he
would huddle in a corner, on a day when so much was going on, and cry because he had not had a pony?

Jack took his hand away.

He said, "So you never had your pony. You've never
had a kangaroo either, nor a king's crown, nor a yacht,
nor a lump of gold. Neither have I and never expect to.
Now put your boots out to that truck and stop sniveling.
You've kept us waiting a quarter of an hour. It'll be dark
before ever we get to the village, and then there'll be all
the unloading and settling to do."

The door rumbled shut behind them. It had no lock,
and never had had. Never until now had there been a
night when a Lee would not have been roused from sleep
by the movement of that door. But tonight nothing inside
the barn was alive or of value. What little was there did
not belong to Lees.

As Jack climbed into the truck and started the engine,
Marge whispered, "Where'd you find him? He's been crying, hasn't he?"

"Yeah," Jack muttered. "Sitting there crying because
he never had a pony. What's ever going to become of him
beats me."

"I guess he just said that. It just happened to come into
his head. He probably feels bad, in some ways, to leave
the farm. Like all of us."

Jack watched the ruts. He knew that he was the only
one who felt bad about leaving the farm. Marge had
never liked it. Deirdre was too young to know one place
from another. Johnny had never tried to milk the cows,
though Old Moll had been gentle as a kitten and gave
down almost at a touch as if she was glad to. He drove
faster.

"All comfy, Johnny?" Marge called back. "You must

be hungry. Here's a biscuit. You be thinking what you want for Christmas. Of course nothing that would cost too much. Like a bicycle."

Johnny took the biscuit. He bit into it and chewed. It clung to his tongue and teeth, a gluey mass. He could not swallow it. Finally he took it out, made it into a dozen little balls, and dropped them, one at a time, through the crack in the truck floor. The rest of the biscuit he squeezed between his hands, then picked it apart, and dropped the crumbs through the crack. He thought of Hansel. And he thought of Linda, who was Gretel. Only Gretel had not come with Hansel. If she had, he would be happy even if they starved, even if they froze to death in the wilderness. Because whatever happened to them would happen to them both. Gretel would go with him, if necessary, even into a witch's oven, her hand cool on his, her eyes full of courage and compassion. Gretel loved whatever Hansel loved, and what he feared she hated. Hansel was incapable of hate. That was why the witch would get him. Because he was alone.

It grew pitch dark inside the truck. He rested his head on his knees.

The kitchen was gone. The farm was gone. The lane was gone. Even the little grotto he and Linda had found in the woods near her house that day — the tiny, grassy room under a roof of ice where Linda said a winter fairy lived. They had cut their hands tucking in a fairy's carpet of moss, a fairy's bed of pine needles, a fairy's table of birchbark, a fairy's acorn cups and saucers; that too, was gone.

Johnny tried to get the grotto back.

Pressing his eyes against his knees he saw pinpricks of light begin to whirl, growing larger with every revolution, until they were wheels flashing faster and faster and merging into one big wheel of incredible brilliance. Within the wheel as within a priceless frame gleamed the white ice of the grotto roof, and through it he could see

the winter fairy setting her birchbark table for supper, filling two acorn cups, turning back the blankets on her pine-
needle bed. She moved gracefully across the velvet floor.
Gracefully and slowly. She was waiting for someone to
come. She tipped her tiny head to listen for his knock
. . . He knocked. She spread her iridescent wings and
flew to the door. She cried, "Oh, darling, come in! I'm so
glad you're here!" She reached up and put her arms
around his neck. But she had to reach up only a very little,
because he was hardly taller than herself. He closed the
door and a bell tinkled with the closing. The sound was
sweeter than any music, even bird songs. And so was
Linda's voice. She said, "There. They can't get us now,
Johnny. Nobody can ever find us now. . . ."

"Johnny!" his mother called. "I declare, Jack, he's
asleep, for all that bumping and lurching! Wake up,
Johnny! Here's our new house!"

Saturday:
The next forenoon everyone was very busy. Jack drove
back to the farm for the front room furniture and Johnny
wanted to go with him but his father said the man next
door had offered to help; it would take two men to handle
the upholstered sofa and the big cherry table and Mar-
gie's parlor organ.

So Johnny stayed in the new house and followed his
mother about. He spread out the rugs but they were not
placed as she wanted them and had to be changed. She let
him help unwrap the dishes and hand them to her to put
away in the cupboards, and she worried for fear he would
break them. He did drop one — one of the set — but it
did not break. She said a piece of the border got chipped,
but he thought the chip had been there when he took off
the paper.

He wanted to talk about all that had happened to these
dishes, where they had been before, the trip they had
taken, but his mother was too busy to listen. So he pre-

tended the dishes could feel and think and hear, and talked to them.

"It's all right, Mrs. Cup," he said. "Mr. Saucer is on the way up. Don't you worry, Mrs. Cup. Mr. Saucer, you go take care of Mrs. Cup. You tell her that shelf isn't a dark place. It just looks like a dark place. She got kind of scared staying in the barrel. You tell her everything's all right . . . Come on, Red Sugar Bowl. You're not scared, Red Sugar Bowl. You're brave . . . Hi, Deedy's Mug! Deedy wondered last night where you'd gone to, Mug! Did you think you didn't have Deedy anymore? Well, you do. She's right over there in her playpen. See? I'll take you to Deedy —"

"Don't, Johnny," his mother said. "She'll only get it dirty. Give it to me."

"That's Deedy's Mum, Mug. You go to Deedy's Mum. Deedy'll have you when she eats her dinner. You'll be with Deedy then, just like you used to be. You won't be lonesome anymore, Mug. You'll be with Deedy."

"Johnny!" his mother exclaimed at last. "That's silly. You're getting me so muddled up I don't know what I'm doing. Here it is 'most noontime. Your father'll be back any minute and I haven't got a thing together to eat."

He was quiet after that.

He went into the dining room. It seemed strange to be in a house which had a dining room. There had been none at the farm; just the big kitchen and sink room, the sitting room where people sat only in warm weather, the front room where people went on great occasions, the back bedroom where his grandfather had slept, and two chambers upstairs. Because there had been no dining room at the farm, this one was empty. His mother hoped to buy furniture for it by and by. A big table, she said, with six chairs and a sideboard. He had asked what a sideboard was for and she said to keep silver and tablecloths and napkins in, and to put flowers and candles on. He wondered where the flowers would come from. He wondered if the candles would be lit at night.

He went on into the living room. This, too, was empty, but today the front-room furniture would come and fill it up. He did not feel at all well acquainted with the front-room furniture. At the farm his mother had kept it covered with old sheets. Sometimes he had opened the door to look in. The sight had fascinated, even as it terrified him. Ghostly chairs, shrouded couch, a table in which he could see his eyes and teeth, ivory keys yellowed by time, ebony keys gray with age. He shivered. In a living room would sheets be spread?

He would rather have the sitting-room furniture here. This was a warm room, a brighter one than the front room at the farm. It had a new, clean, square little fireplace. With the sitting-room furniture it would look all year as the sitting room had in summer. The willow rocker with the green plush seat; the wicker rocker resting in its stand; the phonograph with the big horn and the black and brown cylinder records which his grandfather had loved to hear him play; the Larkin desk with all the pigeonholes and the shelves below where he had kept his toys and books and striped bags of candy behind a flowered curtain . . . But his mother had said the sitting-room furniture was not worth moving; that she would be ashamed for village people to see it; that there was no place to store it in the new house.

The living room had three windows side by side. They filled one whole end. He turned his back on the room and stood looking out at the sidewalk and the street. Cars were coming and going. People he did not know went by without turning their faces. A boy he had seen at school — an older boy — sat on the railing of the porch across the way. He wore a cap with a visor and earlappers. He stared at the house where Johnny was and suddenly caught sight of Johnny. He looked surprised. He gave a shout and another boy came running from a vacant lot. They scooped up snow and made two hard balls which they threw with deadly aim. The balls came splat! splat! against the window before Johnny's face. The snow was wet, and stuck there.

He blinked, but did not move. He stood, impaled on his own fear, between the snow-covered glass and the ghosts of the front-room furniture haunting the emptiness behind him.

Then his mother called, "Johnny! Dinner's ready! Your father hasn't come yet, but we might as well eat."

He wheeled blindly, and ran.

She was by the stove in the kitchen.

It was a small white stove, not a big black stove. No fire crackled in it. But she was there. The same teakettle sang. There was the same smell of crisping bacon, of toasting bread, of cheese and apples. Deirdre was pounding on her highchair tray with her spoon as she always did at meal time.

Johnny's breath came more evenly.

He slid into his chair at the table and felt the warmth of his mother's body as she reached across his shoulder to put a glass of milk beside his plate. His own pink glass. He liked pink glass. It made the milk look rosy.

He smiled up at his mother.

"Gee, Mum," he said. "I bet you're tired."

"Don't mention it," she said. "There's still so much to do I don't know which way to turn."

She pulled Deirdre's chair up beside hers and gave Deirdre a piece of toast, a strip of bacon.

She sat with her right arm resting on the back of Deirdre's chair, and lifted her tea cup wearily with her left hand.

Johnny thought her arm looked very soft. He would have liked to lean his head against it, to rub his cheek against it. He wondered that Deirdre chewed her bacon absorbedly, unaware of her mother's nearness.

"I don't know what's taking your father so long," Marge said.

"I guess," Johnny ventured, "he'll be here anytime now."

"Yes, and then we'll have to start on the living room. I hope we can get the pictures hung. I want to get the curtains up. Somebody might call tomorrow. People do that in town when new folks move in. I wish I had new curtains. But the old ones looked fairly good after I did them up. I mended two or three places. Just small ones. They probably won't show. I'm afraid they're a mite short for those windows, though . . ."

He loved to hear her voice. He loved the way it ran on and on, as if she were thinking aloud. Sometimes he suspected that his father tired of it, but he never did. It flowed smoothly, like a small, quiet river. If only he could always hear it! If only . . . If only it would come closer! . . . If only he could feel it laving his feet, his back, his chest, his shoulders as it had when she gave him his baths! It had not seemed to him then that she bathed him with water from the tank at the end of the stove, but with her soft voice and with something crystal clean and heavenly sweet-smelling which flowed from herself . . .

Suddenly — it seemed sudden to Johnny because he had not been following her words but her tone — she said:

"Isn't it time for your report card?"

He looked at his plate, surprised to find it empty of all she had put on it, and nodded slowly.

"I thought you always got it a week before vacation."

He did. And he had got it yesterday. He and Linda had stood together in the woods, looking at the two yellow cards marked off in little squares. Linda had two E's for Excellent and all the rest G's for Good. E's and G's were beautiful letters, the way Miss Besse made them. He was proud of Linda's beautiful card. He had put his arm around her and said, "Gee, Linda, you're smart."

Linda had looked at the letters on his card and shaken her head.

"You're smarter'n I am," she had said. "Miss Besse's mean. Never mind, Johnny. Next year we'll have Mrs. Curtis. Everybody says she's nice. If only she don't resign. I guess she's getting pretty old . . ."

"Johnny!" his mother exclaimed. "You haven't lost that card, have you?"

He wished he had. He wished it had been dropped into the grotto. There the winter fairy would have brushed it with magic and turned all the letters into E's. It would have become so beautiful that she would have laughed aloud, and they would have hung it on their shining wall to look at and to admire forever.

"Johnny?"

"No'm. It's — I guess it's in my jacket pocket."

"Well, go get it this minute. It makes a terrible lot of work for the teacher if a card is lost, and with the way everything has been turned upside down —"

Johnny looked about the strange room. In the kitchen at home his jacket had always hung on a hook behind the stove.

"I don't know where my jacket is."

"Oh, for goodness' sake! It ought to be in the coat closet!"

But it wasn't. They hunted a long time for the jacket. It seemed to Marge that Johnny looked for it only in the middle of the floor. Finally she pulled it out from a pile of patchwork quilts.

"There. Here it is. Damp, too. I suppose it's dampened the bedding. I'll have to air the quilts now, before I put them away . . . Oh, dear, Johnny, here are two dirty handkerchiefs. Awfully dirty handkerchiefs. One of them smells sour. What in the world . . . And here's your card, all curled up. I declare, Johnny Lee, you don't seem to —"

He saw the pupils of her eyes focussing on the small squares. Reading . . . Spelling . . . Music . . . History . . . Arithmetic . . . Effort . . . School Citizenship . . . Days Absent . . . Days Tardy . . .

At least, for the first time, he had not been absent.

He said, "I didn't miss a day. Did I, Mum? And I wasn't ever late!"

"You can't be late if you catch the bus," she said irritably. "And the bus waits for you!"

She sighed.

"No, and you didn't miss. I saw to that. Mr. Sturtevant said if you didn't stay out your marks would be better. They aren't a bit better. They're — why, they're just exactly the same as last time. Not one single E . . . Only one G, and that's in music . . . All the rest F's, even in reading. In the summer your father says you always have your nose stuck in a book, and in school you get F in reading! F in effort, too . . . There, Johnny. There's the answer right there. You don't try, at school. Do you, Johnny? You don't try; do you?"

Do you . . . You don't try, do you . . . Do you . . . You don't try, do you . . .

"Johnny?"

". . . I don't know."

"You don't know! You don't even know whether you try or not! Well, I can tell you I know I try, and I know your father tries. We've tried all our lives, at school and since we couldn't go to school anymore. We're trying to give you chances we never had. We've sold the farm — and your father loved that place — so you could live in town and learn nice ways to act and ride a bicycle and go to movies and get an education. Sometimes I've thought you might go to college. Mr. Sturtevant says the tests showed you could! But if you keep on this way, you won't even pass in high school. If you won't even try —"

Tears of disappointment and helplessness came into her

eyes. She whirled and turned a faucet. The water gushed out of it, icy cold. She splashed it over her face and groped for a towel. She turned another faucet and the water ran warm. It was almost as magical as anything a winter fairy could do. She wet a cloth and came back to the table to wipe Deirdre's face and hands. She bent and kissed the top of Deirdre's head.

"Mum," Johnny said hoarsely.

She did not answer.

"Mum . . . Could I go to the show?"

She glared around at him.

She said, "The show? No, you may NOT! I'm going to write out some words and give you a pencil and paper and set up the card table in the dining room, and you're going to write nice and spell right before you're through or I'll know the reason why. Now hang your jacket in the closet where it belongs."

He took his jacket and hung it up, but it did not look as if it belonged there.

When he came back into the kitchen, his mother was writing at the table. The point of her pencil was sharp. He could hear it cutting into the yellow paper as she wrote. She wrote across the top of eight lined sheets.

"Now," she said, at last. "Take these, and copy every one times enough to fill the page. When you're through, I'll look at them. If they're not written nice, you can just do them over. Then I'll hear you spell the words."

He took the papers into the dining room.

His mother's writing was very round and plain. It was almost as beautiful as Miss Besse's.

A boy must try to do well.

I go to school to study.

My teacher helps me all she can.

My mother wants me to try hard.

My father is very good to me.

Christmas is a week from Sunday.

I have a little sister.

We have come to live in town.

They were not long sentences. There were no hard words in them. He did not know why they made him want to cry.

After a while he lapped his pencil and began to write.

A boy must try to do well. A boy must try to do well. A boy must try to do well . . .

A truck stopped before the door. The engine raced. His father and another man began bringing in the front-room furniture. They stamped the snow off their feet. They talked and laughed and swore. They paid no attention to Johnny.

A boy must try to do well. A boy must try to do well.

They had been back to the farm. They could go back to the farm because they were big and strong. Johnny could not go back to the farm.

A boy must try to do well. A boy must try to do well.

The farm was sold. The house was sold. The kitchen was gone. The grotto was buried deep under snow. The winter fairy was safe inside, but she was alone. Nobody came to her. Nobody knocked at her door. She sang a sad song, like Redwing.

A boy must try to do well. A boy must try to do well.

When all the furniture was unloaded, and his father had thanked the neighbor and the neighbor had gone home, his mother came through the room with Deirdre in her arms. She did not look at Johnny.

My mother wants me to try hard. My mother wants me to try hard. My mother wants me to try hard.

She stood between the empty dining room and the crowded living room, patting Deirdre's back and talking to his father.

"Well, that's a good forenoon's work. That's all of it, isn't it? Lucky we had good weather today. The sofa fits fine under the windows, doesn't it? I thought it would.

Well, now, Jack, you must be starved. Come on out and eat. I just made fresh coffee. I'll have a cup with you, soon as Deir's tucked in bed."

My mother wants me to try hard. My mother wants me to try hard.

"I've accomplished a lot too. The dishes are all out of the barrels and on the shelves. After you've eaten I'll clean up. It's just nothing to get a meal on an electric stove and wash up with running hot and cold water. Honestly, Jack, I didn't realize — and Deir had such fun in the bathtub this morning. I really think she was swimming. You ought to have seen her. You will tomorrow."

My mother wants me to try hard. My mother wants me to try hard.

She hurried back through the dining room. His father followed her, pulling off his gloves.

"What you doing, Johnny?" his father asked. "Why don't you get outdoors, a nice winter day like this? Afraid somebody'll throw a snowball at you?"

Did he know?

"He's staying in," his mother called crisply from the kitchen, "because I told him to. He's going to learn to write, and he's going to learn to spell. He's got his report card, and it's all F's again. Except in music."

"Can't he learn to write and spell in five days a week," his father asked, "and learn something else on Saturdays?"

But he had gone on into the kitchen and was washing in the warm water which ran so richly from the faucet into the stainless steel sink.

My father is very good to me. My father is very good to me. My father is very good to me . . .

I go to school to study . . .

My teacher helps me all she can . . .

I have a little sister . . .

We have come to live in town . . .

Dierdre had her nap. His father finished his dinner and

they talked and laughed over the coffee cups. They did the dishes together and Marge did not worry for fear Jack would break any of them. Or, if she did, she did not say so, for if she had, he would have stopped drying them. They talked about how good Mr. Schultz had been to help with the heavy moving and not to take a cent in pay. They thought the Schultzes would be fine neighbors. Marge hoped Mrs. Schultz would come to call as soon as the living-room curtains were hung. Mr. Schultz had told Jack he had a boy, Kenny, about Johnny's age. Jack said he was relieved that Johnny was where he could play with boys like Mr. Schultz's son. Too many country boys nowadays were like Bill Sudbury's. A different class lived in the country now than had when Jack was growing up.

Johnny was still writing.

They talked about how cheaply they had managed the moving and how they would earn and save the money to make up the difference between what the farm had brought and what they had paid for this house. Jack said he thought they would have the mortgage cleaned up in a year's time. He reminded Marge of the double garage they had here, and they planned the advertisement they would put in the village paper. Jack said they ought to get ten dollars a month from somebody who needed a place to keep his car.

Marge said. "Every little bit helps, doesn't it? Now let's see if we can get that living room in shape. Oh, Jack, we might be all settled before dark!"

She squeezed his hand. Their two hands were still together when they came through the room where Johnny sat writing.

We have come to live in town. We have come to live in town.

"Of course, it's partly because we haven't much to settle. It'll be a long time before we can afford a dining-room set."

"I'll tell you what, Marge. You can have what we get from renting the garage for your dining-room set."

"Jack! You mean it?"

Jack was feeling fine.

"Why not?"

"Don't you need it for the mortgage?"

"Hundred and twenty dollars would buy the set, wouldn't it? It wouldn't make much of a dent in the mortgage. Heck, no; I'll take care of the mortgage by another Christmas. You rent your garage and get your dining-room set."

"Jack, you darling!"

She hugged him.

Jack looked sheepishly over her head at his son.

" 'Most done, Johnny?"

Johnny shook his head.

"Can't you let him off, Marge? He ought to be outdoors. Come on. It's Saturday. Give him a break."

"We-ell," his mother said, turning her head, her cheek against his father's shoulder.

"I want to finish," Johnny said quickly, urgently. "I don't want to go out, Mum. I'm writing it nice. I'll finish pretty soon. Then you can hear me spell."

"Why, he's really trying, Jack," his mother said proudly. "Leave him alone. He's a good boy."

She pulled his ear gently as she passed on her way to the living room. She looked down at the spread papers.

My teacher helps me all she can. My teacher helps me all she can.

"It's nice writing," she said. "It's real nice writing. Look, Jack!"

"Hm. Good enough. Better than I could do. What does he need to be such a blamed good writer for?"

"So he'll get E in it on his next report card," his mother beamed. "So he'll be on the honor roll and go up to high school with his class."

"Then they'll teach him to use a typewriter, won't

they?" his father asked. "And he'll never write more than
his name again. What the sense of it is beats me. But if he
wants to —"

His mother patted Johnny's shoulder.

"Funny boy," she said. "You've done a few lines on
every sheet, and you haven't finished any of them. What
kind of a way to do is that?"

"I will," he said. "I'm going to."

" 'Course you are."

She went on into the next room.

He wanted to write fast, so that she would come back
to hear him spell. But he could not write fast, because he
must write beautifully.

My mother wants me to try hard. My mother wants me
to try hard.

We have come to live in town. We have come to live in
town.

Johnny called, "Mum!"

They did not hear him. They were putting up picture
hooks.

"Mum!"

"What is it?"

"I thought of something."

"What?"

"If you've got to wait a whole year for the dining-room
set, why don't Daddy bring down the things from the sitting room to put in here?"

"Oh . . . I don't want them, Johnny."

"Just until you get the set, I mean."

"Oh, no. We don't want that old stuff in a nice house
like this. I'd rather go without till I can have what's right.
I'll tell you what I thought, Jack. We can buy another
card table. They don't cost much and they always come
in handy. Then if we want company to a meal, I could
serve it on the two card tables in front of the fireplace
here. Lots of people do that way. I've read about it in the
magazines. Even people that have dining-room furniture."

"Okay by me. As long as we eat, I don't care where we eat. What next?"

"Let's see how the curtains look. They're in that suit box."

We have come to live in town. We have come to live in town. We have come to live in town.

Johnny kept on writing for a long time. He had still not finished when the doorbell rang.

"Goodness!" his mother exclaimed. "Callers already? You go to the door, Jack, while I run fix myself a little."

She fluttered through the room where Johnny sat.

His father opened the door and a deep, pleasant voice said, "How do you do? Is this Mr. Lee? I'm Howard Shawn. Pastor of the Methodist Church."

"Oh, yes. Well, come in, Reverend. Come in."

They went into the living room.

"Just moved to town, have you, Mr. Lee?"

"Into the village, yes. I've always lived in the town. And my folks before me. On a farm up back here. About four miles."

"That's what I heard. I'm new in town myself. This is my first pastorate, as a matter of fact. I only graduated from the seminary last June."

"That so? Thought you looked like a young feller."

"Shouldn't wonder if we're about the same age."

"No. No, I'll never see thirty again."

"Is that a fact? Why, I was just thinking you couldn't be the Jack Lee I'd heard about. Jack Lee who had a son in our primary department."

Johnny's mother went quietly through the room where Johnny sat writing. She had brushed her hair out. It glistened. She had put pink color on her mouth. She was smiling a little.

"This is my wife," Jack said.

"How do you do, Mrs. Lee. I'm Howard Shawn of the Methodist Church —"

"Oh, how do you do, Mr. Shawn! Didn't Jack take your hat? Here, let me. And your coat, too; or you won't feel it when you go out —"

"I'll only stop a minute. Moving day is a busy day."

"Oh, we're just enjoying it. You'll excuse our not being all settled, won't you? It's nice of you to call so promptly on newcomers."

"Well, I know how it is. I'm a newcomer too."

They all laughed. It sounded bright and cosy. Johnny could not see them, but he could hear them.

Christmas is a week from Sunday. Christmas is a week from Sunday. Christmas —

"Is your son at home?"

"Johnny? Yes. He's — studying."

"Studying on Saturday? That's unusual. I hoped he would be here. I wanted to meet him. He is on our Sunday-school roll. I suppose he hasn't been able to get there since the churches gave up sending buses into outlying districts. But he's still our boy, and I hope that now he has come within easy walking distance of us, we'll see him often."

"Well, I hope so, I'm sure. I don't know. He hasn't spoken of it. I know he did go to the Methodist quite a while, and then he changed over to the Baptist, because that was where the little girl he played with went. Children are like that, I guess. But since they stopped sending the bus he hasn't been anywhere."

Jack said, "There's an awful lot to do on a farm Sundays, when a man works away the rest of the week."

"I don't doubt that. Now things ought to be a little easier. Maybe we'll see you all at church tomorrow."

"Well, not tomorrow, I guess. I have to stay with the baby, and Jack's got to haul some wood before he gets back to work Monday."

"I take it you're planning to light up this nice little fireplace. I love an open fire. It's a real inspiration . . .

Could you get Johnny to leave his books and come in for a minute, I wonder?"

"Why, of course."

Johnny's mother came to the dining-room door. She smiled and held out her hand.

"The minister wants to see you, sonny," she said.

She waited until he reached her and drew him into the living room with her arm across his shoulders. Johnny felt like a bird in a nest.

He blinked.

The late afternoon sunshine was streaming in. The front-room furniture was not covered with sheets. He had always thought the upholstery of the sofa and the two big chairs was dark blue, but it was quite a bright blue, and velvety flowers like small daisies stood out all over them. The curtains were milk-white and stiffly starched. There was a white lace runner on the long table. A rug he had never seen lay before the fireplace. It had a dog on it. A curly brown dog with floppy ears.

The man sitting on one end of the sofa, with a soft black hat on his knees, was young and his hair was red.

"This is Johnny, Mr. Shawn," his mother said.

"Hello, Johnny. I've been wanting to meet you. I'm new at the Methodist church, and you used to come there to Sunday school, didn't you?"

Johnny cleared his throat.

"Sometimes," he said carefully.

Mr. Shawn was leaning toward him. He was smiling. There was nothing but friendliness in his face.

"Yes. That's what I heard. You came pretty regularly for a year or more, didn't you?"

"I guess so."

"Well, I just wanted you to know that we're glad you've come to town to live. If you want to go somewhere else to Sunday school, that's fine. I just hope you'll go somewhere to Sunday school tomorrow. It's a pretty nice place to be on Sunday morning, isn't it? Our Sunday school begins at eleven, when the grown-ups have their service upstairs. I think the Baptist Sunday school is at twelve after the morning service. Both places the children sit together and sing and then somebody plays the piano for our children to march off to their different classrooms. I imagine they do the same at the Baptist church, don't they?"

"Yes, sir."

"You like to sing and march?"

"Yes, sir."

"Johnny loves music," said his mother proudly. "He gets G in music at school all the time."

"Well, that's pretty fine. I'll bet he has a good voice to sing, hasn't he? What do you say, Johnny, if we try to get your mother to play something you can sing?"

"Goodness," his mother said, pleased. "I haven't had any time to practice since Deir was born. I don't know how the old organ stood the trip, either. But I guess I can play any hymn that doesn't have more than two sharps or four flats. What do you want to sing for Mr. Shawn, Johnny?"

"I don't know. I can't sing very good."

His mother laughed.

"He's shy," she said.

"Most people are, about singing alone," said Mr. Shawn. "I am myself. But I love to sing."

He was over by the organ, looking through the hymn book. Johnny's mother was on the stool with her hands folded in her lap.

Johnny was by the door, alone.

Mr. Shawn looked over the edge of the book. His eyes were as blue as the upholstery.

"Johnny," he said, "do you suppose your father could stand it if you and I sung 'Faith of Our Fathers'? You know that, don't you? The tune anyway?"

Johnny nodded.

"Sure. Go ahead," Jack said. "I like singing. Always did."

"The words are kind of hard," said Mr. Shawn. "Any we can't pronounce we'll just skim over."

He was holding out his hand to Johnny as his mother had in the dining room. When Johnny was beside him, he too put his arm around Johnny. It felt different from his mother's, but in some ways better. Now he was between the two of them.

> *Faith of our fathers, living still*
> *In spite of dungeon, fire and sword,*
> *O how our hearts beat high with joy*
> *Whene'er we hear that glorious word . . .*

The minister's voice rang out triumphantly. Johnny's trembled. At the end of the first chorus Mr. Shawn drew Johnny hard against him for an instant, sharing his strength, his triumph over dungeon, fire and sword . . .

In the second verse, Mr. Shawn sang more softly, Johnny more steadily.

> *. . . And through the truth that comes from God*
> *Mankind shall then indeed be free.*

This time Mr. Shawn's pressure was gentler, briefer, as if he sensed that Johnny now had what he needed, and was set free.

The last verse Johnny sang alone, in a clear, pure soprano.

> *Faith of our fathers, we will love*
> *Both friend and foe in all our strife*
> *And preach thee, too, as love knows how*
> *By kindly word and virtuous life . . .*

Mr. Shawn came in with the bass on the final chorus, accompanying Johnny, the two of them not quite touching, each standing straight and at his full height, but still together.

As Marge took her hands reluctantly from the smooth old keys, Jack said, "Well, what was the matter with that?"

Mr. Shawn was looking down at Johnny in gentle amazement.

"This boy," he said, and stopped. "This boy has a fine voice. Fine feeling, too. And he read every one of those big words as well as I could. That's remarkable for a third-grader. You must be very proud of this youngster."

"Well," his mother said, "of course we are." But she was embarrassed. She stood up from the stool. "We've got a nice baby girl, too, Mr. Shawn. I hear her waking up now. You sit down and I'll bring her down to show you."

I have a little sister. I have a little sister.

"I'm afraid I have to go, Mrs. Lee," said Mr. Shawn, looking at his watch. "My wife is entertaining the other ministers and their wives at dinner tonight. She'll want me there a little early. I'll call again soon, and see the baby then. I like babies, but, to tell the truth, I'm more interested in boys. Especially boys like yours. Good-bye, Mrs. Lee. Good-bye, Mr. Lee. You've got a nice place here. . . . Good-bye, Johnny. Thanks for singing with me. There's a lot in that hymn, isn't there? You'll be singing in some Sunday school tomorrow, won't you?"

"Sure," Johnny said. "In yours. I'll come to yours."

"You will? Well, it's up to you, son. But we'd be mighty glad to have you."

He went down the little path, putting on his hat. As he reached the sidewalk he turned and saw Johnny still standing in the doorway. He smiled and swung his hand.

"Good-bye, Johnny," he said again. "See you tomorrow."

"Shut the door, Johnny," his mother called. "Before I bring Deir downstairs. You're letting cold in."

He closed it slowly, and went back into the living room.

Surely it would not still look as it had when Mr. Shawn was in it.

But it did. The upholstery waved its velvety blue daisies. The curtains and the lace were milk-white. The hymn book lay open to "Faith of Our Fathers." The organ keys looked warm from his mother's hands. The ears of the dog on the rug seemed to twitch. Indeed, Mr. Shawn seemed to be there. At least, though the sun had gone down, there was still a radiance in the room.

Was that faith the faith of Johnny's father?

"Tell you what, son," his father said, "let's surprise the womenfolks. Let's have a fire here when they come downstairs. I brought a few birch sticks and some kindling on the load this morning. It's in a box in the bottom of the closet."

"Okay," Johnny cried. "Okay, Dad!"

He brought the box. He knelt beside the dog on the rug, careful not to pinch the floppy ear. He twisted paper as his father was doing to make a small flat heap in the center of the bricks, and placed the kindling crisscross of the paper, watched his father lay on a small, speckled log and scratch a match on the sole of his shoe.

The flame sprang up, spread softly through the paper, clung to the kindling, and crackled over the birch bark.

"Nothing like a wood fire," said his father, putting the box away.

"No," said Johnny, on his knees.

"You can't beat it," said his father, coming back and sitting down to light his pipe, "With oil, nor coal, nor anything else."

"No," said Johnny. "I don't think so either, Dad."

"It's got a good sound to it. Like it means business."

"Like popcorn," said Johnny. "Like when we were blocked in with snow up home. And you'd get the popper from the shed chamber. Did we bring our popper?"

"I don't know's we did. I'll have to look for it tomorrow when I go up for the wood."

"You'd better. That's a good popper. Can I go with you when you go up tomorrow?"

"Depends on when I go. If I have to go in the morning, you'll be in Sunday school, won't you? Or won't you?"

Jack's eyes twinkled. Johnny knew his father did not hold much with churches.

But Johnny said, "Yeah. I guess I will."

He wanted to go to the farm, but not as much as he had this morning. He wanted more to go to Sunday school. Mr. Shawn's Sunday school.

His mother came down with Dierdre, and they were both surprised to see the fire. Deirdre crowed and kept creeping toward it. Her mother sat down on the floor to see that she did not creep too close. It was nearly dark now, outside, but in the new living room the fire crackled and sang and made all their faces rosy with its heat and light.

"Now this," said Jack, "is solid comfort."

"My supper's cooking while we sit here," said Marge contentedly. "And you don't have to think of going out to do chores . . . Mr. Shawn was real nice, wasn't he?"

"Pretty good joe," Jack said, "for a minister."

Johnny waited to see if they would say anything about the singing.

But just then Deirdre said, "Go home now. Go ride. Bye-bye, Daddy. Deedy bye-bye now."

She pulled herself up by her father's knee.

"No, ma'am," he said. "No bye-bye tonight. Daddy's got his slippers on."

She looked at his shoes, puzzled. She looked searchingly into his face.

"Go home," she said distinctly. "Go ride, Daddy. Go home. Deedy home."

"Ride on my knee," he said, and put her there, bouncing her up and down.

But she pulled away from him and slid to the floor. She began to cry and crept swiftly toward her mother.

"Mum-Mum! Deedy home! Deedy home!"

"I declare, Jack," her mother exclaimed, "do you suppose she honestly — where's Teddy, Deir? Where's your Teddy, sweetie-pie? Here's Teddy!"

Deirdre pushed the Teddy bear away, and dragged at her mother's arm, crying.

"Ho-ome! Deedy home. Bye-bye now."

Her mother tried to cuddle her, but Deidre kept on crying.

"Come over and look out our nice windows, honey. See the lights? See the pretty lights?"

"Dark," sobbed Deirdre. "All dark. Home now. Go home."

"Turn on the lights, Jack."

The lights in the room flashed on.

Johnny blinked.

"Dark now," sobbed Deirdre. "Go home, Go home. Deedy home."

"Well!" her mother said. "I don't know what to do with her. She'll just have to get over it. I've got supper to take up. You two see she keeps away from the fire."

Jack put a chair on its side across the front of the hearth.

"You watch her, Johnny," he said.

He followed Marge into the kitchen, closing the door behind him. He liked to see her taking up a meal.

Crying, Deirdre crept to the door and pounded on it.

"Daddy! . . . Mum-Mum! Deedy — go — home — now!"

"Why, Deedy!" Johnny said.

She looked at him in surprise. He knew how she felt. She had thought she was alone.

"You said a whole sentence," he told her. "A whole great big sentence. All yourself."

She stopped crying, but her underlip was still thrust out.

She said doubtfully, "All dark, D'onny! Go home!"

He nodded, holding out his hand to her as Mr. Shawn had to him.

"Sure it's dark," he said. " 'Most suppertime. Mum's getting supper. 'Most time for Deedy to go to sleep. Deedy's bed is upstairs. Right upstairs. Right upstairs. So is Mum's and Daddy's. So is D'onny's."

She came and leaned against him, as he had against Mr. Shawn. He held her tight.

He said, "In this home we've got a doggy. See our doggy. Here's his tail. Here's his ears. Here's his mouth. Deedy pat the doggy's paws."

She patted with one hand, clinging to Johnny's shoulder with the other.

"D'onny home?" she asked.

"Sure. I'm home. Deedy's home. Doggy's home. Want D'onny to sing to you, Deedy?"

"D'onny sing."

She crept into his lap. He could feel her breathing against him. He held her foot in his hand. He sang the last verse because he liked the last verse best.

> *Faith of our fathers, we will love*
> *Both friend and foe in all our strife*
> *And preach thee, too, as love knows how*
> *By kindly word and virtuous life* . . .

He sang it over and over.

When their mother opened the door she called softly: "Jack. I want you to look here. Isn't that a picture?" Their father, across her shoulder, said, "Quite a picture."

Johnny smiled at them. Deedy crept toward them. Her mother caught her up.

"All happy now, precious? You had a nice time with Big Brother? Well, now come have your supper. I'll bet you're hungry."

"Bet Big Brother's hungry too," his father said.

And Johnny was. He suddenly realized that he had

never been so hungry. He ate enormously. His mother said she did not know where he put it all. His father said boys had places.

While his mother was putting Deedy to bed, he finished writing his sentences.

I have a little sister. I have a little sister.

We have come to live in town. We have come to live in town.

It was not hard to write them now. It was easy. Almost too easy. Perhaps he was not writing well enough. He tried to draw each letter as if it were a picture.

Christmas is a week from Sunday. Christmas is a week from Sunday.

Why, that was not a long time. A week from tomorrow. Tomorrow he would go to Sunday school. Then in a week it would be Christmas Day. He began to wonder what he would get for Christmas. He had not thought of it before. It did not matter how expensive bicycles were. He did not want a bicycle.

When his mother came downstairs he showed her the papers.

She said, "Johnny, they look fine. You were good to go back and finish them. It was a big job for you to do. Maybe I shouldn't have given you so much."

"Aw, it wasn't much," he boasted. "I can write good now, can't I, Mum?"

"I call it very nice writing," she said, "for a boy nine years old. Don't you, Jack?"

"For nine — or ninety," his father stated, after one quick glance.

"Now hear me spell, Mum?"

"Well — I ought to do the dishes next."

"Oh, hear him spell," his father said. "And have it over with. We'll do the dishes after he's in bed."

So she asked him to spell boy, must, try, well, go, all, hard, very, good, week, come, and live. Then she asked him to spell school, study, teacher, mother, father, little, sister, and town. Even Christmas and Sunday. And he spelled every one right the first time, not forgetting capitals.

"Well, Johnny Lee!" she exclaimed. "I think that's wonderful. I don't believe but Miss Besse would too. You see, you can do it if you try, can't you? After this, will you try at school, too, Johnny?"

He nodded.

My mother wants me to try hard.

He had tried, but he would try again. Maybe it would work. Anyway he would try again.

. . . In spite of dungeon, fire, and sword . . .

Sunday:

It was certainly going to be a white Christmas.

It had snowed heavily in the night, but the big snowplow had been out before daybreak, clearing the streets, and before nine o'clock the sidewalk plow had gone through the village. The pattern was that of a broad band of Hamburg insertion, and two narrow bands, all separated by ruffles of lace, running around the hem of the smooth white cambric petticoat which was the lawns before the houses and the outlying fields which narrowed with distance as if fitted to a woman's waist.

Johnny's father, used to waking early, had finished breaking his path before the sidewalk plow went past, and was there, leaning on his shovel, to wave and grin at the driver and shout, "What did you do, oversleep?"

Johnny, at the window, had seen and heard him.

He wished then that he had not had to take a bath. He wished he had been dressed and down there, to shovel and wave and grin with his father. But his mother had said the snow was too heavy for him; and besides, he had to get ready for Sunday school.

It was still snowing when Johnny left the house, but it did not seem like a stormy day. The sun was not far behind the clouds. Big soft white flakes drifted down through a haze of the faintest possible shade of lemon color. It was not cold, and there was no wind. Great masses of the night's snow clung to the edges of house and garage roofs like the loose folds of warm shawls, and sometimes slid off as ladies might drop them, with grace and luxurious abandon. The spruce and cedar trees in dooryards were decorated for Christmas with a triangle of silver crowning each branch and every tip punctuated by a slender icicle.

Johnny walked fast at first but when he found there was no one else but him the whole length of the street, he moved more and more slowly.

Everything was so still. Everything was so big. And all the bigness was so peaceful.

He could even stare at the houses because no one seemed to be awake in any of them. Smoke came curling out of their chimneys and turned dark gold in the lemon-yellow air. The windows looked at without seeing him. The doors were like quiet mouths. He walked slowly along a narrow band of Hamburg insertion, sometimes stopping to touch the lace with his mitten or to catch a falling flake and see how long it would live with him. When it died, it seemed to go with pleasure and he closed his hand over its going, feeling it melt sweetly into the palm of his hand. He thought God must do that for people when they went — look down at them with tenderness, wait a little in interest and pity because they did not know what He was going to do, and then close His hand over them gently, taking them into Himself.

The church bells began to ring at each end of the village. The first peal was soft, like a mother speaking to wake her child. The next was louder. The two tones ran to meet each other, and blended.

It was like Mr. Shawn and Johnny singing together.

Louder . . . Louder . . . Louder. Loud and strong and true.

Now it was God calling. The village was shaken by the reverberation. Johnny was alone in a strange new country, but it was a friendly country. He was not afraid. He answered.

He tipped his head back, letting the snowflakes fall on his lips and nose and eyes, and, looking up through them, said cheerfully, "Good morning, God!"

He heard doors opening behind him, but he was ahead. He had reached the Square.

To the right he saw the tall, gilded spire of the Baptist church where he had gone several times with Linda, but it meant nothing to him now. Linda would not be there. Linda was far away in her grotto.

To the left was the square bell tower of the Methodist church. That was where he had gone a great many times long ago, and had felt lost and lonely. But it would not be like that today because Mr. Shawn was there. And now he had God.

Johnny turned left.

He passed the post office. Its green shades were drawn. He passed the stores, the bank; all closed. He passed the school, but he did not look at it. He did not have to go to school today. Today he was going to church. Mr. Shawn was there, and God was going with Johnny. Perhaps He would come back with Johnny too, and stay to go to school with him tomorrow. That should make a great difference. He had never been there before; or if He had, Johnny had not known it.

" 'We have come to live in town,' " thought Johnny, writing the words on the seam of his trousers. "This is my town now."

He walked along confidently and when he came to the church did not hesitate, but went straight in at the big door.

Mr. Shawn stood just inside, as Johnny had known he would.

A light broke quickly over his face. His hair gleamed

like the living-room fire. He held out his big, warm hand.

"Good morning, Johnny!"

It was as if God replied to Johnny's greeting in a glad voice.

"You're early. I believe you're the first one here for Sunday school. That's good, too, because I can go with you to your teacher."

They started down the vestry stairs together.

"I'll tell you what I've made up my mind, Johnny. After hearing you sing yesterday, I think you should be in Mrs. Curtis's class. Maybe you won't know many of the boys in that class, because she has the ones who are in the fourth grade at school, and I believe you're in the third, aren't you? But you read so well, I think you will be more interested in what Mrs. Curtis's class is doing than you would be in Miss Kimball's group where you used to be. And you'll soon get acquainted, son . . . Oh, there you are, Mrs. Curtis. This is Johnny Lee. He would like to join your class today."

Johnny looked at Mrs. Curtis's blue serge skirt. It was broad and long.

"That's fine," said a quick voice. "Glad to have you, Johnny. I think I've seen you at school."

"Yes'm," said Johnny. "I'm in — Miss Besse's room."

He thought perhaps he was going to be sick. He had the same feeling he had on school-day mornings. He had heard Mrs. Curtis's voice on the playground and in the halls.

"Step lively there, children." . . . "Come, come, now, David! You know you're not allowed on those steps!" . . . "Nancy, keep on your own side!"

He had seen Mrs. Curtis through the glass door of the fourth-grade room. She was always very busy. She took quick steps, for such a big woman. Everything about her was quick. Even her eyes snapped. It was much quieter next door than it was in Miss Besse's room. He remembered that Linda had said Mrs. Curtis was nice, but he had often wondered what Mrs. Curtis did to make people in the fourth grade so quiet. A boy had told him once that she kept a strap in the closet, and that was why she never sent people to the principal as other teachers did.

"But he reads better than most third-graders," Mr. Shawn was saying. "I think he would like that project your class is working on, Mrs. Curtis. And he has a remarkable voice for singing."

"Well," said Mrs. Curtis, "we'll be glad to give him a try. We certainly need a good singer. Our row usually sounds like a flock of crows, and I caw worse than anybody."

Mr. Shawn laughed.

"Well, I'll leave Johnny with you then," he said, "and get about my business upstairs. I hope you'll enjoy yourself, son. In fact, I know you will."

Johnny was alone with Mrs. Curtis.

"We might as well sit down," she said briskly, "and rest our feet and hands. Some of the rest of my boys are coming downstairs now. I'll know the sound of their steps when they're tramping over my grave. Every blessed one of them. This is our row, Johnny. Take up all the room you can. Looks better. Class will probably be small today. Snowballing's good."

She pushed him ahead of her and settled herself, opening her fur collar, straightening the seams of her gloves, fixing her hat with quick motions.

Following her hands, he stole a glance at her face. It looked exactly as it did through the glass door at school.

She bent sidewise toward him, keeping her eyes front, and whispered, "Am I all right, Johnny? Do I look as if I'd hold together till meeting's over?"

"You look nice," he whispered back. "You look awful nice."

He was surprised. She did look nice.

"Flatterer!" she scoffed.

Her eyes snapped. She reached briskly for hymn books

and passed them to boys pushing past her or coming in from the other side.

"Get ready," she told him. "In a minute here we're going to sing. We're going to sing like sixty."

Two or three boys tried to sit down between Johnny and Mrs. Curtis but she did not make room for them.

"Move along," she said. "Move along."

The row filled up. Soon it had all it would hold. They were all squeezed together.

Johnny had never seen before the boy who sat beside him; a tall boy with sandy hair and glasses who said nothing and kept his eyes on the hymn book. From three seats down the boys who had thrown the snowballs from across the street the day before bent forward to stare at Johnny. One of them demanded, "What you doin' here?"

Johnny did not answer. His shoulder was behind Mrs. Curtis's shoulder.

She answered for him.

She said, "Sit up straight, Wally Stewart. You'll grow taller. Quiet now, everybody. Mr. Richmond is about to begin."

Out of the corner of her mouth she whispered to Johnny, "Can you breathe? I'm just like the old woman in the shoe, here. Only I hope she wasn't as fat as I am." She added, "Keep quiet, Almira Curtis!"

Johnny giggled, and she said, "Sh-h-h," quite loudly, with her eyes fixed on the old man who stood now on the platform.

Upstairs the organ was playing. It sounded far away and majestic. It sounded as if God had withdrawn to his heaven, where all was right and beautiful, but rather too grand for a small boy. God and Mr. Shawn had left Johnny with Mrs. Curtis who was big and quick and snappy eyed and could make Johnny laugh.

"We'll open our program this morning," said Mr. Richmond, "ahem — by singing Number 148. Shall we all stand?"

They stood. Mrs. Curtis held one corner of a hymn book and Johnny held the other.

"Sing loud," she whispered. "Drown me out."

He threw his head back and sang loud.

He looked across the aisle at the boys sitting where he used to sit, with Miss Kimball. There were only three and he knew all of them. They were in Miss Besse's room at school. Kenny Schultz, Pete Barker, and Tarb MacDonald. They were taking pokes at one another. Miss Kimball moved in between Pete and Tarb. A minute later she reached across and shook Kenny a little by the shoulder. She looked as if she thought they were being very silly. Johnny thought so too.

He looked down the crowded row in which he sat and saw that all the boys were singing lustily, even Wally Stewart.

He was glad to be with boys who sang when it was time to sing.

He sang louder than ever.

Then Mr. Richmond prayed and at the end they all said the Lord's Prayer together. It was different from saying it at school. There were so many voices, and upstairs the organ was playing, people were singing, like a heavenly accompaniment to the words.

"A-men," said Mr. Richmond. "Stand, boys and girls."

The piano struck up a march. Mrs. Curtis strode out into the aisle and Johnny followed her proudly up the long aisle and across the back of the room and through a doorway, as if flags were flying and bugles blew. It was not at all as it had used to be when he straggled after Miss Kimball.

"Now," she said, as soon as the door was closed behind the last boy in the line, "let me just get these duds off."

She put her hat and gloves on the windowsill, and smoothed her hair back. She looked ready for business.

"Boys, this is Johnny Lee. He'll learn your names fast enough. Johnny, we've just finished studying about where

Jesus lived when he was your age, more or less, and where
he went with his folks for the Feast of the Passover. They
were Jews, you know. That shows you the kind of people
the Jewish are. A great race. Fine heads, big hearts, and a
faith strong enough to last for thousands of years
through more trials and tribulations than bear thinking
on, almost."

" 'Faith of our fathers living *still*,' " said Johnny. " 'In
spite of dungeon, fire and sword.' "

"Right," said Mrs. Curtis. "Where he lived and where
they went for the feast is all on that map Carl made, over
there. It's a fine map. Nice letters on it. Clear as a bell.
Wally made the pictures. Wally's our artist. You go over
and study it, Johnny. You'll see where Jesus rode his
donkey and where he stayed behind at the temple and
asked questions of the teachers. Jesus wanted to learn
things.

"Now we are going to try to figure out where a boy
would ask questions today. A boy in our time. A boy who
wanted to learn as much as he could about everything that
is important. We'll need a map for this too. Get your
drawing paper, Carl. Put our state on the northeast corner of it — up here — and somebody'll tell you where to
make a star for our town. He might as well start from our
town because he is a boy like you. You boys want to know
things too. What do you want to know about, Slim?"

Slim wanted to know about machinery. Especially auto-
mobile machinery. About engines and cauter-pins and pis-
ton rings.

Where would he go to find out things like that, Mrs.
Curtis asked. The boys decided on Detroit.

"That's on Lake Erie," said Mrs. Curtis. "Draw in
your Great Lakes, Carl. You know how they look. In general. Middle top. That's right. Now how'll Slim get
there? On a donkey?"

They all laughed.

"Not on a donkey? Why not?"

"Because he hasn't got a donkey?" Johnny asked; and added, "Has he?"

They all laughed again, except Mrs. Curtis.

She said, "That's one reason. Too bad, too. Slim would have a lot of fun with a donkey. But he couldn't get to Detroit on one very well. Why not?"

"Too slow," someone said.

"That's right. A donkey is slow, and Detroit is a long way off. How would he go?"

"By plane," cried several. "Draw in a plane for Slim, Wally."

"All right if there isn't a storm. What if the planes are grounded, and Slim's bag is all packed?"

"By train!"

"Or by car."

"Slim hasn't got a car either."

"Maybe he could use his father's."

"You don't know my father," said Slim glumly. "He wouldn't let me go at all. If he knew it. Jesus's folks didn't know it."

"They took him there in the first place. He just stayed behind."

"He didn't mean to, did he, Mis' Curtis? He just forgot."

"I think so."

"His folks was kind of mad, though."

"My folks would be mad."

"Mine wouldn't."

"Well, I don't know. Maybe mine wouldn't."

"Johnny, put in the railroad track. Arnold, you draw the road. Wally'll put the car on the road and the train on the track. We'll get Slim there one way or another. If that's where he wants to go. Because machinery is very important in the world today. There are a lot of things God depends on us to do, now we have machinery, that He didn't expect in Jesus's time. And we need boys like Slim to learn to make it for us and keep it in good order."

Johnny was drawing the railroad track very neatly and carefully. It took a long time. Detroit must be a long way off. He had never heard of Detroit before.

"See what a big country this is," Mrs. Curtis said, "when we start traveling over it. Still it's a small part of the world. See, a map the size of this one we're making now shows all the towns in the part of the world Jesus knew about. This new map wouldn't have room for a fraction of the towns and cities in just our own country. It will take a great many maps of this size just to give an idea of the world that you boys are going to have to know about and help take care of when you're grown up. So we certainly can't depend on donkeys for getting around over it, can we? But the place to begin to learn the things we want to know is right in our own town. Ink in the name of it, Tony; and Detroit on Lake Erie too. Because Slim wants to know where that is, when he is old enough to travel that far alone . . . Now what does somebody else want to know about?"

They took Arnold to Texas to learn about drilling for oil; Wally to California to study airplane design; Carl to Washington to find out about the government; Tony to a Wyoming cattle ranch; Lloyd to a university where he could do experiments in a laboratory; Ernest to New York to learn merchandising . . .

Johnny kept on carefully making the tracks over which they would travel. West and south, south and west from the northeast corner.

"My land," Mrs. Curtis exclaimed. "There's the piano starting again. Who'd believe an hour would go so fast? We've only had time to find out what half of you would like to learn and where you might go to learn it. Well, we'll just have to wait to find out about the rest of you. And then will come the most interesting part. Then we'll have to try to figure out whether we think Jesus would consider it important for him or his friends to learn these things if they were the boys of today, and whether there are other important things we hope other boys will be learning while you are learning these.

"Now, here's your text for next week. A copy for each. Keep it with you. Read it over when you can. Think about it. Use it. You don't need to memorize it. But some of you will. I can't sit with you for the closing hymn today, so show Mr. Richmond it doesn't make any difference whether I'm there or not. He thinks I keep you in order. I know better. Class dismissed."

As she was pulling on her hat she noticed that Johnny was still there.

"Gracious," she said. "They need you to help sing."

"I'm going," Johnny said.

But still he stayed.

"I've got to run upstairs and walk home with my mother," Mrs. Curtis said, "or she'll start right out alone. Good days I let her. But in a storm I don't think it's right. She could fall and break a hip, like anybody else, but she doesn't think so."

"Have you got a mother?" Johnny asked.

"I should say so. Stubbornest old lady you ever saw. Just like me."

"If you've got a mother, you can't be very old. Are you?"

"Old enough. Why?"

"I mean — they said you might be too old to teach. At school. Next year."

"Pshaw," said Mrs. Curtis. "They can't keep me out of school next year unless they put me in jail. Now run along, Johnny. And sing!"

She gave him a little push, and he went. But he did not sing.

Mr. Richmond had announced that the pulpit flowers had been donated, today, to the Sunday school. He believed there were enough for every child to have a blossom to take home to his mother as her first Christmas gift. Each teacher, beginning with the teacher of the littlest ones, was to go forward, call the names of her pupils who were present, and present the blossoms. After the primary classes, all the girls' classes would be called, and then the boys'.

When Johnny took his seat, the small children were already standing with their flowers in their hands. The huge basket of brilliant red carnations seemed hardly to have been touched.

Now the third-grade girls were going forward, one by one. Johnny recognized Nancy Bennett, Gloria Nash with her yellow curls, Joyce Mathes in a green coat with a leopard plush collar. He wished Linda were there. Linda would look prettier than any of them. Linda would like to take a red carnation home to her mother. And Linda, on her way back to her seat, would smile at Johnny.

But they did not send the Sunday buses anymore.

The fourth- and fifth-grade girls . . . The sixth- and seventh-grade girls . . . The junior high school girls . . .

"Gosh," muttered Wally. "They're most gone. All the best ones are gone. Why do darned old girls always have to be first?"

"Sh-h-h," whispered Johnny.

He was thinking of what Mrs. Curtis had said.

"Shut up," growled Wally. "Who set you up anyway, and never cropped your ears? I'll fix you, when we get out of here!"

Johnny tried not to hear what Wally said. He tried not to be afraid. He tried to put his mind on the carnations. He tried to imagine his mother's face when he brought in her first Christmas gift. A real flower. A real, living flower, in December. A flower that smelled sweet . . . He thought she would cry, "Oh, Johnny!" and sniff it and hold it out for Deirdre to sniff, but not let her take it, because she might break it. Then he would bring the thin green glass vase, and they would run water into it from the faucet, and then they would put the flower in it, and carry it into the living room. His mother would put it in the center of the white lace mat.

His father would say later, "Where did this come from, Marge?"

And she would say, "Johnny brought it to me."

Surely the flowers would last. There were quite a few left . . .

"Miss Kimball next, please," Mr. Richmond said.

Miss Kimball hurried forward, her crisp veil going in and out with her breath. She was very thin and bent forward as she walked. She turned quickly, as she reached the platform, and found that Pete and Tarb were already wrestling on the bench where she had left them.

"Peter Barker," she called sharply.

Peter fell over Kenny's out-thrust foot. He picked himself up and gave Kenny a punch. He went down the aisle and took his carnation.

"Tarbell MacDonald," Miss Kimball had already called.

As the two boys met, Pete hit Tarb with the carnation. Tarb ducked and grinned.

"Kenneth Schultz," said Miss Kimball, in haste and desperation.

"Ah," said Mr. Richmond kindly. "Ah — I'll just sit with those young men of yours, Helen, while you read Mrs. Curtis's attendance sheet. She was obliged to leave early. You're — ah — handier with flowers than I am."

He did not say that he was handier with boys than she, but Pete, Tarb, and Kenny became suddenly models of good behavior. They sat quietly beside Mr. Richmond with angelic faces.

Miss Kimball peered through her veil at Mrs. Curtis's list. How long it was! At least three times as long as hers! What did Almira Curtis do to bring so many boys regularly to Sunday school? Her own were always dropping out. Her room had not had the attendance banner for months. She wondered if Almira brought something for her boys to eat. It was against the rules, but you could never tell about Almira . . .

She looked at the names on her list.

The first one was John Lee.

John Lee. John Lee. Johnny Lee . . . Why, he used to be in her class. He should be in her class now. He used to come down from the country on the bus. Then he had changed over to the Baptist Sunday school. Her brother's wife had told her about it, at the time. Miss Kimball had not been able to imagine why. Now he was back here today. He was one of the changeable kind nobody could depend on, apparently. And he was on Mrs. Curtis's list instead of hers. That just showed that Mrs. Curtis was doing something in her room which attracted wanderers.

"Carl Crawford," Miss Kimball said, passing over Johnny's name because she could not bring herself to say it.

Carl went down the aisle.

Johnny counted the carnations. He could see six across the front of the basket. Surely there were more behind the ferns.

"Wallace Stewart," read Miss Kimball, snatching up the flowers and handing them out. "Antonio Watkins, Leonard Mitchum. Lloyd Keyes. John Lee. Arnold Nash . . ."

Mrs. Curtis's boys were coming and going swiftly. Pupils who had their flowers were becoming restless, especially the little ones. The older girls slipped on their coats. The pianist was taking her place at the piano. Sunday school was nearly over for another week. It was time to go home to dinner.

Probably no one heard Miss Kimball say to Johnny, "Why don't you get your flowers at the Baptist church, young man?"

No one but Johnny.

He had already put out his hand. He stood below her, blinking . . .

Perhaps she did not mean to keep the flower from him. Perhaps he could have had it if he had reached a little higher.

But he turned and stumbled back up the aisle. Arnold Nash took the carnation Miss Kimball was holding, and she reached for another.

A few minutes later Mr. Richmond announced the closing hymn but Johnny did not sing it.

Johnny was not there.

Monday:

I do believe it's going to make all the difference in the world, said Marge to herself, his not having to go on that old bus.

She could not remember another school morning in two years when she had not been obliged to call Johnny at least three times before she heard him moving about in his own room, and after that to run upstairs and hurry him down, to remind him to wash, to urge him to sit down at the table and to get up from it. But today when she called, he answered "Okay, Mum," in a clear voice. A minute later she heard water running in the bathroom. When he came downstairs, the cuffs of his shirt were buttoned, his suspenders were straight, his face was scrubbed clean and shiny, and his hair was combed.

"My, Johnny! How nice you look!" his mother said, smiling.

He slid into his chair, tucked his napkin inside his collar, and picked up his spoon. He did not smile back at her, but perhaps it was too soon to expect a school-morning smile. She guessed that he had something on his mind — something important to him — but she did not feel that it was an unpleasant thing. His eyes were big, but not altogether sad. There was a kind of purposefulness in them; almost a gleam of hope.

"What you thinking about, Johnny?" she asked curiously.

"Nothing," Johnny answered.

They both knew that was not true. A boy says "Nothing" only because he is unable to say more.

He ate part of his egg, a few bites of bacon, half a slice of toast. It was not much, but it was more than usual, and he did it without dawdling, without pausing to rub his stomach uneasily or to rest his head on his hand.

He said, "That's enough, Mum. I'll go brush my teeth."

She was too astonished to ask him to try to eat more. He had never before brushed his teeth without being told.

I do believe, she thought, it's going to make all the difference in the world, his not having to go on that old bus . . . I'd like to know what he's got on his mind.

She saw no reason at all to be worried until she noticed that it was half-past eight and he had not yet come downstairs. School began at quarter of nine.

She called, "Johnny! It's half-past eight."

"Okay, Mum."

"School begins in fifteen minutes."

"I know it."

Five minutes later she called again.

"What are you doing, Johnny?"

"I'm — in the bathroom."

"Well, hurry up. You mustn't be late the first morning you have to get yourself to school."

"I won't be."

In three minutes she called again.

"Johnny Lee! You've got just seven minutes to get to school."

"I'll make it, Mum. I'll make it." This time there was a note of desperation in his voice.

She wanted to go up, but intuition told her it was better not to. She moved aimlessly back and forth across the small kitchen, watching the clock, watching other children hurry along the street.

Oh, dear, she thought anxiously, now there isn't a bus driver, am I going to have to take him to school? I can't. I can't leave Deir. And if I have to get her ready and take her, he'd be so late I don't know what they'd say. I wish Jack was home. He'd see —

At exactly nineteen minutes of nine the bathroom door opened, Johnny came clattering down the stairs, stepped into his boots, grabbed his jacket and lunch box from her, and ran out saying "Bye, Mum" without turning his head.

Sighing with relief, she watched him race down the street faster than she had ever seen him move. There was not another child in sight. All the others must be safely on the school grounds already.

She looked at the clock. Eighteen of. He was disappearing. He probably would make it, as he had said he would. But what did it mean?

She shook her head. She could not think about it any longer, for Johnny's clattering had wakened Deirdre.

Johnny had calculated perfectly. He reached the school grounds as the last of the second-graders were filing in past Mr. Sturtevant. Panting, he wriggled in between two third-grade girls.

"You were almost LATE," said one of them accusingly.

"Where you been, hayseeder?" muttered Wally Stewart, from behind. "Why don't you try gettin' into the fourth-grade line here, like you did at Sunday school? I was layin' for you, long as I could, and I will be again, don't you forget it. I'll get you yet!"

"Silence in the lines," said Mr. Sturtevant in his dry, cold voice. "Third grade, pass!"

I'll tell Mrs. Curtis, thought Johnny. If I have to, I'll tell Mrs. Curtis.

It was fine to know that there was someone, at last, whom he could tell about things other boys said or did to him, if they were bad enough, if he had to. There never had been anyone before. It was no use to tell his mother for she could not do anything about it and would only worry; and he did not dare to tell his father because his father would say he should stand up for himself, show a little spunk, fight his own battles. Only Linda knew what he had been obliged to take from other boys, and she did not know all of it. At school boys and girls were separated on the playground. Linda knew what she had seen, but he had never told her the rest. What she did know had made her cry with helpless rage, because Johnny was small and could not hate, and she was a girl. Seeing Linda cry was worse than being hurt. He wanted Linda to be happy. Someday he would be so big that he would not need to hate; then he would take care of himself and Linda and she would be happy all the time.

He tried to catch sight of Linda by stretching his neck and peering ahead, but a teacher touched him with a ruler as he passed her, and he shrank into his place. He thought perhaps Linda had not come today. Perhaps she had caught cold playing in the ice.

"Move along," said Miss Besse. "Move along."

It was what Mrs. Curtis had said yesterday but it did not sound the same.

Then, as he was hanging up his jacket, he saw Linda sitting at her desk, bent over, taking off her overshoes. He felt much better. He started up the aisle — her aisle — with his lunch box in his hand. He thought that as he went by he would swing his lunch box against Linda and she would lift her head and look around at him. He would not speak, of course. Miss Besse did not allow speaking without permission, in the room. Anyway, he did not have anything he needed to say to Linda. He only wanted her to look at him.

"Johnny Lee!" said Miss Besse. "Your own aisle, please!"

She saw everything, he thought. She probably could see into Johnny. She saw that he wanted to make Linda look at him and because it was what he wanted it was what she did not want. But this time she did not have her way. For once, she guessed wrong. The minute Miss Besse said "Johnny Lee!" Linda's head flew up. She did not look at Miss Besse. She looked straight at Johnny, and smiled, and hunched her shoulders, lifting her eyebrows. He knew what that meant. It meant, "Mean old thing, isn't she?"

"Johnny Lee, take your seat," said Miss Besse. "Linda, I don't like your attitude."

Several children snickered.

Everyone knew that Johnny was Linda's boyfriend. They had known it since subprimary. Many of them remembered how, in their first days at school, Johnny had wanted to play on the girls' side, to be with Linda. They might not have remembered it — because at that time none of them had realized there was much difference between girls and boys — if after they had seen him playing there with Linda for two days (a pair of strange children from upcountry whom no one knew or noticed much) their teacher had not appeared around a corner on the third morning and said:

"Johnny, this has gone on long enough. You aren't a girl, are you? So why are you playing on the Girls' Side? Get over on the Boys' Side where you belong!"

If Johnny had grinned and ducked and run, they might not have remembered it.

But Johnny had stood still and said, "I want to play with Linda."

Miss Secord laughed, exchanging glances with other teachers.

"My, my," she said. "So young, too! Well, I'm sorry, but you can't play with Linda on the school grounds."

The other children gathered around. They liked to hear Miss Secord laugh. They laughed too.

She took Johnny by the shoulder and steered him around the building to the Boys' Side.

"There," she said. "See you stay here. It's the Rule."

Johnny stood staring at other boys chasing one another, pushing one another down, throwing hard balls at one another. Someone bumped into him. Someone hit him, said, "You're It," and ran away. Johnny stood staring, until the bell rang.

"What's the matter with ya? Ya dumb?" a big boy asked, knocking off Johnny's cap.

The next recess Johnny went back to play with Linda.

"You can't play with her," the other children cried. "You're a boy! You're a boy! Get over on the Boys' Side where you belong!"

"You leave him alone," Linda told them savagely. "He can too play with me. He always plays with me. You shut up. I like him best of anybody. You leave us alone."

She put her arms around Johnny and kissed his check. She had never done that before.

"Missecor! Missecor! Johnny's on the Girls' Side. Linda's kissing Johnny!"

Miss Secord descended upon them.

She said, "Hush. That's tattling. But what are you here for, Johnny Lee? Didn't I tell you to stay on the Boys' Side? Now listen. I'm going to take you back there just once more. If you come over here again, do you know what will happen to you? Do you know what we do to a boy that goes on the Girls' Side? We decide he wants to be a girl, and we put a girl's dress on him and make him stay over here. Then do you know what the boys do — and the girls too? They call a boy like that a sissy."

Johnny blinked. His first blink.

Miss Secord took him by his shoulder again.

"March yourself," she said. "If any teacher ever sees

you over here again, you know what will happen. And NOBODY likes a sissy."

The next morning Johnny felt sick when it was time to go to school. He never had before.

He never went on the Girls' Side again. He never again played with Linda at school. But everyone knew he was still Linda's boyfriend because he stood across the line and watched her, or tossed a rubber ball back and forth across the line to her whenever they could escape the attention of the others long enough. It was a popular game with the others to snatch their ball and to drag Johnny and Linda in opposite directions, until they were out of each other's sight. Linda around the corner of the building or behind the hedge where the girls had to let her go before she bit their hands or broke their ankles with her kicking, Johnny submerged under a heap of squirming boys who tore his clothes and rubbed snow or mud on his face.

"I hate 'em. I hate 'em all," Linda said, over and over, as they rode home on the bus at night. "Don't you, Johnny?"

But that was Johnny's trouble. He could not hate.

> *And preach thee too, as love knows how,*
> *By kindly word and virtuous life.*

He looked up now at Miss Besse, who stood behind her desk with the Bible in her hands. She looked determined.

"If you are all settled," she said, "please listen to me for a moment. This should be a very pleasant week for us all. It is the last week before Christmas. On Friday we shall have a Christmas party here in our room. If you work well until recess time, after recess we shall begin making decorations for the room and for the tree which will be delivered this afternoon. I am sure you will all enjoy that. Sometime soon we shall exchange names, and each of you may bring a gift for the person whose name you draw. It must not cost over a quarter. That is a new rule which Mr. Sturtevant has made this year, and I think it is a very wise one. The value of a gift is not the amount of money you pay for it. Now I must ask you to remember that we must not neglect our work for pleasure. The work is to be done first, and well. I shall now read from the second chapter of the Gospel according to St. Luke . . . 'And it came to pass in those days, that there went out a decree from Caesar Augustus, that all the world should be taxed. . . .' "

Johnny listened and thought of Joseph and Mary going to Bethlehem to be taxed, and their baby being born; but it was not their home, and the three of them "returned into Galilee, to their own city of Nazareth."

Miss Besse's reading stopped there, but Johnny's thinking did not stop there. He thought of the child growing older and stronger, and becoming a boy who went up to Jerusalem for the Feast of the Passover and staying behind, when it was over, to listen to the wise men in the temple and ask them questions. He wondered how Jesus had dared to ask them questions. Jesus must have been a very brave boy. . . . He thought of the map at Sunday school which showed the way Jesus had traveled to the temple; and then of the map which showed the ways Slim, Arnold, Wally, Carl, and the other boys might travel to find out what they wanted to know. He wondered what he wanted to know, and where he would go to find it out. He made railroad tracks slowly and neatly on a wrinkled bit of paper. He knew the marks started from this town where he was now, but he could not see where they led to. He thought that if he kept on making marks, carefully, God would tell him where they were going.

"I am very much surprised," said Miss Besse distinctly, "very much surprised — that while the rest of us were praying, someone was playing with his pencil! . . . Singing books, please. Who would like to choose the first Christmas carol of the season? Debby?"

They sang carols, and, as he sang, Johnny pretended that he stood between Mr. Shawn and Mrs. Curtis.

Miss Besse thought, That Johnny Lee has the best voice in the room.

But of course she could not say so.

They saluted the flag, and she noticed that Johnny stood as straight as any soldier and that he looked neater than usual today.

She thought, If he hadn't acted the way he did when he came in, and diddled with his pencil during the Lord's Prayer, I'd think maybe we'd begun to make something of him at last. But it's probably only that now he doesn't come on the bus he's trying to look and act like the town boys. He'll be as fresh as the rest of them in a few weeks, I suppose.

She passed out workbooks for the arithmetic lesson and sent several of the best pupils to the blackboard to figure the problems. It did not occur to her to send Johnny because he was not a good pupil in arithmetic and, besides, she never sent Johnny to the blackboard. The second-grade teacher had written in her report that almost every time John Lee was sent to the blackboard he just stood and looked at it, but did not write anything. If she stood over him and made him use his chalk, he cried. When she had tried everything else, she gave him the ruler. The next time after that he would not even leave his seat, but just put his head on his desk and cried. Miss Besse had resolved that she would let him stay away from the blackboard the whole year, and see how he liked that. Most of the children loved to use chalk, and she had too many problems already without trying to handle a crybaby in the third grade.

The assignment in the workbook was finished before recess. Miss Besse checked a few of the books while the children were on the playground and found them reasonably satisfactory. When the children came back, she passed out materials for making paper chains.

Linda Morris was very skillful with her hands. Miss Besse, watching her at work, wished the fingernails were cleaner, and the hair of the bent head, but she tried not to be prejudiced against children who came from poor homes.

She held up Linda's chain and said, "Try to make one like Linda's. See? The edges she has glued down are perfectly even. She has used deep, bright colors which show up, and she has put the color on smoothly. There are no streaks."

The chain swung lightly from Miss Besse's decent, middle-aged finger.

Johnny looked at it with admiration. He was proud of what Linda had done. He looked at his own chain and saw that its colors were pale and streaked, that the places where the edges of the loops came together were not even. He asked for clean paper, chose crayons of a deeper, brighter shade, and began again. He had not finished his second chain when Miss Besse sent the collectors around.

"Slowpoke!" hissed Georgia Raeburn. "I've made three already. Give me the one you have got done, stupe."

She snatched the pale, streaked chain with the uneven edges, and tossed it on the growing heap on Miss Besse's desk. Her skirts rustled as she switched back to her seat.

"Put your materials away," said Miss Besse. "Rise. Pass to the cafeteria."

Johnny saw Mrs. Curtis in the cafeteria.

She was the only teacher who sat with her grade at lunch. The other teachers had a table by themselves. There was a place for Mrs. Curtis at the teachers' table but she never used it. She was talking rapidly as the third grade filed in, and Johnny tried to hear what she was saying but her words did not carry beyond the fourth grade table.

"Gee, I bet Four's gettin' the devil," one third-grader

said to another. "Least, Miss Besse leaves us alone to eat."

Johnny was thankful for that, too. But he wished he were beside Mrs. Curtis. He knew now that whatever she was saying would be good to hear.

He passed quite close to her, with his tray, but she did not see him.

"I climbed a tree," she was saying. "I did, too! I was scared to death. You can do things when you're scared that you can't do any other time. It makes you strong."

Johnny thought about that all through lunch. Being scared had never made him feel strong. It made him feel weak. He wanted to ask Mrs. Curtis why that was.

He had tomato soup with the sandwiches he had brought from home. He did not like tomato soup, and when Tarb kept bumping his arm so that the soup spilled out of the spoon, he stopped trying to eat it. He munched his dry sandwiches and wondered if Mrs. Curtis had ever really been scared and if it had really made her strong. He wanted to ask her about it. He wondered if he would dare to ask her, if he had a chance. Yesterday he would have dared to ask her anything; while she was with him, he could have asked her questions he could not even ask his mother, if he had thought of them. But she was not with him here. She was with the fourth grade.

He thought, The priests weren't with Jesus. They were in their temples. Jesus went where they were, to ask them questions. Jesus dared.

He made up his mind that as soon as Mrs. Curtis left the cafeteria he would go upstairs and look through the door of her room. If she was inside, he would knock on the door, and she would call him in, and he would ask her about being scared and being strong. After that, maybe he would ask her whether it was wrong for him to want to play with Linda; and, if it wasn't, how he could play with Linda now that he no longer lived near her. After that, maybe he could ask her what he really wanted to know most today; that was whether he would ever see Mr. Shawn again, and whether he could ever be in her Sunday-school class again, and if a person couldn't be a Methodist if he had ever gone to a Baptist church. He wanted to find out, too, why Wally was laying for him and why so many other boys in his grade and other grades laid for him, pushed him, knocked him down. He thought perhaps most of these questions were not important to anybody but him, and that surely Jesus had not dared to ask unimportant questions of the priests; but what Johnny needed to know was all mixed up and rolling over and over in his mind and he thought Mrs. Curtis would understand that he did not know which was important enough to ask about and which wasn't. Perhaps even Jesus asked some questions of the priests which did not seem important to them, but they took him in and let him stay three days, just because he was a boy trying to find out and they wanted to help him.

He began to feel braver than he ever had.

He thought, She may not be in her room. If she isn't, she may be on duty on the playground. If she is on the playground I will ask her questions there. Unless she is on the Girls' Side.

He was the last third-grader to leave the cafeteria. He had tried to keep Mrs. Curtis in sight but in his haste to return his tray he tipped over his bowl of soup and had to mop up the floor with paper towels. Then he had to wash his hands because they looked blood-stained.

When he reached the hall and started upstairs, Mrs. Curtis had disappeared.

Mr. Sturtevant, the principal, stood there, talking with a teacher. Without looking at Johnny, he put out a hand and stopped him.

Mr. Sturtevant finished what he was saying to the teacher.

Then he looked down and asked, "Where do you think you're going, young man?"

Miss Kimball had asked, "Why don't you get your flowers at the Baptist church, young man?"

"To — to find Mis' Curtis," Johnny said, very low.

"Mrs. Curtis. Are you in Mrs. Curtis's grade?"

". . . no."

"No, sir."

"No, sir."

"Who is your teacher?"

"Miss Besse."

"I see. Well, Miss Besse's boys are outside this door. They are sliding on the ice. You go right along and slide on the ice until I ring the bell."

Mr. Sturtevant opened the door, pushed Johnny through it, and closed the door.

It was very cold outside. Johnny stood on the step, blinking.

He was not one of Miss Besse's boys, if she had any. Even though he was in the third grade, he was not Miss Besse's boy. But because he was not in the fourth grade, he was not one of Mrs. Curtis's boys either. He was nobody's boy, at school.

He stood on the step, blinking, until Kenny Schultz pushed him off.

"Wha's'a matter?" Kenny grinned. "Can't you slide? Can't you do nothin'? My father says why don't you never come ou'doors sence you moved down here. He said go get you but I tol' him you wouldn't come. I didn't tell him why, but I know. 'Cause you're yeller, you're yeller, you're yeller. You don't dare slide for fear you'll fall on your tail!"

Johnny did not answer. He moved away, trying to appear as if he had not heard. He did not run, at first, because he knew he would be overtaken. But when he saw Tarb come off the ice, and heard Wally shout, "Hold him for me, kids!" he ran. He ran as far as he could. He nearly reached the boundary of the Boys' Side. Sometimes if he was close to the Girls' Side, the boys let him go because of the teachers over there. As he felt them close in on his back and begin to drag him down, he thought, Somebody may stop them. Mrs. Curtis may be over there. If she sees them she will stop them — I guess.

But either she was not there, or she did not want to stop them. Nobody stopped them. They forced him down against the frozen ground. They pulled his hair. They stuffed snow inside his belt.

When they left him, he stood up slowly. He could not see. He could hear only faintly. What he heard was the bell ringing. He went in the direction of the eerie sound.

He was entirely alone.

Even back in his room, when he heard Linda saying hotly, "Miss Besse! Kenny and Tarb threw Johnny down in the snow! I saw 'em!" he was alone.

"Don't tattle, Linda," said Miss Besse. "Most of you are down in the snow most of the time."

"But they threw him down!"

"I don't see any bruises on him."

"Well, they're not on his *face* —"

Several children giggled.

"That will do, Linda," said Miss Besse, flushing. "Language workbooks, please. As I said this morning, when the workbooks are finished, we shall continue making preparations for Christmas. Not before. Page forty-three. At the top of the page, it says —"

Johnny groped for his pencil. He filled in blank spaces in sentences. Sentences with capitals and periods made him think of the sentences he had written on Saturday.

My teacher helps me all she can. My teacher helps me all she can.

He thought once more of Mrs. Curtis. Tears came to his eyes. He blinked them away. He had been to the Feast, but he had not stayed at the temple. The priests had not noticed him at all. After the Feast they had gone inside and locked the temple doors. His family had traveled homeward, left him behind, and he was alone. It was desert all around and the sand was cold because the sun had gone down.

"That is all," said Miss Besse. "Assistants, collect the books and pass out the materials for making paper candles. The prettiest candles will be pasted on our windows. The tree will not be here this afternoon, I understand, but you may see it when you come into the room tomorrow morning."

There were no trees where Johnny was, and would not be. He drew and colored a candle. It would not be one of the prettiest ones. This did not matter. His hand trembled as he cut it out.

As Miss Besse passed his desk, he mumbled, "May I get a book?"

"What did you say?" she asked, turning in surprise.

He repeated the words, with difficulty.

"Yes," she said. "But quietly. The others are interested in Christmas."

No one looked up as he tiptoed to the bookshelf. Not even Linda. She was on the far side of the room and her head was bent over the beautiful candle Johnny knew she was drawing.

He took the first book his hand touched, and crept back to his seat.

It was a good book. It carried Johnny out of third grade, out of the town, even out of the time in which he had been born, as good books often did, and as only books and music ever had.

It picked him up, wafted him into the middle of another century than his own, and set him down on the bank of the Mississippi River. When he looked at himself he saw that his feet and legs were bare, his shirt was old and soft, his straw hat was broad and ragged. His name was Huck and he smoked a corncob pipe. He had no family. He did not have to go to school. He was alone and he liked it. He was thinking of floating down the river on a raft . . .

Tuesday:

Miss Besse sniffed appreciatively as she entered her room.

She had cleaned it herself the afternoon before. The janitor was no more thorough in his cleaning than most men. She bought a powder for the floor which both disinfected and deodorized as she swept — or so the label said — and a polish for the desks which cleaned as it polished. She bought these materials out of her own small salary and used them at least once a week. Last night she had been at it, a towel around her head and a sweater on, windows wide open, until after five o'clock. Then she had allowed the big boys to bring in the spruce tree with which they had been waiting, impatiently, in the hall. She had a corner cleared for it. The tip nearly reached the ceiling. It was a well-shaped tree, and she was pleased with it. After that she had pasted the prettiest candles on the windows, and drawn Christmas designs and greetings with colored chalk on all the blackboards.

She had been late home to supper but it was worth a few scowls from her landlady to know that her room would be gay, ready, and in perfect order the next morning.

It was not only that; it was also fragrant with the smell of spruce which had been spreading through it all night.

She put a pile of workbooks on her neat desk and hung her coat in the tidy closet.

It was still early. The bell would not ring for ten minutes. The children were not allowed above the basement until after the bell rang.

She sat down at her desk and opened a workbook. It had been corrected. She had no work to do, but she wanted to appear busy if one of the other teachers should look in. She did not want a visitor. She wanted to enjoy this little time alone, before the children came in and began to absorb the clean fragrance, to replace it with the odor of their clothes, their hair, their grubby little fingers, and to nibble away at the neatness until it became like the shell of a squash from which mice have secretly gnawed out the inside.

But she was not to have this privilege.

An eighth-grade girl knocked, with cafeteria tickets, asking how many Miss Besse would need. The nurse sent word that two third-graders had enlarged tonsils and she had received no reply from the notices she had sent their parents. What did Miss Besse know about the families of these two pupils? A member of the Christmas Seal committee stopped in to ask how many third-graders had taken seals to sell and how much money had come in; and would Miss Besse make sure that all money was collected and unsold seals returned by Thursday at the latest, as the principal was to announce on Friday which grade had proved to be the best sales force.

Miss Besse had all these records in books in her desk drawers, though little was known about the two with the large tonsils except that they came on the bus, had no telephone, one of them had seven brothers and sisters, and the other did not have the same last name as that of her mother.

The member of the Seal committee had not left the room when the children came tramping in. She was a former teacher, now married and — Miss Besse assumed — proud of her accomplishment, secure in her husband's protection, and quite certain that her own period of teaching had been highly successful from start to finish.

"I'll have the report for you Thursday afternoon, Mrs. Galway," said Miss Besse. "Several of the children have taken a second sheet of seals. Only three dollars and a few cents have come in so far, but — Kenneth, pick up your cap off the floor before it is trampled on! Girls, girls! Sh-h-h!"

"Goodness," murmured Mrs. Galway. "That closet is so crowded, Miss Besse. Isn't there danger of — well, creeping things?"

"I have forty-six pupils," said Miss Besse. "It's too

many for the space. I'd like to push the walls out, but I can't."

She was afraid she had sounded crisp. She smiled, to soften it. She wished Mrs. Galway would go, but she had to be polite.

"How do you like our tree? Nice shape, isn't it? The children are looking forward to decorating it today. They made the paper chains yesterday — "

"Did they really like doing that? My subprimary class made paper chains. I shouldn't think third grade —"

"Some of them liked it," said Miss Besse. "Some of them made very nice ones, too. Better than subprimary children could. If you are going to visit us, Mrs. Galway, won't you take this chair? I have to call them to order now —"

"I should think so," said Mrs. Galway, wrinkling her dark little nose. "No, thanks, I can't stop. I still have Christmas shopping to do."

So do I, thought Miss Besse. And the chances are it will never get done. But hers will. And when she's tired from her Christmas shopping, she'll stop at the drug store for coffee and a cigarette. The only place I can have a cigarette in this town is in my room with the door closed.

"I know how that is," nodded Miss Besse pleasantly. "Well, I'll have the report for you Thursday afternoon. Good-bye, Mrs. Galway. Debby, open the door for Mrs. Galway. Now, children, I know you noticed our lovely Christmas tree, but — Deborah, close the door! — *but the way you have been behaving since you came into this room is not the way to win the pleasure of decorating a Christmas tree, or any other kind of pleasure!* What were you thinking of to be so noisy and kick your clothes around and push one another when Mrs. Galway was in the room? Were you trying to show off? Or did you think you could get away with it because we had a guest? I was ashamed of you. I was thoroughly ashamed of you. If

that was what you wanted, you got it. This class will have
no recess this morning. If that was also what you wanted,
now you have it. If you cannot take off your outdoor
things and go to your seats properly, you may stay in your
seats. Sometimes I think you act younger than the children
in the subprimary. It is very discouraging, especially just
at this season of the year when grown-ups are trying to do
more than ever for people of your age. Some of you, at
least —"

She paused. The door was opening. A small boy with
big eyes closed it softly and scuttled toward the coat
closet. He did not look at Miss Besse nor at anyone in the
room. He took off his boots, cap, and jacket with his head
down and his shoulders hunched.

Miss Besse particularly disliked his manner. It suggested that he thought if he pretended to notice no one, no
one would notice him. She thought of an ostrich with its
head in the sand. She waited in silence, watching him try
to find a hook on which to hang his cap and jacket. There
was none. She watched him try to make them cling to
other hanging caps and jackets. They slid off, taking
other caps and jackets with them. She sighed audibly.
Some of the children giggled. They watched him hang up
the other caps and jackets and stand there, holding his
own, with his eyes on the floor and his shoulders hunched.
They watched him, finally, lay his jacket and cap on his
boots, and tiptoe to his seat.

"Some of you, at least," resumed Miss Besse, "do not
deserve what is being done for you at Christmastime . . .
Johhny Lee, why were you late?"

Johnny swallowed and blinked.

"Stand up," said Miss Besse.

He stood up.

"Why were you late?"

"I — didn't start soon enough."

"Why didn't you start soon enough?"

He did not answer. She repeated the question.

Linda raised her hand.

"Put your hand down, Linda. Johnny?"

"Don't know," Johnny whispered.

"You don't know," said Miss Besse. She regarded him severely. "You will stay in at the morning recess. The others are staying in because they were noisy. You will stay in because you were late. I shall stay in for no good reason. We shall all suffer together. And this afternoon, John, you will take home a note to your mother informing her that school begins at quarter of nine. You may sit down now. Take positions for the opening exercises which must be brief today because we have already wasted much valuable time."

She read a few verses. They repeated the Lord's Prayer. They sang "America," and saluted the flag.

"Now, Group One, open your readers to page 47. Study the following two pages. Group Two, open to page 93 and read silently to page 97. Group Three, page 129. Debby Marshall, stand and read, please."

Group One was the slow group, Two the average, and Three the best readers. The numbers ran backward to prevent the children from guessing what they meant. Everyone knew who got the most votes in elections, who wore the best clothes, who passed in the neatest papers, who were the best ballplayers, who got E's on report cards, who made the prettiest paper chains; but that or why some children were given more advanced work than others was, insofar as possible, concealed.

Miss Besse did not question the system. The results of intelligence and placement tests came in to her at the opening of each school year and she divided the class accordingly, for each area of work. Some pupils were in Group Three for reading and in Group One for arithmetic (Johnny Lee was one of these) and some the other way about, but the majority studied with the same group all day. It was rather like teaching three different grades, but she had developed the ability to keep them all busy, and, by this plan, she had an opportunity to concentrate on other shortcomings as well as that of not knowing that "house" and "home" are two different words or that three multiplied by four make twelve. She realized now that in the past she had spent undue time on slow children and let the quick ones do as well as they would, since they were always ahead of the others anyway.

The fact that Debby Marshall pronounced words well was not enough. She must learn to read with expression.

"Wait, Debby," said Miss Besse. "Let me read that sentence to you."

Miss Besse read as she wrote, beautifully, admirably. "Now try it again, Debby."

Debby did much better on her second try. Miss Besse told her so. It was comforting to work with a child who responded to suggestion as Debby did.

Some of the others, however, reacted quite differently. Johnny Lee, for instance.

When she called on him, he began to read where he sat. He knew better than that.

"Stand up, John," she said.

He slid out of his seat slowly, provokingly, and began to read with one hand on his desk top. As he read, his hand moved gradually toward the far edge of his desk, until he was all but lying on it.

Miss Besse interrupted again.

"Stand up, John. Out in the aisle. Away from your desk. Don't touch anything but the book. Stand like a man. Now read to the bottom of the page."

When he finished, she went to the front of the room.

"Now, class," she said. "I want your comments on that recitation. What did you think of the way John read?"

"He read good," said Linda.

"Read well," said Miss Besse. "I was not asking you,

Linda. You are not in this group. And he did not read well. He pronounced all the words properly but he did not read well. Why not? Donald?"

"He leaned on his desk."

"After he stopped leaning on his desk . . . Debby?"

"He said the words all in the same tone. All run together."

"That is true. He had no expression. What was another reason why the words ran together? Elizabeth?"

"He read too fast."

"That is right. I noticed something else about John's reading. I wonder if anyone else did."

Olivia Hemingway waved her hand wildly.

"Olivia?"

"He put in words that weren't there at all!"

"Exactly. These are John's reading faults which we have been pointing out to him for months now. First, he does not stand properly. Second, he never changes the tone of his voice. Third, he reads much too fast. Fourth, he frequently puts in words which are not printed on the page. I cannot see that he has improved in his reading since the first of the year. He seems to be interested only in sitting down again as soon as possible. That is the reason, John, why you continue to get an F in reading. I am waiting and hoping for signs of improvement. Donald, continue, please."

It was a long forenoon without benefit of recess for either teacher or pupils.

Toward its close, Miss Besse passed back the language workbooks which she had corrected the night before, and directed the children to observe carefully the marks and comments which she had made in them.

This gave her ten minutes in which to get information about the two children with enlarged tonsils and to copy it off for the nurse. Her head ached. It seemed twenty-four hours ago that she had had her breakfast. Three more days after this before vacation! She wondered if by Friday night she would be capable of packing her bag and taking a train for her home in Connecticut. If she was, she knew that the minute she got there she would go to bed and sleep the clock around.

In Johnny's workbook there was written in red pencil: "All your mistakes are careless ones. You must spend more time on your work. Take no more books from the shelf this week."

A boy must try to do well. A boy must try to do well . . . All your mistakes are careless ones. All your mistakes are careless ones . . . My teacher helps me all she can. My teacher helps me all she can . . . First fault, second fault, third fault, fourth fault. I cannot see that he has improved. That is why he gets F . . . Take no more books from the shelf. Take no more books from the shelf. Take no more books from the shelf . . .

The Feast was over. The guests had departed. The temple doors were closed. And Huckleberry Finn had floated out of sight on his raft. Johnny was alone in the desert.

After lunch Miss Besse had the boon of a half hour in the teachers' room. She sat in a wicker rocker with her feet against the radiator and leafed through a new magazine bright with pictures of Christmas dinner tables, gift-wrapped packages, and toddlers hanging their stockings in chimney corners.

It occurred to her to wonder what happened to children between the ages of four and nine to make them change from the adorable cherubs they had once been into sly monkeys, proud peacocks, scared rabbits, and dull little grubs. Everyone loved subprimary children. They came with clean faces. They liked to wash their hands. They boasted of brushing their teeth. They did everything as well as they possibly could. They were eager to learn. They were responsive and affectionate. They were loyal to one another. In first grade they were less so; in second grade still less so; by third grade they were dirty and said they liked to be dirty, they were lazy, they cheated, they lied, they acted as if teachers were their mortal enemies, they kicked and mauled and told on one another. It seemed as if, the more that was done for them, the less civilized they became.

"Oh, well," sighed Miss Besse, "they aren't all so bad. They weren't all noisy this morning, but I punished them all. Now I'll reward them all, even those who don't deserve it. I'll give them a happy afternoon if it kills me. And if all Aunt Maude gets from me this year is a pretty card instead of a best seller."

She dropped her magazine into the rack, sprang to her feet, snatched her coat, and hurried uptown to buy forty-five fudgsicles.

Hurrying back with her arms full of paper bags, she caught sight of Kenny Schultz balancing perilously on the edge of the step which separated the school walk from the sidewalk. Pupils who did not go home for lunch were not allowed off the school grounds.

"Careful, Kenny," she said good-naturedly. "Stay where you belong, now. It's almost time for the bell."

"He don't dare step off," yelled Pete. "He don't dare. He's got a dime and he don't dare spend it. He don't dare. He don't dare."

Miss Besse smiled and hurried into the building.

A few minutes later she told the third grade that they were going to have a nice afternoon together. First, they would each have a fudgsicle as an extra dessert; she hoped they had not eaten so much that they had no room for fudgsicles. They screamed that they had not, and she hushed them, still smiling. She said that when they had finished their treat, each one would draw the name of a classmate to whom he would bring a gift on Friday. Then they would hang their paper chains on the tree, and also the tinsel, the icicles, and the bells and balls and tiny silver trumpets which she had ready in her closet.

"Now stand and file past my desk," she said. "A fudgsicle for each of you."

She smiled at every pupil as he passed her, and nearly all smiled back.

But when they were seated, there was one fudgsicle left. She looked at it in surprise.

"Is someone absent?" she asked. "I thought everyone was present this morning."

"Kenny ain't come back," said Pete, rolling his eyes.

"Kenny? Where did he go?"

"He didn't go nowheres. He started, but Mr. Sturtevant see him an' made him come back and took him up to the office. He's gittin' a terrible lickin'."

"Oh, dear," said Miss Besse. "Oh, no, I don't think so. But he shouldn't have gone. And you shouldn't have dared him, Pete. I heard you dare him. Children, you all know it is the Rule that you must not leave the schoolgrounds during noon hour or recess unless you have special permission. Never, never do it . . . Well, we mustn't let this spoil our nice afternoon. Have your fudgsicles and then we'll draw names. I'll put Kenny's out on the window ledge so it won't melt."

The children lapped and sucked. Miss Besse refrained from making any suggestions about their manners.

The subprimaries lap and suck, she thought, and we think it's cute. I'll try to pretend I'm teaching subprimary this afternoon.

But it was not easy.

After a few minutes the door opened and Mr. Sturtevant pushed Kenny into the room.

"This boy of yours left the schoolground without permission," said Mr. Sturtevant to Miss Besse.

"St, st," said Miss Besse. "I am sorry to hear that."

"I have dealt with this offense," said Mr. Sturtevant. "If it is ever repeated, it will go harder with him."

He turned on his heel and went out.

Kenny stood by the coat closet, grinning. His face was red.

"What'd he do to you, Ken?" Pete asked.

"Never mind, Peter. Take your seat, Kenneth," said Miss Besse.

"Tell what he did. We want to know what he did. Come on, Miss Besse, let him tell," cried several girls.

Miss Besse knew they were getting out of hand. She tried to think of a way to get them back without spoiling the afternoon.

"Aw," Kenny said, "hit me with a ruler; that's all. Tried to make me cry. What'd he think? Nothin' but a little old ruler. He can't hit harder'n a fly. He says, 'Put out your hand.' So I did. 'Bend it back,' he says. So I bent it back. Then he hit it four, five times. 'Nuts,' I told him, 'that don't hurt none.' "

"Kenneth," said Miss Besse, rising, "I don't believe a word of it. And your grammar is terrible. Sit down and wash out your mouth with this fudgsicle. Come, children, finish your treat, and then we'll draw names."

They lapped and sucked again. Kenny sucked louder than any of the others.

Miss Besse began writing names on slips of scratch paper.

Suddenly Linda Morris cried, "Teacher! Look at Johnny! Johnny's — going to be sick!"

And he was.

Wednesday:

A number of people noticed Johnny Lee on Wednesday, though they did not think much about him at the time; not until later.

Mr. Shawn saw him from across the street, at about twenty minutes of nine, hiding behind the filling station which neighbored the school. He waved to Johnny, but the boy was looking in another direction. Mr. Shawn thought of crossing the street to speak to him, but supposed this would reveal the hiding place to Wally Stewart and Kenny Schultz who seemed to be the seekers in the game; besides, Mr. Shawn was on his way to visit a parish member who had suffered bereavement in the night. He thought he would call on the Lees late in the afternoon when Johnny would be at home; but this turned out to be impossible because the young widower was desperate in his grief and Mr. Shawn stayed with him until after the doctor came in the evening with sedatives to help the poor fellow get some rest. Then Mr. Shawn went home in need of food and sleep and his wife's gentle services.

Mrs. Curtis saw Johnny marching down the hall past her door, and thought, "How pale that child is. He didn't look that way Sunday. Must be coming on with something. If he were in my grade, I'd send him home."

But he was not in her grade, and passed from her sight.

Linda did not see him that day. Her mother was ill and she stayed at home to take care of her small brother.

Miss Besse saw him, of course, when she took attendance. She could prove that because she had marked him present, and she remembered later that she had noticed him especially because, after his illness the day before and his hour's rest in the nurse's room, she had thought he seemed well enough to walk home but might use that episode as an excuse to stay out the following day; or possibly he really had some virus thing, such as others had been having, though the nurse had said it could not be that because he had no fever, in fact his temperature was a bit below normal.

The nurse must have been right, for Johnny was in his place today and on time too. Like Mrs. Curtis, Miss Besse observed he was paler than usual, but that was natural after a stomach upset, and Johnny never had much color.

She drew attention to the beauty of the tree glittering in the morning sunshine, and allowed those pupils who had brought gifts to put them around the base.

"Don't they look mysterious!" she exclaimed. "Now who do you suppose that thick square one in the red paper is for? And this tiny little one in the white box! Good things sometimes come in very small packages, you know. Well, no one must peek at the labels. All will be revealed day after tomorrow. Do you think you can wait?"

There was a chorus of no's. She did not notice whether Johnny was one of those who said no. If he was, she thought later, perhaps he meant it. At the time she was not looking his way. She was concentrating on trying again to create the happy atmosphere which Kenny had punctured and Johnny, by being sick, had torn apart, the afternoon before.

"Well, we have to," she said smiling. "It will be good discipline for us. Today we'll open our morning exercises by singing, 'O, Little Town of Bethlehem.' "

She did not read from the Bible that day. She asked the children to repeat only the prayer and the pledge to the flag. The rest of the exercise period she let them sing, and she was quite sure, later, that Johnny sang with the others. She thought he must have, because she knew he liked to sing and had a good voice; her book showed she always gave him G in music.

"Now," she said, "it is ten minutes past nine. Before we take up our schoolwork — how many of you have brought in money from the sale of Christmas seals? Mrs. Galway is going to collect our grade's contribution tomorrow afternoon. We hope it will be a big one. Remember that tomorrow morning you must bring in all money for the seals you have sold, and all the unsold seals you have. I must have the record exact for Mrs. Galway. If any of you have seal money today, bring it to the desk and I will check it against your name."

Ten or fifteen children gathered around her. Some had money tied into the corner of their handkerchiefs so securely that only adult fingers could wrench the knot apart. Some had it in purses they could not unclasp. Others had it in their pockets in pennies and counted each coin aloud as it came forth. Still others waved dollar bills from which fifty cents was to be taken, or forty cents, or seventy cents.

Children who had change coming back wanted to buy lunch tickets, wanted Miss Besse to keep the money for them until after school, dropped nickels which rolled under Miss Besse's feet where only she could retrieve them. Children who had not brought money pushed in upon the circle asking how many seals they had taken, how much money they had already brought in, if they must return seals which people on the street had given them money for but had not taken because they had plenty of Christmas seals at home. The subject of money had a fascination for them all, Miss Besse knew. The sight of it made their eyes widen and glisten. The poorest children, who usually were the quietest, had neither money to contribute nor questions to ask, but they hovered close, too, looking at the money, hearing it clink, jumping and staring when a piece rolled across the floor, as if it might explode or set fire or, by chance, turn the whole room into Midas gold.

"Lunch tickets later," Miss Besse said over and over. "I only want seal money now. I have to keep the seal money straight for Mrs. Galway. Keep your change until later. Sit down, please, as soon as you have paid me. If you don't have seal money, don't come to the desk, children. Sit down until I have finished with this. Then we'll go on to other things."

She pushed back her hair distractedly. She could scarcely breathe. She wanted to ask someone to open a window but it was too much effort to make herself heard. She was not sure whether the same children still surrounded her or had been replaced by others. She was not sure she always gave the right change, or put it into the right hand. She was sure of only one point. That was that whatever was paid her for seals was accurately entered on her book and properly deposited in a box which had formerly held paper clips. She had to be sure of this because Mrs. Galway was coming the next day to collect.

At last no more money was being proffered. Miss Besse rose and told all the children to take their seats. She closed the paper-clip box and opened the cafeteria box. She found relief in the plan of having each child who wanted a lunch ticket come alone to the desk. After that she took the change with which she was to serve as bank, and put it into envelopes which she kept for the purpose. She wrote the owner's name on each envelope.

"There we are," she announced valiantly. "Now in ten minutes I am going to ask you to write your spelling words. We won't spell orally first, as we usually do. So get out the lists I gave you yesterday and study them carefully. Then I'll pass out your spelling books."

She tidied her desk until they were all at work. She had raised a window a little but her throat still felt dry. She went into the hall to get a drink from the fountain, and hastily pushed a few bobby pins more securely into place. She had left her door open. She was out of sight of her desk, but she could hear every movement in the room and was certain that no one left his seat.

When she reentered the room three minutes of the ten still remained for studying. She sat down and looked again at the total of the third grade's Christmas seal sale so far. It was not large. Only $4.80. She was rather surprised. Perhaps a good deal would come in tomorrow. She opened the paper-clip box and idly counted the contents . . . She counted them again, swiftly and anxiously . . . again, incredulously.

Then she stood up. Her chair slid back against the wall behind her with a thump.

She said "Children!"

They all looked up, startled.

"Children, there is a shortage of fifty cents in the Seal money box! I am positive there was no mistake in the total of what I put in there. I counted each pupil's money twice. I entered each amount by the name of the pupil who gave it to me, in my book. I am positive — and yet I shall give you the amounts to add. Turn over your spelling lists and put down these figures."

She read the figures aloud distinctly, adding them in her head. It came to $4.80.

While they added, she searched the top of her desk thoroughly, though she knew there was no loose money there; she had tidied it only five minutes ago.

"$4.80," called someone. "$4.80" . . . "$4.90" . . . "No, $4.80" . . . "I got $4.40."

Sighing, she asked all pupils who did not get a total of $4.80 to work the sum on the blackboard. Mistakes were rectified in all cases. $4.80 was the right answer.

"But," said Miss Besse, sadly, "there is only $4.30 here."

She counted it aloud, holding up each bill and piece of metal. She asked five different children to come to the desk, one by one, to count it.

"Two dollar bills. And fifty cents make $2.50. Three quarters make $3.25. Six dimes make $3.85. Two nickels make $3.95. And the rest pennies. One, two, three, four, five, six . . . It comes out $4.30, Miss Besse."

"And I entered $4.80 in the book. I put $4.80 in this box. And now there is only $4.30 here. Fifty cents has disappeared. Fifty cents which we owe to Mrs. Galway. Fifty cents which was to make sick people well again. There has been no one in this room but us. I am the only one who has been out of the room. I did not take the fifty cents. I want all sick people to have a chance to be made well again. I am sure you all do, too. Perhaps the person who took the fifty cents did not realize what an important purpose it was meant for. You are all very young and none of you is sick. Please bring me the fifty cents and we'll say no more about it."

She waited hopefully. All their eyes were on her. But no one moved.

"I think," said Miss Besse, at last, very gently, "the pupil who took that fifty cents is sorry he did it now, and ashamed. He doesn't want the rest of us to know he did it. We can understand that, can't we? We have all made mistakes which we were sorry for. Let's all think of this as just another lesson which has been learned. We shall be proud of the person who returns the fifty cents. We shall not blame him for his mistake. Come, bring it to me."

There was an embarrassed shuffling of feet, but no one came forward.

"Perhaps he is not quite brave enough," said Miss Besse, "while so many are watching and listening. Put your fingers in your ears, children, and put your foreheads on your desks with your eyes closed. Don't look and don't listen. When the money has been returned I'll open the windows wide. You will feel the cold air, and that will mean that the money is safely back and we can go on with our work."

She sat for a few minutes looking at all the heads on all the desks with all the elbows thrust out.

Then she passed along the front row touching each child and telling him to touch the one behind him until we were looking at her again.

"It has not come back," she said. "When you have rested a minute, we'll all cover our eyes and ears. Then not even I shall know who returns the money. He may open the window and after we feel the cold we'll stay as we are until we are sure he is back in his seat. . . . Now I want to speak directly to the pupil who took the money. We don't know who you are. If you return the money after all of us put our heads down, we shall never know who you are. But we shall always know there was no really dishonest person in our class today. We shall be able to trust one another after this just as we have before. We shall be glad and proud to have Mrs. Galway's money to give to her tomorrow. We shall be glad and proud none of us kept fifty cents which would have helped some sick person to get well. Every fifty cents is needed. Every dime is needed. Every penny is needed. You will return the fifty cents, won't you? You will return it now, won't you? You will leave it on my desk and open the window and take your seat, won't you? Then this will be all over, and we can forget it, and do our spelling, and be ready to go out for recess . . . Now, children!"

All their heads went down. Hers went down. She waited to feel a small figure approach her. She waited until spots began to flash before her eyes. Just then she felt it. She saw no one; she heard no one; but she felt him and she knew it was a boy.

She waited for the cold to come in from the windows. It did not come. In his excitement he must have forgotten the signal.

She raised her head slowly, cautiously, looking only at her neat desk top. There was a dime there. She stared at it.

"What on earth is this?" she exclaimed sharply.

Several children looked up. Their ears could not have been very tightly closed. An instant later all were facing her again, a few alarmed, others curious.

"The fifty cents has not been returned," she informed them. "But someone has put a dime here. What does that mean? It was five dimes, or two quarters or a half-dollar which was taken. Is someone trying to put back stolen money on the installment plan? Or does someone think this is a joking matter? Who put that dime on my desk?"

No answer.

"Very well," said Miss Besse, icy cold now. "Since no one will speak on request, every one will speak on order. We shall get to the bottom of this if it takes all day. We'll begin in this left-hand corner and go up and down every row. Deborah Marshall, did you take fifty cents from my desk?"

"No, Miss Besse."

"Kathryn Whitcomb, did you?"

"No, Miss Besse."

"Rupert Cailler, did you?"

"Nope."

"No . . . Gail Murphy, did you?"

"No, I didn't."

At the bottom of the fourth row she came to Johnny Lee.

"Johnny Lee, did you?"

"No —"

His voice did not fall, as the others had. It hung suspended.

Miss Besse gave him a long look. He had the palms of his hands pressed against the corners of his desk and was staring at the blank space between them.

"Johnny," she said, "perhaps you have something more to tell me."

"No," he mumbled. "Well — I didn't — take the fifty cents —"

"Did you see someone else take the fifty cents? If you did, it is your duty to tell me. For the sake of the person who did it. And for the sake of the class."

"I — didn't," Johnny managed. He blinked desperately. "I mean — I didn't see. I don't know. But I — but I —"

"You what, Johnny?"

"I put the ten cents on your desk," he said very fast. "I felt — I mean — as if — I thought if I give that, and maybe four other people had dimes they could — spare — why — why, then the — the sick people could get well and we wouldn't have to talk any — anymore about it."

After a minute Miss Besse said, "I see. I see what you were thinking, Johnny. But you were mistaken. That fifty cents which was taken by someone in this class was given by someone else to help sick people get well. That fifty cents belongs to the sick people. Other money is all very well, but it is that money we must have, because it does not belong to whoever has it. When that has been returned, if any of you children wish to add to our fund from candy money — where did you get this dime, Johnny?"

"My — mother gave it to me."

"What for?"

"For — lunch."

"I see," said Miss Besse again. "Then it must be spent for lunch. It would not be honest to use it in any other way."

She dropped the dime into the cafeteria box and walked down to Johnny's desk to leave his yellow ticket there. A yellow ticket bought soup, milk, and a piece of fruit to be eaten with a box lunch brought from home.

"Peter Barker," she continued, "did you take fifty cents from my desk?"

"No, ma'am."

"Lawrence Kennicott, did you?"

When she had asked them all, they had all said no.

"I am sorry," said Miss Besse. "I am more sorry than I can say. Deborah, go for Mr. Sturtevant and ask him to come to my room."

Every child was searched; every desk, every lunch box, every piece of clothing in the closet was searched. The third grade was not allowed to leave the building until the end of the afternoon session. They were kept separate from the other grades in the cafeteria. They were taken to the auditorium and questioned and searched again, while the room they had left was searched in their absence.

At the close of school, the money had not been found. Miss Besse gave a letter to each pupil to take home to his parents, explaining what had happened in third grade that day, and asking each parent to talk with his child that night, and to send a reply in the morning. She said no child would be readmitted to the room without this reply from his parents.

She noticed that Johnny's face was very white, but so

were the faces of many of the children. She felt like a ghost herself.

That night, at supper, Johnny gave Miss Besse's letter to his mother.

She said, "What's this, for goodness' sake? More trouble?"

She read it and pushed it across the table to his father.

"Somebody in Johnny's room stole fifty cents," she told him. "Miss Besse wants us to talk with him about it."

"If a kid of mine stole money," Jack Lee growled, "I wouldn't *talk* with him about it! . . . Johnny, did you do it?"

Johnny shook his head.

"Then what makes her think you did?"

Johnny shook his head again.

"She don't," his mother said. "I don't s'pose —"

"Then what's she sending us this letter for?" his father demanded.

"Why don't you read it and find out?" his mother snapped.

"You read it, didn't you? You must know what she's driving at."

"Well, she says she's writing to all the parents —"

"What for?"

"Oh, Jack! You don't have to get so mad. I'm just as worried as you are. Miss Besse doesn't know who stole it."

"She thinks Johnny did, though."

"Well, no —"

"Then what's she writing us a letter for? That's what I want to know. What in thunder is she writing us letters about stolen money for, if she don't think Johnny stole it?"

Deirdre began to howl.

"Now look," Marge said. "You've scared the baby. I'm trying to tell you Miss Besse doesn't know who stole it. She's writing to all the parents for them to —"

Deirdre drowned out the rest of the sentence.

"Shut that kid up," roared Jack. "I'll speak as I want to in my own house, and when I want to —"

"Well, nobody can hear you," Marge said, beginning to cry.

She got up to lift the howling baby from her high chair.

"I'll take her," Johnny said quickly. "Let me take her, Mum. I'll take her in the front room. Come with Brother, Deedy. We'll go in and see the doggie and sing, like we do every night. Come, Deedy. Come."

He led her away, holding both her hands. The door closed after them.

Jack and Marge were nearly an hour threshing out the meager bits of information in Miss Besse's letter and debating as to whether she had any good reason for sending it to them. When they had calmed down, they agreed that Marge would write briefly, after the children were in bed, to say that they had talked with Johnny and were satisfied he had not taken the fifty cents.

"He's never touched a penny in his life," said his mother, "except what we've given him. I'm just as sure of that as I am that I didn't take the money. But I can see Miss Besse's side of it. She's in a bad spot."

Johnny did not hear her say this. He was in the front room with Deirdre.

When their mother went in, she found the baby asleep in the corner of the sofa, and Johnny sitting on the floor beside her. He had been crying, and his mother did not wonder. She had cried her own eyes nearly out. But that was over now.

She picked up the baby and said, "It's kind of chilly in here. I hope you didn't catch cold. I ought to have built a little fire. You might bring up an armful of wood from the cellar, Johnny, and leave it in the box in the front hall closet, where it will be ready when I need it. Then you'd better go to bed."

His father did not speak to Johnny as he went through

the kitchen with the wood. Jack thought he had said enough for one night. Maybe too much.

Thursday:
It did not storm the next morning but the sky looked threatening.

Johnny was late coming down to breakfast. His mother had to call him twice. When he came she thought his face had a pinched look.

"My goodness," she said, "you look gloomy. Don't you know it's almost Christmas? Isn't it tomorrow you have your school party?"

Johnny nodded.

"I used to love Christmas parties at school," she said. "Drink your orange juice, Johnny."

He took a swallow and sat moving the glass here and there, pressing it down. It left circle marks on the red plastic table cover.

"Don't do that," his mother said. "Drink it before you spill it. Here's your cereal. We used to draw names, to give presents to. Have you drawn names?"

Johnny shook his head. He was not sure. Perhaps they had drawn names while he was in the nurse's room, sick. But he shook his head anyway.

"Well, after you get home from school, maybe we'll put Deedy on her sled and go downtown to buy a present for Miss Besse. Hurry up, Johnny. Eat."

"Mum —"

"What?"

"Could I — stay home today?"

The old refrain!

She laughed.

"Johnny Lee, we're away past that. It's almost time for school, and you're going. You couldn't stay home today of all days. You've got to take this note to Miss Besse, or she'll think you took the fifty cents."

He thought, Linda hates Miss Besse.

He said, "Linda wasn't there yesterday."

"Maybe she's sick."

He could not imagine Linda sick. He could only imagine her inside the grotto. She was so small, as he imagined her, that she was scarcely visible. It was so long since he had seen her, to speak to her, that now it was as if she lay dead in a tiny coffin of ice which he carried in a pocket of his mind.

"Mum —"

"Johnny, I wish you'd eat. It's twenty-five minutes of nine. Remember, you've been late once this week already, and Miss Besse said —"

"Mum —"

"What, Johnny?"

"Would Dad take us up home in the truck tonight? We could — go out in the pasture and get evergreens to make wreaths."

"The idea!" his mother scoffed. "I guess your father'll be tired enough when he gets home from work without bouncing out into the country. We don't need wreaths. Johnny, you have to go. Take a big spoonful . . . There, here's the letter for Miss Besse . . . And your dime, and your lunch. Get your jacket —"

"Mum —"

"Johnny!"

"Mum, could I come home to lunch? This once?"

"Oh, Johnny, no! I've got your lunch all put up. Get your jacket! . . . Wait! Johnny!"

He stared at her, blinking.

"Johnny Lee, you've torn your sweater! Your practically new sweater! When did you do that?"

"I don't know," he mumbled.

"You do, too. When did you tear that sweater?"

"Well — last night. I guess."

"Where? What were you doing?"

"When I — got the wood. Down cellar. On a nail."

"Oh. Down cellar. On a nail. The whole cellar to walk

around in and you've got to get hung up on a nail! I declare, it's a shame. The only decent sweater you've got, practically a new one, and you not only tear it, but don't even mention it until you're ready to go, and there it is all raveling out! I could cry!"

"I'd better," Johnny said low, "I'd better — stay home — hadn't I?"

"Stay home!" his mother exclaimed. "Stay home! Stay home! No, you will not stay home. You'll leave that sweater here, though. Come, take it off! You'll go without a sweater. You tell Miss Besse you can't go out to play. You've got to stay in because you haven't any sweater, because you tore your sweater, because it's here for me to spend an hour mending, and I don't know whether I can twotch it together or not. It's just about ruined!"

She was dragging it off over his head. She was pushing on his jacket over his shirt sleeves.

"I'll be late," Johnny whispered.

"All right. So you'll be late. You brought it on yourself. Now get there as fast as you can. And remember! You're not to go outside today until you're ready to come home! You tell Miss Besse!"

He had reached the sidewalk, running.

He called back, " 'Bye, Mum," over his shoulder. He could not say it very clearly.

If she answered he did not hear her. He did not think she answered.

He ran as hard as he could all the way to school. The sobs kept swelling up in his chest until it seemed as if his chest would burst. One would come out in a gust, and another was already swelling. His eyes burned, but he shed no tears. He wished he could. It seemed as if his tears had dried up from the heat inside.

The schoolground was deserted when he entered it.

The school door was closed, and it stuck. He thought he was not going to be able to open it, but at last he did. He went up the stairs and along the hall on tiptoe because it was the Rule, but panting loudly because he could not help it.

"Late again," said Miss Besse.

Johnny nodded. He hung up his jacket and left his boots. He saw that Linda was there, but she looked big and far away. She seemed like a stranger.

Miss Besse sighed.

"Why are you late again, John? Weren't you ready to start on time?"

"Yes'm."

"Then why didn't you get here on time?"

"I had to stop to take off a sweater."

"You aren't ready on time unless there is enough lee-way for taking off a sweater," said Miss Besse. "If you weren't, you could have left the sweater on." But she did not press the matter that day. She asked, "Did you bring a letter from your parents?"

"Yes'm."

"Put it here with the others. After the exercises, children, you will have a study period while I read these letters."

The morning dragged. Miss Besse looked grim. She wore a dark dress with no collar. The plain silver pin at the point of the V was not quite straight. She said very little to the children. She read the letters, sighing frequently. After a while Mr. Sturtevant came in and she showed some of the letters to him. They talked in low voices, glancing darkly at the children from time to time.

Finally Miss Besse said, "Put your books away. Stand for recess."

She sounded as if it would be a relief to be rid of them.

Johnny raised his hand.

"Hands down," said Miss Besse. "No questions now. First row, get your clothes! You see, Mr. Sturtevant, Mrs. Galway may be in this noon. It seems to me — Second row! It seems to me we shall have to present the case exactly as it is. Third row! Sometimes I wonder if it is really best for collections to be made in schoolrooms, however — Fourth row! — however worthy the cause. But I don't mean that by way of excuse. Fifth row! If you can give me any advice, I'll certainly follow it. Sixth row! I admit I'm baffled. I hardly slept a wink last night . . ."

Johnny was out in the yard, with no sweater under his jacket. His mother had expressly directed him not to be there, to tell Miss Besse that he was not to be there; but Miss Besse had not allowed him to tell her that he was not to be there. He tried to think what it was best to do, when he was obliged to be where he had been ordered not to be. He thought the important thing was not to catch cold. He tried to stay out of the wind, but where there was no wind there was no sun. He jumped up and down in the shade, and swung his arms, but he could feel the cold creeping up his sleeves. He went out into the wind and the pale sunshine, and found it colder there. He decided to go back close to the building. No one seemed to notice him. He was thankful for that.

He had no trouble, except to keep warm, until the bell rang.

The ringing of the bell, the knowledge that he would soon be inside and might be able to tell Miss Besse, before noon, what his mother had said brought him a minute of something like peace.

He looked about him for the first time, saw the sun wading manfully through clouds like big gray snowdrifts, wondered if the sky over the farm looked the same, and noticed a man going down the front walk from the school building.

It was a small, elderly man, with a soft hat pulled low over his eyes. Johnny knew the man's name. It was Mr. Dwight, the new superintendent of the school union. He went in and out of the building two or three times a week. Sometimes he waved his hand and smiled as he passed the third-grade room. But he had not yet been inside.

The line was forming. Johnny went to find a place in it,

but when he stood behind Pete, Pete lunged back into him and nearly knocked him over. He could not risk falling in the snow. He drew back, and Kenny Schultz ran up and kicked his shins.

Johnny stood well to one side, hoping Mr. Sturtevant would not notice him. When all the others were ahead, Johnny could follow.

He watched Mr. Dwight step into his car at the end of the walk.

As he did so, something brown fell to the ground. Johnny stared, hearing the engine start.

His eyes were very keen. He could see that the object was longer than it was wide. It looked like a billfold.

The car was moving slowly, in low gear.

"Gee," Johnny whispered, "What'll I —"

The line was moving away from him. He looked for Mr. Sturtevant, but the principal, having rung the bell, had gone into the building.

"Maybe he'll turn," Johnny thought. "Maybe Mr. Dwight'll turn around at the gas station. I can give him what he dropped and be back to go in with the next grade."

He ran to the end of the walk. He could not explain to anyone what he was doing because it was the Rule that no one could speak after the bell rang. He could not shout to catch Mr. Dwight's attention because if one was not allowed to speak, surely he could not shout. But he ran as fast as he could.

The object was a billfold. It had come unsnapped as it fell and Johnny could see the edges of bills. There were a great many of them, pressed together like leaves.

He stood watching Mr. Dwight's car slowly approach the gasoline station. But it did not turn in. It began to move faster. Mr. Dwight was not going to the southern towns in the union. He was traveling north.

"Gee," Johnny whispered again, "what'll I —"

The single traffic lights of the town turned red at the

corner. Mr. Dwight would have to stop. Johnny had no time to lose. If he ran fast enough he would get there before the car could go through.

He doubled up his arms and ran as he had learned to run when boys were chasing him, his head down and his feet flying.

"Mr. Dwight," he kept whispering. "Mr. — Dwight —"

The last time he must have said it aloud. Mr. Dwight looked through the window of his coupe, and reached over to open the door.

"What is it, son?" he asked. "Going this way? Want a lift?"

His voice was smooth and pleasant. He had bright dark eyes.

"No," Johnny panted. "No — thanks. You dropped — this."

He laid the billfold on the seat, and closed the door.

"Wait a minute," Mr. Dwight called. "I want to speak to you. I'll just pull over to the curb out of the way."

Johnny scuttled to the sidewalk.

"Now," said Mr. Dwight, opening the door again. "Do you know what you've done for me, young man? You've prevented my losing the biggest sum of money I've carried in my pocket for a long time. I haven't opened a checking account since I came here, and I am on my way to pay the bill for a new refrigerator my wife just bought. What do you suppose she would have said to me if I had lost all that money?"

Johnny shook his head. He could not imagine that anyone would say anything very bad to a man like Mr. Dwight. He was thinking how different "young man" sounded when Mr. Dwight said it than when Mr. Sturtevant said it.

"Well, I don't know either," said Mr. Dwight. "I was very careless. But thanks to you, she can keep the new refrigerator. What's your name, son?"

Mr. Shawn had called him "son," too.

"John. Johnny Lee."

"Well, Johnny, I want to give you a reward —"

"Oh, no," Johnny said, backing away. "No. That's all right."

This was what his father would have said.

"Wait a minute," said Mr. Dwight. "I know it would be all right with you, but it wouldn't be all right with me. You see, I'll feel better if you take a reward. I might have paid around two hundred dollars for being careless. I'd feel guilty if I didn't pay a little. Here, take this for something you would like to have . . . And I'll see you again, Johnny Lee — when we can talk longer."

He nodded and smiled, and drove past the green light.

Johnny stood looking after him.

For a long time Johnny had been alone, except for Linda. Then he had been taken away from Linda. But the next day Mr. Shawn had found him, and the next morning Johnny had found God. Then, in the twinkling of an eye, God and Mr. Shawn had left him with Mrs. Curtis. Mrs. Curtis had been the best of them all; like a mother and a father and part of Linda and as much of Mr. Shawn-and-God as a small boy could be comfortable with. But he had had her for only an hour. After that, for a day and a night, he had kept a feeling of being with her, but it was only a feeling; it was not so; she, too, had gone away. Since then he had been entirely alone.

Until five minutes ago.

For five minutes he had been with Mr. Dwight.

Now he was alone again.

The wind pulled at what he held in his hand.

He looked down at the bill.

Five dollars. He had a five-dollar bill.

He spread it smooth between his hands and stared at it.

Mr. Dwight had said for him to use it for something he would like to have. Five dollars was a great deal of money. But what of all that Johnny wanted would it buy?

Would it buy the farm so that he could go back and play with Linda? Would it pay his way to a part of the school grounds where he could play with Linda? Would it make up for his having gone to the Baptist church? Would it, divided, bribe Wally and Pete and Tarb and Kenny to leave him alone? Would it make him one of Mrs. Curtis's boys for good and all? Would it even help him to stand straighter and read more slowly and write more neatly and so bring him the privilege of taking books from Miss Besse's shelves?

He did not think so.

The town hall clock began striking the hour of eleven.

Johnny raised his head and looked at the clock.

He was late! He was later than he had ever been before!

Would five dollars, if he passed it to her silently, prevent Miss Besse from saying, "Late again!"? No.

He started moving woodenly toward the silent school grounds. Then, suddenly, he stopped.

He was worse than late. This was much worse than being late. He had left the school grounds without permission.

He could try to explain — if the words would come out — but Miss Besse did not like excuses. She would send him to Mr. Sturtevant. He could not explain to Mr. Sturtevant. If he tried, Mr. Sturtevant might not believe him. The only proof he had of where he had been was the five-dollar bill. Miss Besse and Mr. Sturtevant might think he had stolen the five-dollar bill. If anyone would steal fifty cents, he would steal five dollars. Mr. Sturtevant would say, "Put out your hand. Bend it back." He had not been able to make Kenny cry. But Johnny would cry. And nobody liked a boy who cried.

Johnny felt a pushing up in his chest. He did not know whether a sob was coming, or a sickness. He started running. He ran past the school and stores and up the street toward home.

Then he stopped.

He could not go home. It was not time to go home. It was a time when he was supposed to be in school. His mother would send him back. She would have to send him back. And he could not go back.

Besides, he could not explain to his mother why he had seen Mr. Dwight drop a wallet on the walk. He was not supposed to have been where he could see it. His mother had told him to stay inside that day. She had told him to tell Miss Besse that he must stay inside. And he had tried. *My mother wants me to try hard.*

He had tried, but it was like all the other times and ways he had tried. It did no good. It was no use.

He stood still.

He was all alone.

He stood there until he heard a truck which sounded like his father's truck. Then he darted down a side street and ran as hard as he could until he reached the bushes which lined the river bank. He cried there for a while, and rested. When he had stopped sobbing and panting, he went on down the river bank to the railroad bridge. It was not a very high bridge and he climbed the side of it and walked across on the tracks. He did not know where the tracks led, but he knew that when he had crossed the river he was in a different state. He remembered the tracks he had drawn for Mrs. Curtis. He had not known where they led, but she did. They went in many directions, all in search of what some boy most wanted to find out. One of them must lead to what he, Johnny, most needed to find out, though he did not know what it was. Perhaps this was the one. It was the only one he could see. He had no other choice. So he followed it.

A little way beyond the bridge, where the track curved into pine woods, he heard a train coming and stepped off into deep snow.

It was a fast train. It passed him with a thunderous roar and a rush of wind which made him shrink back. But when it had been gone a little while the strange woods seemed vast and empty. The singing of the pine needles was a ghostly sound. He shivered with cold, and wallowed through the snow back to the cleared track. Looking ahead, he saw the two black rails converging into one. He ran toward the convergence until he felt warmer, but the two rails were still separate and he was still alone, walking between them . . .

An hour later he came out of the checkerboard of dark woods and white fields, and saw ahead a cluster of houses close to the track.

He had never seen these houses before. He had never seen houses like them before. They were all small and square, all painted white with blue blinds and stone chimneys, all with a patch of lawn before them and a drying yard in the rear.

It was like a toy town.

Johnny's eyes widened.

It seemed to him that if he could leap over the intervening distance, he could kneel among these shiny little houses and move them about according to a plan of his own. He could find a little store and have it handy by for children to buy their candy in, and ice cream. The store might also sell pencils and blocks of paper. Or he might have two stores. But there would be only one church. Only one. With a bell in the steeple through which God's voice would speak to everyone; and in its vestry Mrs. Curtis would teach all the classes. If there were enough Mrs. Curtises to teach all the classes in a school, and Mr. Dwight would come to superintend it, there would be a school. Otherwise, there would be no school. The children would play all day in the fields behind the houses, and every child would do whatever he wanted to do as long as he hurt no one else. If any child hurt another, he would be put in a yard by himself until he had learned how to play without hurting. There would be Mrs. Curtises to help the children who were in yards by themselves.

Johnny knew this was a dream. Nothing real had ever been that small. There were not that many Mrs. Curtises. There was only one, and she was back in the world from which he had been driven forth, a small exile.

What he saw ahead was a real town. The nearer he came to it, the more clearly he saw that it was an outlying section of a city. Beyond the little new houses were bigger, older ones, with porches and bay windows and elm trees. Beyond the bigger houses were tall brick buildings, taller cement buildings, and many church steeples. Not one, but many.

It looked like a very great city. He wondered if this could be Detroit. Or New York. Or Washington. Texas, California, Wyoming . . .

Mrs. Curtis had said people must travel on trains or planes or by car to reach those places. She had said it would take too long to ride there on a donkey. But he had been walking a very long time, and part of the way he had been running. Other people were going there by train. They were going there faster. But he was going there too.

He had to step off the track now while another train went by. This made two trains which had passed him, filled with people riding to Detroit or Texas or Washington or whatever it was.

He began to be excited. Perhaps this was the place where he could find out what he needed to know. Perhaps even now the feast was being spread and the temple doors stood open. Perhaps wise men were waiting for boys to ask them questions.

Johnny did not return to the track. The sidewalk was comforting to his feet after the miles of ties. He looked skyward at the tallest building he could see and began to run toward it, though he could not run fast because his feet were sore and his legs were stiff.

There were cars, trucks, and buses stopping, starting,

and honking. Lights flashed at every corner. Lights ran around in circles. The sky was so dark now and there were so many lights that it might have been night. Or perhaps he was in a mighty cavern. The great buildings stood around like walls, with lights sparkling in row upon row of tiny windows.

It was beginning to snow. The air was full of big white flakes falling like silver feathers.

The sidewalk was crowded with hurrying people. None of them noticed Johnny.

He stood still and looked at them. Their faces were neither kind nor unkind. Their eyes were fixed on something farther on. They bumped into him, drew back, and hurried past in the way they had been going. His view was shut off by fur coats and paper-covered packages and bulging bags.

They must all be going to the feast. The temple must be ahead.

He ran on. He tried to keep up. He stayed with the crowd.

And at last he passed through a great doorway.

He did not know what he had expected to see. Certainly not what he saw.

Immediately before him there was a long, narrow, high white table. As smooth as glass, but milk-white like marble. Behind it a white mist rose and rolled in clouds, like the smoke from a geni's arrival.

Johnny stood staring.

The mist was not only beautiful to see. It was beautiful to smell. Better than wild strawberries on the pasture hill in June. Better than garden peas and sliced cucumbers on the Fourth of July. Better than the big orange in the toe of a Christmas stocking.

Then the geni's face appeared through the mist. It was round and red, with snapping black eyes. It grinned at Johnny.

It said, "You hungry, boy?"

Hungry? . . . Everything went wavy before Johnny's eyes. He felt as if he were being taken into the beautiful mist, dissolving into it.

He could not answer, but he must have nodded, for the geni said, "Well, hop up on a stool. What'll you have? Hamburger? Hot dog? Piece of apple pie? Ice cream? Cup of hot chocolate? Coke or ginger ale?"

Hamburger . . . Hot dog . . . Piece of apple pie . . . Ice cream. . . . Cup of hot chocolate . . . Coke or ginger ale. . .

All the things Johnny liked best!

He saw a high, round, empty stool waiting for him and climbed slowly onto it as if he were being lifted. Now he and the geni were together in the soft, warm, sweet mist.

Johnny opened his mouth.

He whispered, "I'd like — a hot dog. Please."

"A hot dog?" repeated the geni in a big, firm voice. "I knew it. Right you are. A hot dog. Dinner for a prince."

Dinner for a prince!

The geni turned to where a pan of frankfort sausages sizzled gently. He took a long white roll from a drawer and tossed it into the air. It somersaulted three times before he caught it on a toasting rack.

His wide grin flashed out of the mist as he turned his head toward Johnny.

"Mug of chocolate with the dog?" he asked. "Warm you up."

Johnny, hunched down inside his jacket, with his hands between his knees, was already growing warm from the outside, but inside there was a cold, dry channel in which it would be wonderful to feel a hot chocolate river flowing.

He nodded.

The geni touched a handle and rich liquid bubbled out. With one sweep of his hand he placed a steaming white mug before Johnny's chin. With another he set the ruddy sausage in a golden-brown blanket beside the mug. The fragrant steam from the two combined to make a cloud which was entirely Johnny's.

Johnny said in a low voice, "I'm not a prince."

The geni gave him a quick glance which Johnny did not understand.

"Don't tell me," he said. And then, "Where's your money, bub?"

"Money?" . . . Oh, the geni knew about that five-dollar bill.

"It's here," Johnny said, amazed. He took it from his inside jacket pocket.

The geni whistled.

He said, "If a boy wasn't a prince, how'd he come by that kind of money?"

"You know, don't you?" Johnny asked.

"Oh, sure," the geni grinned. "A feller gave it to you."

He took the bill. A minute later he piled up four bills, a fifty-cent piece, and a quarter beside the mug.

"Put it in your pocket, Prince," he said. "Before you lose it."

He disappeared. Johnny put the money carefully into his pocket. It was bulky against his chest. He drew a long breath and began to eat.

The hot dog was the best he had ever tasted. Probably another such hot dog had never been made. He did not stop eating until he had finished it.

Once only the geni's arm and hand appeared, leaving a big smooth blob of whipped cream in the top of the mug.

Now Johnny drank. As he drank, not only was his thirst quenched, but he was warmed all through, his heart stopped pounding, his feet were no longer sore, and he began to feel happy.

"A piece of apple pie?" asked the geni, appearing. "Scoop of ice cream on it?"

Johnny nodded.

"Right you are."

The pie was there. The ice cream rode on it like a cap, melting softly and spilling over.

This was bliss.

As Johnny scraped up the last creamy drop with a spoon, the geni appeared again, his whole head and shoulers.

"What's next on your program, Prince?" he asked. "Where do you go from here?"

Johnny wiped his mouth and fingers with a paper napkin. He smiled at the geni.

"I want to stay," he said bravely. "I want to ask a man some questions."

"Right you are," the geni said. "Our Answer Man is in the next aisle. I'll call him over. Mr. Fenton!"

Johnny turned on the stool to watch him come. He was young, Johnny thought, to be an Answer Man. Not even as old as Mr. Shawn. He had no beard. His face was smooth and fair, and he had bright blue eyes like Mr. Shawn's. He wore a white shirt, like Mr. Shawn's, and a green and white necktie. A red carnation was pinned on the lapel of his dark coat.

"Mr. Fenton," the geni said, "here's a young prince who's just had a good lunch, and now he wants to ask you some questions. Where's your money, Prince?"

"Right here," Johnny smiled, touching his pocket.

"Let's see it again."

Johnny took it out and spread it on the high table.

"Look at that," the geni said. "Quite a fortune." He took one of the quarters and gave Johnny a dime so new and shiny that it seemed never before to have been touched by human hands. "Put it away, Prince. Until you need it. Now I'll turn you over to the Answer Man."

He disappeared.

The Answer Man looked down at Johnny.

"What did you want to know?" he asked.

Johnny hardly heard what he said, he was so eager with his first question.

"Where did you get that red flower on your coat?"

"Counter One."

"Are there any more?"

"Thousands. Do you want one?"

"I want —" Johnny said. He paused. Then he said bravely, "I want three."

"This way. Follow me."

It was not far. Only a few steps, and there were red carnations in baskets and pails, on floor and counters, and on shelves reaching to the high ceiling.

From among them a girl's face smiled at the Answer Man and Johnny.

"I have a customer for you, Lorene. He wants three red carnations."

"Which ones?" Lorene asked. Her throat was white, whiter than the pearls around it.

"That one," said Johnny. "And that one. And — that one."

"Oh, my," Lorene said. "You chose the very biggest ones. They will be fifty cents."

"He has the money," the Answer Man told her. "Alex says he is a prince."

"Oh, my," Lorene said again.

Johnny took fifty cents from his pocket. Mr. Dwight had said this money was for something he wanted. He had wanted a hot dog and chocolate and pie and ice cream. Now he wanted red carnations.

"They're for my mother," he said.

"Oh, won't she be pleased! Are you going home now? Or are you going to get some other presents first?"

Johnny regarded her gravely.

"I'm not going home for a long time," he told her.

"Then why don't you let me keep the flowers in water until you're ready to go? I'll put your name on them. What is your name?"

"John. Johnny Lee."

"All right, Johnny Lee. They'll be here when you want to take them."

She had a little space between her two front teeth, like Miss Besse.

"Thank you," he said, staring up at her; and as he stared, she disappeared.

"Can I do anything else for you, Johnny?" asked the Answer Man.

"Oh, yes, sir . . . How many can I have?"

"How many what?"

"Questions."

"Quite a few. What else do you want to know?"

"Is this Detroit?"

"Detroit? . . . No. This is Treadwell. You don't live here, Johnny?"

"Oh, no, sir."

"Where do you live?"

"Very far away. Is this a temple?"

"This — no, this is — ah — an emporium."

"In an em-porium can I find everything I need?"

"I should think so. What do you need?"

Johnny wrinkled his forehead.

"Well, there's a lot of little things. And there is a big thing that I don't know what it is. That's what I came to find out."

"What are some of the little things?"

"Well . . . One is what would make my teacher look more like — Lorene, when she looks at me. Maybe it's beads. Like the ones Lorene's got around her neck . . . And something to make Mrs. — another teacher remember me. I guess something to wear on the front of her dress. So when I look into her room I can see it on the front of her dress, and I'll know she remembered me when she put it on. You see, she can't remember me now because she's so busy with a lot of other boys . . ."

Between pauses Johnny talked faster and faster. It was

easy to talk to the Answer Man because he did not interrupt, even during the pauses. He just nodded now and then, scribbling in a little book he held in the palm of his hand.

"I need a little badge to show I am a Methodist . . . And something to make four boys stop plaguing me . . . And something to give a girl that likes me — she's the only one that likes me; at school, I mean — only I don't hardly ever see her anymore because I moved away and I can't go on her side of the schoolground . . . And a book to have to read at home when Miss Besse won't let me read at school. A book about — about a boy that smoked a pipe and went down river on a raft . . . And something to show my father I'm tough — like that boy was . . . And something alive for my little sister. A small animal. It would have to be a very small animal because it would have to live in the house. All she's got now to pat is the picture of a dog on a rug . . . And I need something to play music for her, too. Because she likes music. Not the radio. She likes the same piece over and over. She's little, and she'll get lonesome when it comes dark if I — if I'm not there to sing to her —"

He felt his eyes filling with tears, and blinked them back.

"Well, that's quite a list," the Answer Man said. "We'd better get started on it. Follow me."

Johnny followed him. He found that an emporium was more vast a place than he had ever imagined a temple. The ceiling seemed as high as the sky and was blue like the sky at night, with stars twinkling. He could not see the outer walls. To either side of the corridor through which he followed the Answer Man wonders were massed. Whatever there was one of there were thousands, like the carnations. Thousands of dolls. Thousands of little jars with sprigs of holly on their covers. Thousands of dishes. Thousands of Christmas wreaths. Thousands of balloons.

Thousands of everything. And thousands of people looking and touching and talking and laughing.

When the Answer Man stopped, Johnny asked, "Has it
always been here?"

"What?"

"The em-porium."

"No. It's new. Brand new. This is Opening Day. Lots
of bargains. . . . Now here are the beads you mentioned. Pearl beads. Like Lorene's."

The treasures were given to Johnny, one after another.
Pearls for Miss Besse, in white cotton, inside a little white
box. A twisted gold pin for Mrs. Curtis with the words "I
Love You" on it. A plain gold bar on which a machine
inscribed the letters METHODIST, big and plain. Four
giant chocolate bars. A picture of Johnny himself, taken
by himself by pushing a button from where he sat in
a brightly lit closet, looking into a mirror. A square fat
book with *"Tom Sawyer* and *Huckleberry Finn"* on the
cover. Two corncob pipes with short stems; one for
Johnny and one for Johnny's father.

"You won't smoke yours," said the Answer Man. "But
you can chew on it, while he smokes his."

Johnny nodded.

The Answer Man was not always close beside him.
Sometimes he had to go away to answer other people's
questions. But he was never out of Johnny's sight, and
while he was gone Johnny looked at the things in the
paper bag with handles which had been given him and
which had "Main Street Emporium" printed in red on the
side. He looked at the white box, and the pin on the card,
and the candy, and the picture of himself, and the book,
and the pipes. He pinned the Methodist badge on his
jacket. And all the time Lorene was keeping his mother's
carnations, far more brilliant and beautiful than those
which had been in the pulpit basket.

Once when the Answer Man came back, Johnny looked

up at him and said, "It seems as if this is a magic country. Of course it isn't. But it seems as if it is."

"It's better than that," said the Answer Man. "It's America. Now, you wanted a music box. This way."

The music box played "Lullabye and Good Night" when Johnny turned the handle.

"And a small animal. Follow me."

They went to a corner where a big yellow cat lay on a blue carpet. A small black and white kitten was cuddled against her side. A bigger, yellow kitten was lapping her ears. Two three-colored kittens were eating from a pink saucer.

"Would your little sister like one of these?"

"Oh . . . Yes, sir."

"Which one?"

"One of those eating from the saucer. The other ones are too — too little to leave their mother."

"That's right. Which one of the three-coloreds?"

"The biggest one. You have to be as big as you can — to leave your mother."

"That's right."

The geni, Alex, had kept saying, "Right you are." The Answer Man kept saying, "That's right." In this place Johnny was almost always right. In other places he was almost always wrong.

"Put the biggest three-colored kitten in a box," the Answer Man told a man in a blue shirt. "Punch holes in both ends."

"You picked a beauty," said the man in the blue shirt. "You picked a beauty, my boy."

The Answer Man tucked the big box under his arm.

"That's all on our list," he said. "Except the carnations. How will you carry them all, Johnny, if you have far to go?"

"I can't carry them," Johnny said. "They will have to be sent."

"Sent where?"

"To — Mrs. John Lee, North Bainbridge, Maine."

"Then you need cards on them, don't you? Since they are for different people? Here are our gift tags. Ten in each package. And here is a desk where you can write them. I'll take the kitten down to Lorene. If you finish writing before I come back, just wait for me here."

Johnny sat in a chair which exactly fitted him. He dipped the pen in a little inkwell. He had never used a pen before.

He wrote slowly and carefully, "Miss Besse from Johnny Lee"; "Mrs. Curtis from Johnny Lee"; "Wally" and "Kenny" and "Pete" and "Tarb" from "your friend, Johnny Lee"; "Linda with love from Johnny"; "Dad from Johnny, and the other one is for me only I will not smoke it until I am older if you do not want me to but some boys do and I could"; "For my mother, to make the front room smell sweet when she plays the organ, Johnny"; and "Deedy, so you will not miss me, your big brother."

He did not make a single blot. He was sure he spelled every word right.

He did not know why writing the cards made him want to cry. It must be that any writing made him feel that way. It was a habit he must get over. He could write very nicely here in the emporium. Even Miss Besse would think so.

He wrote "John Lee, Junior" in the front of his book.

He was tying the tags to the gifts, making hard knots in the red strings, when a voice said, "Well, Johnny Lee! Hello!"

He looked up, startled. It was Mr. Dwight.

Johnny got up from his knees and smiled.

He said quickly, "Hello. See all the things I've got. You said I could use the five dollars for something I would like to have. I didn't know five dollars was so much money. You hadn't ought to give me so much. It isn't all gone. You can have some back."

He took change from his pocket and held it out.

"That's yours," Mr. Dwight said cheerfully. "I had enough to pay for the refrigerator. And I've just bought some refrigerator dishes here for my wife for Christmas. But you certainly have made a haul for less than five dollars —"

"He helped me. The Answer Man," said Johnny, pointing over Mr. Dwight's shoulder.

"It's opening day," said the Answer Man. "That helped. Johnny, is Mr. Dwight a friend of yours?"

Johnny did not know what to say, but Mr. Dwight did. He said briskly, "I certainly am."

"He is of mine, too, Johnny," the Answer Man said. "He was my teacher when I was your age. In fact, I guess you and I might call him a Head Answer Man."

Johnny looked at Mr. Dwight with new respect.

"Are you?" he asked. "Honest?"

"I've answered a lot of questions in my time," admitted Mr. Dwight. "The best answers usually are the ones people find for themselves. Well, Johnny, what do you say — want a ride home with all this stuff?"

Johnny was silent. Nobody else said anything.

Finally he whispered, "I wasn't going home. I was going to send them."

"I'll tell you," the Answer Man said. "I'm kind of worried about sending the kitten. She isn't used to being shut up. She's meowing quite a lot now . . . And the fact is those carnations would freeze, this weather, if they got left in a cold place. Like on a baggage truck at the station."

"My car's right outside," said Mr. Dwight. "The heater would warm it up before the cold got through to the carnations. And you could take the kitten out of the box and hold him on your lap."

"Well, couldn't you — couldn't you take them home for me?"

"I couldn't tend the kitten and drive too. If I opened the window to signal, he might jump out. It's snowing

great guns. It's getting dark. It's going to be a wild night
. . . Don't you want to go home, Johnny?"

"Yes," Johnny whispered. "Yes, I — want to —"

"Then come along," said Mr. Dwight briskly.

"Follow me," said the Answer Man for the last time.
But this time he put his arm around Johnny's shoulders.

Lorene gave them the flowers wrapped in paper, and
the cat box. The Answer Man went as far as the car and
put the cat box on Johnny's lap.

Before he closed the door, he tore a handful of sheets
from his notebook and gave them to Mr. Dwight.

"It's Johnny's list of the things he needed," he said.
"You and he may want to check it over. I think we got all
the little things, but there was one big thing — you talk
that over with the Head Answer Man, Johnny. Good-bye
and good luck. Be sure to drop in at the Emporium whenever you're in Treadwell."

He waved and smiled. Mr. Dwight headed the car out
into the traffic. They rode without talking until they were
in the country.

Then Mr. Dwight said, "Tell me about since I saw you
this morning, will you, Johnny? It must make a good
story. I like to have someone tell me a story when I'm
driving. It keeps me awake. How did you happen to go to
Treadwell?"

The kitten was out of the box now, and Johnny had her
cuddled inside his jacket, against his stomach, with only
her chin sticking out. He was keeping her warm and she
was keeping him warm. It was easy to talk, riding along
through the stormy dark, scratching a kitten's chin.

". . . I didn't know I was going to Treadwell," he
concluded. "But I had to go somewhere. I was afraid to
go back to school and I was afraid to go home. Mis' Curtis said being afraid made you strong. Does it?"

"Sometimes," said Mr. Dwight. "Some people. It depends."

"Brave people, you mean?"

"Maybe they're brave. Maybe they're just the fighting kind."

"I'm not. Linda is, but I'm not . . . Does that mean I am a sissy, do you think?"

"Have you read much about Jesus, Johnny?"

"Some. And Mis' Curtis told us about him."

"Do you think he was a sissy?"

"Oh, no, sir."

"A lot of people did. Some still do. Because he said that if anybody was hit on one cheek he should turn the other."

"I think that was brave."

"It's one of the hardest things in the world to do. And I bet you've done it a lot of times."

"No. I run away."

"I didn't mean when somebody hit you with his fist. I meant when somebody was mean to you. You weren't mean back. You kept on trying to get along with him, didn't you?"

"Yes. Because I was afraid."

"Partly because you were afraid. Maybe that is how being afraid has made you strong. Without your even knowing it."

"I'm afraid to fight. Abraham Lincoln didn't like to fight. . . . But he did."

"There you are. He didn't like to. But when it was right, he did."

After a minute Johnny said, "I would fight. If it was right. If there was any chance I could beat."

"Ah," said Mr. Dwight gently. "It is a foolish man who fights when there is no chance of beating. Unless there is no other way."

"I couldn't beat Wally Stewart in a fight. Nor Bill Sudbury. Nor three or four together."

"You shouldn't have to. I couldn't fight a husky young gangster. Much less a bunch of them. I should call a policeman."

"I don't know any policeman."

"Maybe North Bainbridge needs more policemen."

"I couldn't fight Mr. Sturtevant. Nor Miss Besse. Nor — my father."

"You shouldn't have to."

"They're too big . . . And even if I could I wouldn't want to."

"No. They're your friends."

"Yes," said Johnny faintly. He added, "But they're not — not like you are."

Mr. Dwight rested his hand for an instant on Johnny's knee.

He said, "There's been a misunderstanding here. A lot of misunderstandings. Don't worry about it, Johnny. It isn't your job to straighten them out. It's mine. I'll explain to Mr. Sturtevant and Miss Besse. And to your father too. They'll understand when I explain it to them. There won't be any trouble when you get home, nor when you go back to school. I promise . . . How's the kitten?"

"She's fine," Johnny said. "Gee, she's cute."

He felt all over as his foot felt sometimes when it had been numb, and then full of hot prickles, and now was his own foot again.

"What are you going to name her?"

". . . Lucky. They say a three-colored cat is lucky."

"This has certainly been a lucky day for both of us . . . How did you get to Treadwell, Johnny?"

"I walked."

"That was a long walk for a boy your size. Tell me about it."

Johnny told about the bushes by the river, and the bridge, and the track, and the train going by, and that reminded him of the tracks he had made on the map for Mrs. Curtis. Suddenly he laughed aloud.

He said, "When we did that at Sunday school, all the other boys knew what they wanted to find out, so we could tell where they would have to go. I didn't know what I wanted to find out, so there was no way to tell where I would have to go. But it was easy. I just got on the only track I could see, and I went to Treadwell. And then I found out."

"What did you find out, Johnny?"

"There is an em-porium. It's even better than a temple. You can ask questions, and you can get things too. You can eat when you want to, whatever you want to eat. It tastes good. People don't scold you. They help you. It's full of wonderful things, and you can look at them all, and nobody sends you away, and you can have some of them. It seems like magic, only it's real. The Answer Man said it was better than magic; it was America . . . But North Bainbridge is in America. And there's no em-porium in North Bainbridge; is there?"

"Maybe," said Mr. Dwight. "Maybe there is. You keep on looking for it. It would be much smaller than the one in Treadwell, of course, because North Bainbridge is a much smaller town. And it would seem different to you in many ways besides size."

"Why?" Johnny asked.

He was growing sleepy.

"Because North Bainbridge is home, where you are a small boy and people see you that way and treat you that way. It can be a good way, until you are older. Today you were old enough to go to the emporium in the big city of Treadwell, and there you were treated as grown-ups expect to be treated. When you are older still, you will probably go there again, and stay longer."

"I want —" said Johnny sleepily.

"What do you want, Johnny?"

"To stay in the em-porium always when I grow up. I want — to be an Answer Man."

"If you want to enough," said Mr. Dwight, "you will. All in good time . . . Don't think, though, Johnny, that life is always as you saw it there today. Grown-ups are not always treated as they would like to be. Life is not often easy. But when life is hard for a child it is harder than it could be for anyone who has lived through the process of growing up. What I can't see is why so few adults realize that. They think children are happy enough just because they are children. So when life is hard for adults and they can't fight back successfully at people of their own size they often strike out at children. That's why some children are the most miserable creatures in the world. That's why some of them run away. That's why some of them never come back."

He knew Johnny was asleep. He was talking to himself.

In the principal's office Mr. Sturtevant had just replaced the telephone receiver on its hook.

"Well, Miss Besse," he said, "there's little news, and what we have conflicts. The boy is apparently not in the village. Mrs. Lee's husband has come from the shipyard and they are on their way here. Scouts are scouring the countryside. The crossing tender saw a boy about Johnny's size in a brown hooded jacket like Johnny's walking up the track when he went out to stop the traffic for the twelve o'clock express to go through. He shouted, but the boy gave no sign of hearing. He went on along the track out of sight. The train was a minute or two late. Nothing has been reported by the trainmen. The mailman thought he saw a boy sitting on a girder under the Forks Bridge when he drove by about eleven o'clock. He thought nothing of it at the time, but remembers it now. They couldn't both have been Johnny."

"No," agreed Miss Besse. "Funny how people always —"

"Perhaps I should try to contact the superintendent. But he is in upper towns in the union. I doubt if I could reach him."

"I wish you would try," Miss Besse said.

Mr. Sturtevant frowned. He preferred that the superintendent should not know that a boy had left his school without permission.

"I've reported to the police," he said. "Too bad we don't have a more efficient force here. They just say they never had any complaints about the boy before. I told them this was no complaint, only that the boy may be in trouble and we've got to find him. It's a cold day —"

"And it is growing dark," Miss Besse said, shivering.

"I think he'll be back when he gets hungry," Mr. Sturtevant said. "His mother says he has no money."

I wish he had, thought Miss Besse wildly. I wish he had stolen that fifty-cent piece we made such a fuss about. But he didn't. There it was wedged under my desk all the time. Some rascal like Kenny Schultz must have pushed it there with his toe. It never got there by itself. If I hadn't moved the desk myself, it wouldn't have been found until next summer. . . . If Johnny had money, I could think maybe he had gone where he could use money. Not into the woods . . . or into the river . . . or under a train. But without money —

The young, red-headed Methodist pastor came into the principal's office. He looked very grave.

"I've just heard," he said, "that Johnny Lee has disappeared. What have you found out? What can I do? It's nearly five o'clock, and a storm is blowing up. He had only a cotton shirt under his jacket, because he tore his sweater yesterday."

"Do you know Johnny?" Miss Besse asked eagerly.

"Not as well as I wish I did."

Did anybody know Johnny?

"Last Sunday he came to our Sunday school and . . . there was an unfortunate incident."

"What happened?" asked Miss Besse.

"I didn't hear about it until just now. It was our Sunday-school superintendent who told me. Since he heard of Johnny's disappearance he just remembered that last Sunday the pulpit flowers were offered to the pupils, one blossom for each. When Johnny went up to receive his, the —

well, the person in charge, who knew he had been to the Baptist Sunday school since he had been to ours, said, 'Why don't you get your flowers at the Baptist church, young man?' So Johnny didn't take one. The superintendent thought it too bad at the time, and meant to try to explain it to Johnny, but when he looked for him again he had gone."

"Huh-huh," Mr. Sturtevant laughed, without mirth. "Well, a flower — I can't imagine a nine-year-old boy caring much whether he got a flower or not."

"Oh, I believe Johnny would like flowers," Miss Besse said. "He used to pick goldenrod on his way to school last fall."

Yes, and she had told him to leave it outside because it gave some people hay fever.

"Even if he did not want the flower," Mr. Shawn said, "perhaps it hurt him to have it refused, in such a way, when he had gone up to receive it." He looked distressed. "But hardly enough —"

"No, no," Mr. Sturtevant agreed. "Such a little thing —"

That was Sunday, Miss Besse thought. Yesterday was Wednesday and I spent most of the day trying to find out who stole the fifty cents that was wedged under my desk. Tuesday I told Johnny, before the class, that he was careless. I punished him by telling him he could not have a book to read all the rest of the week, and Johnny loves to read.

She thought, I feel skinned, as if all my nerve endings were bare. I've never felt this way before. I don't think I can stand it —

The minister was waiting for the principal to tell him what he could do.

Mr. Sturtevant was rubbing the desk hard with the eraser of his pencil.

Then the Lees appeared silently in the doorway. Jack wore his work clothes. He was tired and tense but he had a strong grip on himself. Marge had put on her best coat, over her housedress, and tied a kerchief over her hair. Her eyes were red and swollen.

"Come in, Mrs. Lee, Mr. Lee," the principal said nervously. "Sit down. You know Mr. Shawn? And Miss Besse, Johnny's teacher?"

Jack nodded shortly. He fixed his eyes on Mr. Sturtevant.

Marge smiled faintly.

"Mr. Shawn has called," she said. "He's been real nice to Johnny." Her lips trembled. She turned to Miss Besse. "I ought to have been to see you before," she apologized. "Johnny was always asking me to come. But I don't know. I couldn't seem to leave the baby."

You've left her now, haven't you? And don't talk about Johnny in the past tense, Miss Besse wanted to scream.

But instead she said humbly, "I should have come to see you, Mrs. Lee. We should have talked about Johnny. We might have helped each other to help him more."

I'm talking about him in the past tense myself, she thought.

Mr. Sturtevant looked at his watch. It showed half-past five. Jack glanced at the window. The streetlights had gone on.

"I can't stop here long," he said. "I've got to get going."

Mr. Sturtevant rubbed his hands.

"Wait a minute," he said. "Let's put our heads together. How did Johnny seem to feel when he left home this morning, Mrs. Lee?"

"Same as always, I guess," Marge answered, low. "He never can eat much breakfast. He didn't want to come to school. But you told me, Mr. Sturtevant —"

"Yes," the principal answered uneasily. "The state law requires regular attendance, of course. The school system — it's the same in all schools."

"I can't see why he felt the way he did about school,"

his mother said. "I always loved to go. And he said Miss Besse was nice to him."

Miss Besse's every nerve end shrieked denial.

"There are so many children in my room," she said. "What helps one may hurt another. It's hard to know. Johnny was so bright I — may have expected too much of him."

Mr. Sturtevant raised his eyebrows as if this did not make sense.

"It is a teacher's duty to see that a child's achievement is commensurate with his ability," he said. "I checked Johnny's rating on the intelligence test given him when he entered school. It was — er — very high. He should be an honor pupil. But on the report which went out just last Friday I find he had no E's, only one G, and the rest F's. Naturally, Miss Besse —"

"I knew he could get E's," Marge admitted. "His teachers always said so, but he never did. He didn't show me his card until Saturday. He was helping his father on the truck Friday night. We moved into the village. When I saw it, I asked him why it wasn't better and he said he didn't know and asked if he could go to the movies. That made me kind of mad. I guess I was tired. I told him to stay in and write his spelling words."

That was Saturday, clicked off Miss Besse's mind.

Jack cleared his throat.

"Maybe he felt bad about leaving the farm," he said. "I found him crying in the barn two, three times last week. But I couldn't keep a farm up and carry a full-time job besides. So when I found a house in town we could get into, I sold the farm. I thought it would be better for Johnny to be where he had other kids to play with. Boys, I mean. He was by himself too much."

"The only other young one near us, out there, was Linda Morris. You know," Marge said to Miss Besse.

Miss Besse said, "I guess they were friends. Maybe Johnny missed her."

"But aren't they both in your grade?" Mr. Sturtevant asked Miss Besse.

"Yes," Miss Besse answered. "But boys and girls are separated on the playground, Mr. Sturtevant."

Mr. Sturtevant cleared his throat.

"That's true," he agreed. "Yes, certainly. It's the practice in the majority of schools."

It seemed to strengthen Mr. Sturtevant to think of how many principals did as he did, right or wrong, Johnny or no Johnny.

Mr. Shawn bent forward.

"Did he say anything about Sunday school after he got home last Sunday, Mrs. Lee?"

"No. I don't remember. Nothing special, I guess."

Jack stood up.

"I don't see as this is getting us anywhere," he said. "It's almost six o'clock. Johnny might have gone out to the farm. I'll run out there."

He crossed to the principal's desk. He bent over and spoke low but Miss Besse was near enough to hear every word.

"I'm going to get a bunch of guys to go with me. There's a lot of woods out there a little feller could get lost in if he wasn't paying attention to where he went. And the firemen've offered to . . . drag the river. I wish you'd call the police in the other towns around, and get 'em going. Wish you'd call the newspapers and the radio station —"

Miss Besse moved over beside Johnny's mother. Their shoulders touched.

"Don't you go," Miss Besse said. "Stay here with me. Everything'll be done that should be."

"I suppose I ought to go and get the baby," Marge said dully. "I left her with a neighbor I don't know very well. She isn't two years old yet, and when it begins to get dark, she cries to go home, to the farm. Johnny . . . Johnny used to comfort her."

She covered her face with her hands.

"Oh, I wish he'd worn his sweater today. I wish I'd got it mended. I wish I hadn't scolded when he tore it. It was only that he caught it on a nail in the cellar. It was a strange cellar, and he was getting me some wood, and he didn't know there was a nail —"

Miss Besse put her arm around Johnny's mother.

"He should have had an E in reading," she said. "He was the best reader in the class. That is, he read best for meaning. But I never told him so. I said the things I shouldn't have said, and didn't say the things I should have said. It's hard to do right by so many."

But excuses did not count now.

Where was Johnny?

Jack stopped by his wife.

"Don't cry, Marge," he said hoarsely. "We'll find Johnny. You want me to take you home?"

She shook her head.

"I've got to stay here, Jack. How can I go home? I just brought the tree in from the garage this morning after Johnny left, and set out the trimmings. I was going to surprise him. I was making a wreath for the door when . . . when they called me. It's there on the kitchen table. How can I go back there? It can't be . . . it can't be Christmas without —"

"You let her stay with me, Mr. Lee," Miss Besse said quite steadily. "I'll walk up with her by-and-by. It's better for her to be here."

But not in my room, she thought. Not in Johnny's room. Because there is a Christmas tree there, with a paper chain that Johnny made, and paper candles pasted on the windows, and the books I wouldn't let Johnny read. Nothing else but forty empty seats — all of them Johnny's now.

As Johnny's father was going out, he met Mr. Dwight, the superintendent, coming in.

"Well, Mr. Dwight," Mr. Sturtevant said, rising.

"Didn't expect to see you back today. I — er — was just going to telephone you."

Johnny's father tried to pass the superintendent, but Mr. Dwight did not move aside.

He said, "How do you do? I think you're Mr. Lee. Wait a minute, please. Why were you going to telephone me, Mr. Sturtevant?"

His voice was low and pleasant. His glance was like a firm rein which caught up everyone in the room.

Mr. Sturtevant cleared his throat.

"Mr. Lee's son — one of our third-graders — left the playground at morning recess. We assumed he had gone home, but when I checked with his mother, she hadn't see him. We haven't been able to find him. I'm just about to — er — send out an alarm to neighboring towns, and I wanted to check with you on that before I did. Of course, huh-huh, no doubt he'll turn up for supper."

"What makes you think that?"

"Well — huh — a hungry boy —"

"Perhaps Johnny has been hungry a long time. Are you Johnny's friends?"

Mr. Dwight looked at the two women.

"I'm his teacher," Miss Besse said, very low.

"I'm his . . . mother," Marge whispered.

"I see. And what have you all been doing here?"

"We were trying," Miss Besse said, "to think why Johnny would want to go away."

"And did you find reasons?"

"None," said Mr. Sturtevant, "sufficient —"

"I did," Miss Besse murmured. "I think they were quite sufficient."

Mr. Dwight regarded her approvingly.

"Those reasons must be remembered," he said. "We must try to make good use of this knowledge, if Johnny comes back to us."

"Oh, surely," Miss Besse said, "he will come back."

"Why should he?" Mr. Dwight asked.

"I don't know," Miss Besse answered. "I mean, he shouldn't. But I think he would, if he knew."

"Why do you think he would, Miss Besse?"

"Because — because children are like that!"

Mr. Dwight's eyes on Miss Besse were wholly kind.

He said gently, "I think you could be Johnny's friend."

Johnny's father said, "I've got to go. It's getting late and cold. I've got a feeling that he might be up at the farm. Maybe in the barn. He liked that barn."

"We've got a little barn where we are here," said Johnny's mother. "We thought we'd fix it into a garage to rent. But Johnny could have it, couldn't he, Jack. We could bring down some hay. He could keep rabbits —"

"I'd been thinking of a bicycle for Christmas, but we could get him a horse," his father said. "He always wanted a pony. He's too big for a pony now. But he could have a small horse."

It's present tense again, thought Miss Besse. Present tense for Johnny.

"When he's learned to ride," his mother said, "he can go out to Linda's whenever he wants to, on his little horse."

She stood up in her excitement and pushed back her kerchief. Her hair was short and soft.

"Oh, Jack, if you go up there, bring down something from the sitting room. Johnny wanted that furniture. I didn't think we'd need it. But we will now. If we don't rent the garage. I can make it look nice, with some new cretonne. I guess he'd like that . . . Oh, if we can just find him —"

"He can't have gone far," said Mr. Sturtevant positively. "He had no money."

"Yes, he did," said Mr. Dwight quietly. "Johnny had money."

They all stared at him. He came into the room, sat on the edge of the principal's desk and smiled at them.

"Let me tell you," he said, "I am a very careless man."

(*Accuracy is not enough, John. We must learn not to be careless.*) "When I left this building just as the bell was ringing at the end of recess, I dropped my billfold on the walk. Johnny saw it, and chased my car to the edge of the village to give it back to me. I had two hundred and fourteen dollars in it. I saw that Johnny was a very honest boy; his jacket was unbuttoned and I saw he wore no sweater; and I saw that his eyes were sad. I made up my mind to find out more about him later. I asked his name, and I gave him five dollars as a reward . . . But I forgot there is a rule that no child is to leave the playground without permission. If I had remembered that, I should have returned with Johnny or given him a note. Because a boy with eyes like Johnny's is fearful. Such a boy has been made fearful by the very people who should have helped him to be unafraid."

But Mr. Dwight's eyes were still kind. His voice was gentle.

"So Johnny had money," he continued.

"And what," Miss Besse asked, "do you think he did after that, Mr. Dwight?"

"I think he kept on going because he did not dare come back to school and he did not dare go home. I think he followed the railroad track because he knew it went somewhere. I think when he came to Treadwell he spent his five dollars mostly for Christmas presents. In fact, I know he did."

"How?" his father asked. "How do you know, sir?"

"Because," Mr. Dwight said gently, "a former student of mine pointed him out to me in Treadwell an hour or so ago. I gave him a ride back here. He is outside in my car now, with presents for his mother, father, and baby sister, his teachers, a little girl named Linda, and four boys whose names, he says, are Wally, Pete, Tarb, and Kenny. He said they weren't his friends but he wanted to be friends with them, and he thought if he put chocolate bars on the school tree for them tomorrow, they might like him better. I asked him to wait while I came in to explain to Miss Besse and Mr. Sturtevant, and I said that after that I would take him home and explain to his parents. I've told him that he has nothing to fear from any of you."

"Why — er — no," said Mr. Sturtevant. "As a matter of fact, he has missed only part of the day: the — ah — records are all straight."

"The important record," said Mr. Dwight, "is in Johnny."

"I don't know how to thank you," Johnny's mother sobbed. "I'll — I'll write you a letter tomorrow, Mr. Dwight. But now all I can think of is — seeing Johnny."

She was already starting toward the doorway.

"Wait," Mr. Dwight said quietly. "Take time to compose yourself, Mrs. Lee. You mustn't make Johnny feel he has been the cause of any distress. Tell him just that you are here because you had begun to worry about him. He will hear later how much concern has been felt, and it will be all right then; he will know he is not blamed for it. It will help to prove to him how much people cared. But tonight just show him you are pleased that he is back, and ask about his shopping. He almost forgets to be afraid when he thinks about the presents he has bought. You will see one of those he has for you as soon as you see him, Mrs. Lee. I hope you like red carnations."

Miss Besse did not shed a tear until the Lees had gone and Mr. Shawn and Mr. Sturtevant had gone too.

Then Mr. Dwight let her cry for a while. He seemed busy at the desk.

Finally he said, "Fortunately, Miss Besse, we still have the tomorrows."

Miss Besse stood up, tucking her handkerchief inside her cuff.

"Yes, Mr. Dwight," she said.

She went downstairs. As she passed the fourth-grade room, Mrs. Curtis opened the door.

"Poor Mabel!" she said. "What a day you've had! But

it's come out all right, hasn't it? Mr. Shawn was just in and told me. Don't blame yourself, Mabel. It's no more your fault than everybody else's. We're all in the same boat. I had that boy in Sunday school. If I'd had my wits about me, I'd have helped you more with him this week than I have. I will after this. We'll right him around, now we've waked up. You see if we don't."

Miss Besse went on into her own room, and the Christmas tree branches were tilted up. The wreath on the door looked fat and gay. The paper candles on the window-panes were white against the dusk.

She thought, *Tomorrow I'll praise accuracy where there isn't neatness, and neatness may follow. I'll praise neatness where there is little or no accuracy. We'll sing as long as the children want to sing. We'll all have Christmas because of Johnny. Because Johnny has given Christmas back to us.*

hristmas 1950

"We haven't made very much headway today, have we?" said Miss Farley with a faint smile. "I had hoped we might finish our trays at this last meeting before Christmas, but it is hard working in gloves, isn't it? It makes our fingers all thumbs . . . Well, put your materials into your bags, and Maxine and Sheila will serve refreshments . . . Joyce has her tray nearly finished anyway — why, look, girls! Joyce's is *all* finished! Isn't it beautiful?"

She held up the disk which Joyce had painstakingly created of strips of tin cut from cans and woven like basketry, then trimmed into a circle with heavy shears. The edges had been turned under and hammered down.

The other seven members of the All-Girls Club of Cambrook looked at it apathetically. They knew from experience that making it had been a hard job. They saw that it was neatly made. But it was hardly an object of beauty. Anyone could see that it was just strips of tin put together and trimmed and hammered down. It was no use to say anything about it because Joyce could not hear. Joyce was totally deaf. She had been born that way. Joyce had never heard a sound in her life. And these trays had been planned as Christmas gifts for the girls to give their mothers, but Joyce had no mother. The whole idea of making these trays was tiresome and dreary. Most of them would never be finished. The one which had would serve no purpose.

For Joyce's sake, some of the girls put on an admiring expression — because Joyce could see — and Miss Farley stroked the smooth edge and squeezed Joyce's hand. Joyce looked proud, and tucked her tray into the side of the stroller where her baby brother slept.

Joyce always brought the baby to club meetings. She took him everywhere she went. She had to, because there was no one else to care for him. Their mother had died when he was born, and their father slept all day and worked nights. The neighbors had thought at first that the state should take the baby since Joyce was only thirteen by the calendar and nobody knew how old she was in her mind. People who have been deaf all their lives only make queer sounds when they try to talk. But she loved the baby, fed him and kept him clean, and he was as healthy as any baby in town. The doctor said Joyce was doing for him all that a mother could do, so everyone had gradually stopped talking and thinking about them.

Sheila brought in the jelly pudding she had made in custard cups. She must have held them in hot water too long, to unmold them, because they were not quite firm and there was red liquid trickling across each plate. The dabs of whipped cream were small and sort of buttery. Maxine passed little sponge cakes but they were not homemade. She had bought them at the grocery and frosted them green. Nobody was fooled.

It was so dreary, sitting there in Miss Farley's room with her bed made up to look like a couch and the door open into the closet where she kept her electric plate and dime-store dishes, eating soppy pudding and store cake, and knowing they were supposed to be happy because school had closed and Christmas would be next week.

"Now wasn't that delicious," said Miss Farley with false enthusiasm. "Joyce and I'll take care of the dishes this time. The rest of you run along. Don't forget your paper bags. Try to finish the trays before Christmas Eve. You have a whole week. Merry Christmas and happy New Year! See you at school!"

She let them out into the dusky hall. Her landlady never turned on the hall light until she turned on the porch light, though there was only one small window.

"Thank you, Miss Farley. Have a nice vacation," the girls called over their shoulders.

What they said carried no conviction. Their shoulders drooped. Their feet dragged.

Miss Farley sighed, closing her door.

Joyce was already picking up the dishes, humming tunelessly.

Joyce had stayed after the others because she always did. She never had to hurry home, for the baby was always with her. She was picking up the dishes because they were there to be picked up.

"Bless you, Joyce," said Miss Farley. "You don't need to hear. You know without hearing. But I do wish you could talk. Maybe you could tell us what we need to hear. Nobody else seems to know what it is. I'm sure I don't. All the people who can talk are saying things that make us more mixed up. Maybe it's because you can't hear that you aren't mixed up. Maybe that's why your face is so calm and sweet and happy looking. Maybe that's why when you have a tray to make, you can settle down and make it."

Joyce stood watching Miss Farley's lips. She did not know what they were saying, but she could tell that they were expressing approval of her. She nodded and smiled, and poured hot water into the pan from the teakettle.

"Now Mr. Smith is perfectly right that we need that gymnasium, and so are the other people who think so," said Miss Farley, drying as Joyce washed. "The young people in this town have no place to play basketball, no place except the movies to go in the evenings, no suitable place for club meetings or parties or exhibits. The school children have no place to get exercise during school days in winter. It is different than it was fifty years ago when children walked long distances to school, could slide on the pasture hills and in the streets, had wood and water to carry and barn stock to take care of; and when teachers thought it was good for lively youngsters to sit still for hours at a time."

Joyce nodded and smiled.

"But Mr. Dyer is perfectly right that raising taxes to pay for that gymnasium is going to be very hard on a great many people in this town who can't afford it. They need their taxes reduced instead of increased. As he says, it isn't only property owners — like your father — who are going to suffer. People who rent will be affected, too. With prices what they are, already some families aren't getting enough to eat. I know if Mrs. Worster asks any more for this room, I can't even buy one meal out a day on my salary, and I don't think I can stand getting all my meals on this hot plate. Then there are the farmers trying to get a living off their rocky acres. Many of them don't have money to pay doctors' bills. And the people who own woodland are going to sell off the lumber half grown because they can't pay the taxes on it. Then the town will lose the taxes, there'll be a greater fire hazard and droughts and — Joyce, there must be some way out!"

Joyce nodded and smiled.

"The people who went to that special town meeting last summer were mostly the ones who were sure that we must have a gymnasium. They were so enthusiastic they went early and took all the seats. Many people stayed away or left because they knew Mr. Smith and Mr. Dyer were going to have a dreadful battle and they didn't want to hear it; and they thought the polls were going to be open all the next day for them to vote. Country people can't get to an evening meeting in town very well anyway. But then Mr. Smith made a motion around midnight to vote then and there on raising three hundred thousand dollars for the gym, and it passed, so there was no chance to vote the next day. That made people mad. And it scared them. Now it seems that three hundred thousand isn't enough to do the job, so there has to be another special meeting right after New Year's. If this town doesn't blow up before that night, it will then.

"Because people on both sides are getting madder and more scared every hour, and saying worse things about one another. Poor Mr. Paige is begging and pleading every Sunday in the pulpit for cooperation and understanding and constructive suggestions and the use of democratic procedures, and now some people are angry with him and more are laughing at him. Some say that all the resentment of Mr. Smith is because he is a newcomer in town and Jewish. Others say the only reason Mr. Dyer is against the gym is because he is a politician and wants the money to use for his own purposes. Others say that Father Renaud is against it because it is to be built next to the public school instead of halfway between that and the parochial school.

"Now I don't believe any of this. I don't believe those opposing the gym even knew Mr. Smith was Jewish before his friends brought up the race issue, nor that it makes the slightest difference to anybody; many of the opposition haven't lived in town even as long as he has. As for Mr. Dyer, he's been chairman of the town board of selectmen ever since I came here to teach ten years ago, and I've never heard one word against him until this matter of the gym came up; but I heard a great deal about how much money he saved the taxpayers, how good he was to the poor, and how he had devoted his life to the town. Every word Mr. Paige has said is true and wise and good and people should be ashamed to twist it the way they have. And I don't know how anyone dares say what Father Renaud thinks about the gym because no one can be found who has heard him say one word about it, for or against, anywhere at anytime. To his people who go to him for advice in the campaign he just says, 'Pray . . . And beware of thinking that the end ever justifies the means.' Which is just what Mr. Paige is telling his people.

"No, the real trouble isn't Mr. Smith or Mr. Dyer or Mr. Paige or Father Renaud," said Miss Farley, shaking her head.

Joyce smiled and shook her head.

"They're doing and saying what they believe is right. The trouble is that the rest of us are so mixed up by what they've told us. We're the ones who have to decide and either way seems to be wrong, so we talk and talk and think of nothing but trouble, and it grows worse and worse. I'm afraid there isn't any heart for Christmas in this town this year. Even the children are affected by it. That's why they couldn't finish their trays."

The dishes were done, the sink scrubbed. Joyce snapped the button on the dish cupboard door. The baby stirred and crowed.

Miss Farley put her arm around Joyce.

"Your baby is awake, dear," she said. "You take him home for supper and I'll pack my bag and catch the night train for Boston. I'm just going to believe that things will be better after Christmas. I've thought of one way maybe

I can help you. I'm going to find out about sign language, and get books on it and start learning it myself. Then maybe I can teach you. I don't know why I haven't tried that before. Why, Joyce, next year we'll be talking together!"

Joyce smiled and nodded, saw the baby's feet waving, and went to put on his bonnet.

The other seven members of the All-Girls Club had gone slowly down the street. At the corner they waited by the old stable for Sheila's father to come from work and take Sheila and Emily home. Sheila and Emily lived on farms up-country.

It was cold and they wished the sun would come out before it set. They kicked at the frozen turf of the stable yard. They wished it would snow.

An old man came out of a house nearby, leaning on his cane.

He asked, "When you kids goin' to move that paper?"

They knew what he meant. The stable was full of papers and magazines they had spent most of last summer collecting. It was to have brought money for playground equipment.

Maxine shrugged.

"Nobody wants it," she said. "Nobody'll buy it."

"Well, can't leave it there," said the old man. "Somebody drop a match into it and the whole town'll go up in smoke. Can't sleep nights myself for thinkin' of it."

"Mr. Dyer told us we could store it there," said Thelma. "It's Mr. Dyer's stable."

"Stable!" growled the old man. "It's nothin' but a ruin. It's an eyesore and a menace. It ought to be cleaned out and tore down. If 'tain't, either a high wind'll blow it onto somebody or it'll ketch afire and the whole town'll go up in smoke. Might be a good thing if it did."

He stamped back into the house. The girls moved to the other side of the stable and stood shivering. Sheila saw her father's car and ran out to stop him. She and Emily climbed in and rode away. They seemed glad to go. The five who were left — Maxine, Thelma, Patty, Janet, and Ellen — plodded down the street to the center of town.

They stood staring in at the shop windows. There were toys there, but they were too old for toys. There were nylon slips, but they were too young for nylon slips. There were ties for fathers and jewelry for mothers, but fathers and mothers seemed not to care what they wore lately. Mothers and fathers were all the time reading newspapers and writing flyers, answering the doorbell, and calling people on the telephone.

The plastic sprays of holly and strings of paper evergreen looked silly.

They straggled inside one of the stores. Two women stood by the counter but they were not buying anything. They were arguing, and the saleswoman was looking anxiously from one to the other.

"You don't have children, so of course —"

"I should feel just the same if I did have children. Children should have everything we can afford to give them. But we're not rich in this town. We can't afford these luxuries."

"We certainly can't afford the 'luxury' of juvenile delinquency!"

"It's the parents' responsibility to prevent that!"

"It's everybody's responsibility!"

"Come on out," muttered Maxine. On the sidewalk she said, "They talk all the time about children. They don't care anything about us. They're not even going to make Christmas. I keep asking my mother about the wreaths and the tree and she just holds her head and says, 'Don't bother me now.' Nobody's paid any attention to us for weeks only Miss Farley, and we shan't see her again all vacation. I was getting kind of sick of her anyway. Her and her old tin cans." She glared at the paper bags. "I don't think they'd know it if we died."

"Like Laurel McAllister," said Janet, hoarsely.

They had hardly known Laurel, except that she had come to live in the big brick house when she was four years old, and that Mr. and Mrs. McAllister had bought the hill behind the house and fenced it in as a playground for Laurel. They had seen Laurel through the hedge several times, playing with her kitten. They had seen her once or twice walking up the hill, led by a woman in a white uniform. That was all. They remembered Laurel for three reasons. Because before the McAllisters bought the hill and fenced it in, anyone who wanted to could go up there, and after that they couldn't; because the roof they could see among the pines at the top of the hill was said to be the roof of a wonderful playhouse the McAllisters had built for Laurel, a house just like a real house only smaller, with a sink and running water and little electric lights and furniture and rugs and curtains at the windows; and because Laurel had died this fall, not more than a year after she came to the brick house.

Thelma and Patty blinked. Was it as bad as that? That children really could die? And nobody would notice?

The expression on Ellen's face was startled too, but in a different way. Ellen was startled by an idea.

She said, "I know what! I know something to do! Let's go to the brick house and ask if we can go up the hill to see the playhouse!"

"You wouldn't dare," gasped Patty.

"No, but Maxine would. Maxine would dare. Wouldn't you, Maxine?"

Maxine shrugged. "Why not?"

But even Maxine looked a little excited. She turned at once to march up the street toward the brick house, and the others followed.

"They'll never let us, will they?" Janet whispered to Ellen.

"You can't tell," Janet whispered back. "They might."

Maxine pushed open the gate, went straight up the walk between the bare syringa bushes and rang the doorbell. The others waited. Mr. McAllister stood there. His hair was white, though his face was quite young.

"Hi," Maxine said quickly. "Do you care if we kids climb the hill?"

He looked puzzled.

"Why, no; certainly not." His voice was deep and pleasant. "But isn't it too late, tonight? It's cold and nearly dark."

"We don't care," Maxine told him. "It won't take us long. We just want to see the little house."

"Well, then," said Mr. McAllister, "follow that path to the backyard and you'll see where it leads up the hill. But hurry back before dark. You might get lost."

"Oh, no," Maxine said scornfully. "We couldn't get lost on that hill. We've been up there dozens of times. Anyway you come down right in the middle of town. Come on, kids."

Ellen wished Maxine had not spoken in that tone, when Mr. McAllister had been so nice. As she passed him she looked up and smiled. The wind was blowing his white hair all around.

She said, "Thank you, Mr. McAllister."

"You're very welcome, my dear. . . . What's your name?"

"Ellen —"

She was almost around the corner of the brick house. The wind took her voice and carried it back to him. She hurried after the others.

Maxine was ahead. Maxine was running. So they all ran.

The path up the hill had been made broad and smooth and paved with crumbled white seashells. It wound gently in and out among the pines and so was not steep at all.

"Who'd get lost with a path like this?" Maxine shouted back. "Anybody could find it in pitch-dark!"

When they caught up with her she was staring at the little house.

It was not at all as they had imagined it. It was really only a shelter. It had a roof and three walls, but the side facing west was completely open. It was made of rough brown boards and timbers, and there was no sink in it, no lights, only a square hole in the back for a window, and no furniture at all except a small bunk in the middle of the east wall. The bunk had a rusty spring.

"Well!" Janet panted. "Is that all? That's no play-house! What made people think it was?"

"What makes people think a lot of things?" Maxine shrugged.

"Because it was Laurel's, maybe," Ellen said. "They thought it was for her to play in. I guess it was for her to rest in . . . It must have been a nice place to rest, too. In the summer, you know. In the afternoon the sun would come in. The bunk must have had a mattress, and pillows and a blanket. She probably brought her dolls."

"Br-r," shivered Thelma. "It's just bleak now. It might be nice to have a picnic in, but will it ever be time for pic-nics?"

"Let's go back down," said Patty. "It's almost dark. And I'm hungry."

"Oh, look!" Ellen cried. "The lights are coming on!"

She stood on tiptoe on an outcropping of ledge which was the crest of the hill, and the others ran to join her. The town made a circle around the foot of the hill, as Maxine had said, and, as they watched, the lights from the houses and store windows seemed to ignite the head-lights of cars, and the moving cars in turn seemed to switch on streetlights which stretched in all directions like the ribbons of a maypole.

"Oh," Janet gasped, "I never saw that happen before. I didn't know it did."

"Maybe it didn't," Ellen said. "Or hasn't for a long time. Because nobody was here to see it. They say things don't happen unless people see them happen, or hear them, or feel them."

"The wind's stopped blowing," said Thelma. "It's warmer all of a sudden."

"Maybe it's a miracle," said Ellen. "It looks and feels like a miracle, doesn't it? Maybe it's the beginning of Christmas."

"Not down there," growled Maxine. "They're still fighting —"

"We don't know," said Ellen quicky. "We're not down there. They don't know what's happening up here either. I wish they did though. If they could just see how the town looks now! . . . I know what! Let's get them up here! Let's tell them there's going to be a miracle up here next — next Wednesday night!"

"Why next Wednesday night?"

"Well, it's two nights before Christmas. That leaves time . . . And it's prayer-meeting night, so let's have the miracle at seven o'clock and then they can go to church. It'll be kind of on their way —"

"Lots of people can't climb a hill."

"Lots of people can. We'll have to do something else for the people that can't come. We've got to think. Can you all come to my house after supper and make plans?"

"Ellen, the McAllisters won't let us do it."

"He let us this time, didn't he? After we've planned, we'll talk to him first."

"Not me," said Maxine. "He'll think we're crazy."

"I will, then," said Ellen. "He's nice. I like him. He asked me what my name was."

The next day, late in the afternoon, Patty and Thelma stopped in at Mr. Smith's store. He was busy talking with a group of women, but as soon as they left, he said, "What can I do for you, young ladies?" They told him it was very confidential, so he took them into the backshop, and they told him McAllister's Hill was going to be open to the public next Wednesday night. They asked Mr. Smith if he would dress up like one of the Wise Men, with a scarf covering all of his face but his eyes, and not let anybody know who he was, but just come up the hill about seven o'clock by himself. He said he did not know what he would look like in a Wise Man's costume, but he would ask his wife, and they would do their best.

At the same time Ellen and Janet were at the Town Office. Mr. Dyer was sitting at his desk listening to three men. Two of them were telling Mr. Dyer that the day of the politician was over, that the people were aroused, and now they were going to run the country themselves. The other one said, "How? By cutting it in inch pieces and passing it around like wedding cake? You going to throw out the party system? What have you got to put in its place?"

After a while Mr. Dyer got up from the desk and came over to the girls. Janet said they had a secret to tell him, and he said there couldn't be a better place to tell a secret because he was the only one in this office who ever listened to what anybody said and sometimes he didn't, but he certainly would listen to them. They told him what Patty and Thelma were telling Mr. Smith. Mr. Dyer seemed very pleased. He said he would welcome a chance to be almost anybody else but Charlie Dyer for even fifteen minutes. He said they could count on him, and wrote the date and time in his book.

Ellen and Janet went across to the post office to join Patty and Thelma. Then they all went to the parsonage to see Mr. Paige, and from there to Father Renaud's house. When they left Mr. Paige he looked almost happy and said, "God be with you till we meet again," like the hymn. When they left Father Renaud, he spread his big hands, touching two of their heads with each, and his lips moved and his eyes shone.

"I think he blessed us," said Janet in awe.

"Just as if we were Catholic children," said Patty with a skip.

"Mr. Paige did too," said Ellen "It makes you feel peaceful, doesn't it?"

After supper that night they all met at Maxine's.

"Okay," she said as soon as she saw them. "Nobody's here but me. They've gone to a meeting. Spill it. They all said you were crazy, didn't they?"

They told her nobody had said they were crazy, that all the people they had talked to seemed to like children. Mr. McAllister had not been at home when they got there, but Mrs. McAllister was. They had never seen her before. She was tall and pale and very beautiful and wore rings. She said she would have a new gate made in the fence so that people could reach the path without going through the yard, and that a sign saying OPEN TO THE PUBLIC would be hung on the gate at six o'clock Wednesday night. Mr. McAllister had come home just as they were leaving, and remembered them, and asked them to call again at the brick house.

They told Maxine that Mr. Smith and Mr. Dyer had both promised to be Wise Men — though neither knew about the other, or ever would probably — and so had Mr. McAllister; and that Mr. Paige and Father Renaud had heard their whole plan, as far as it had gone, and said it was good.

"So now," said Ellen triumphantly, "cut out the cardboard for the posters, Maxine, and start the drawing. We'll color and put on the letters."

Maxine was very good at drawing. She drew a steep hill with pines all over it, the path going up, a little house at the top, and a big Christmas star in the sky. They colored the trees green, the house brown, and the star crimson in the center, softening to orange toward the points and gilded around the edge. The rays coming down from the star were gold, too, and just reached the roof of the house.

Toward the base of the hill they printed, "MIRACLE ON MCALLISTER'S HILL WEDNESDAY, DEC. 23, 7:00 P.M. OPEN TO PUBLIC. FREE. COME TO THE MIRACLE."

The next day at Sunday school they tried to tell Sheila and Emily about it. Sheila and Emily could not understand at all.

"Nobody'll believe the posters," they said. "Nobody'll come. And what do you think is going to happen anyway?"

"We don't know. It will be different for different people," Ellen told them. "Things always are. According to the way we think. But it will be some kind of a miracle. I don't mean a great miracle to put in books. Just a Cambrook miracle. I think it's begun already, really."

"Look," said Maxine. "Ellen's turning mystic or something. You know me. My feet are on the ground. We're going to get people up there. Some people anyway. If it doesn't storm. They'll see how pretty the lights of the town look from up there, and that will make them feel better. Then they'll look at the little house because we'll have a lantern lit inside. It'll make them think of the manger in Bethlehem because we'll have hay on the floor and the little bed made up."

"You going to put a doll in it?" Emily asked.

"Oh, no," Ellen said. "The bed will just be made up. So it will look cosy. And Mr. Paige will be at one end of the house to make a prayer, and Father Renaud will be at the other end to say a benediction. We'll be out back to sing 'Silent Night' and 'O Little Town.' Can you come?"

"You left out the Wise Men, Ellen," said Maxine, "after all the trouble you went to to get them. Mr. —"

"Sh-h," said Janet.

"Okay," said Maxine. "But she also left out the trays which we're nearly killing ourselves trying to finish. I can't do them in gloves and I'm covered with cuts. But we've got to have three made before Wednesday night. They're for the gold, frankincense, and myrrh. We're going to put them on the step of the house, and if there is any gold, frankincense and myrrh it will be to help pay for the gym. That's really the main idea."

"I don't think so," said Ellen. "It's just the tail end of the idea. So if the miracle makes people want to do something, they can."

"Well, I don't see what the miracle is going to be," said Sheila. "And anyway we can't come. My father never takes the car out after dark. It's all I can do to get him to bring us to Sunday school. Lately especially. He says gas costs money. There — he's calling me now!"

Ellen ran after her.

"Sheila! You and Emily be the shepherds. You and your folks, and everybody else you can get! You all be outside at seven o'clock Wednesday night looking down toward McAllister's hill. I think you'll see something to remember. I'm almost sure you will."

That evening on their way to church she and Janet knocked at the side door of the fire station where the firemen played cards every night. The fire chief himself came to the door and they whispered to him. He chuckled and said, "Sure. Sure. I guess so. I'll see anyway. Never can refuse a kid."

"Gee," said Janet, hopping over sidewalk cracks, "a lot of people do like us, don't they?"

Monday, posters began going up in all the store windows and at the town office and on fences and tree trunks. MIRACLE ON MCALLISTER'S HILL WEDNESDAY, 7:00 P.M.

"What's this?" people asked, frowning.

"Kids' work," others answered, smiling. "A bunch of kids from Miss Farley's room, I hear. The McAllisters seem to be in on it. Better go up. Better give 'em a little support. Don't know how many years it's been since I climbed that hill. Seemed to get steeper while I was growing older. But they've got a good easy path now, they say."

The girls saw Joyce looking intently at the posters while she ran the baby buggy forward and back, forward and back, just as she looked intently in store windows and elsewhere about her. Of course the words meant nothing to Joyce, since she could not read, but perhaps the picture suggested Christmas to her; there was no way of knowing. They wished they could tell Joyce what they were going to do, because of course she was part of it, as a member of the club. But Joyce could never know what was going to happen until it happened.

Wednesday night Maxine and Thelma called for her on their way to McAllister's Hill, but she was not there. Nobody was there.

"Too bad," said Thelma. "I guess she would have liked it."

"She likes everything," shrugged Maxine. "As far as anybody knows. Even likes dragging that baby with her everywhere she goes."

They met Patty, Ellen, and Janet at the church. They were all a little late because there had barely been time for supper when they got home from carrying up the hay, cutting the pine boughs, lighting and hanging the lantern, and making up the bed with the mattress, pink blankets, and white ruffled pillow Mrs. McAllister had let them take. But being a little late did not matter. Everything they could do was done. Even the three trays were finished, and the cards propped up behind them.

GOLD . . . FRANKINCENSE . . . MYRRH . . .

The new gate with its sign, OPEN TO THE PUBLIC, stood ajar.

They slipped through.

"It's strange," murmured Ellen. "All of a sudden, I don't feel as if we had anything to do with this. It's as if— as if —"

There were several groups of people ahead of them, walking slowly, talking a little in low voices. Others were coming behind.

It was dark, but it was not cold, and the sky was clear. The stars were very bright. The white path stood out distinctly among the trees, against the brown needles which covered the ground. Flashlights had been fastened to low branches where the path curved. A light wind made a singing in the pines; and you could smell them.

As those ahead reached the clearing at the top they paused beside those already there, looking down into the valley. The girls reached them and paused too. No one was talking now. The whole hill was perfectly still, except for the singing of the pines. Even those climbing made no sound which reached the summit.

Below lay the little town, its lights stretched in all directions like maypole streamers. A few cars were moving, not many. The starry canopy of the sky hung softly over it.

The crowd was growing and growing. The winding white path was completely obscured by climbers becoming silent as they neared the top. It had become a steady procession, a pilgrimage. People filled the cleared space on the top of the hill, standing so close that they could feel one another's breathing, and men held small children on their shoulders so that they, too, could look down on their town.

Suddenly, across the silence, there was a puff of sound like the indrawn breath of a giant. Everyone turned toward it. A stream of light ran up into the sky, and a great star formed there, among the others. It found its place. It hung, seeming to vibrate, to come alive, for a long instant, and then went out. But in the darkness it left, other stars shone with greater intensity than before.

Then the first church bells rang out in the town . . . Distant. Clear. Sweet as the call of a child. . . .

And everyone in the darkness was looking into the rough, lantern-lit building.

There, among the pine boughs and the hay, was the little bed to which Laurel had once gone to rest. On Laurel's mattress and Laurel's ruffled white pillow, under Laurel's pink blanket, lay a baby! At his head knelt a very young woman, a white scarf over her head, her face calm and sweet between the white folds! Her shining eyes were fixed on the baby, and the baby's shining eyes were fixed on a silver disk which she was holding where it caught the light from the lantern for him to watch! It made a circle like a halo behind him.

"Bless you, Joyce," Miss Farley had said. "You don't need to hear. You know without hearing."

Why had Joyce come here? How long had she been here? What was she thinking? No one could tell. Perhaps no one would ever know.

"Come," Ellen whispered. "Behind the house. We have to sing. And if Joyce should see all the people out in the dark she might be frightened. We should be near her."

> *Silent night, holy night*
> *All is calm, all is bright*
> *Round yon virgin Mother and Child*
> *Holy Infant so tender and mild* . . .

The Church bells had stopped ringing.

"Dear Father of us all," said a voice out of the dark, "we thank Thee for the blessing of our children and for the town of Cambrook in which to grow up. We ask Thee for the faith which is theirs, and for willing hearts and minds to learn again from them the wisdom with which all of us are born. We know we have only to open the door and Thou wilt come in.

"Tonight we have stood in awe of the beauty, the tranquillity, the promise of our town as we looked down upon it. We see that we have builded well together. Help us to build higher on this foundation.

"We have had a glowing reminder of the wonder of that night long ago when a new Star appeared in the sky over Bethlehem. And now we have before us a singularly touching scene, more than usually reminiscent of the first Christmas Eve. Here is a girl we all know, and the child she has taken to care for as her own. She cannot hear what we say. She does not even know that we are here.

But Thou knowest, O Lord, what is in her heart and in ours. Help us to follow Thee as she has followed Thee, confidently, up the long path, among the dark trees, to the shelter, the comfort, the shining loveliness which awaits us at the top.

"Thou hast given us this vision through our children. This is the miracle Thou has granted us in our great need, because of their faith. Our gratitude is immeasurable. Help us to use throughout this Christmas season, the coming year, and all the years ahead, this great lesson which, through our children, Thou hast taught us tonight.

"In the name of Jesus, Thy son, our guide and master, we ask it.

"Amen."

> *Joy to the world, the Lord has come;*
> *Let earth receive her King;*
> *Let every heart prepare Him room,*
> *And heaven and nature sing . . .*
> *He rules the world with truth and grace,*
> *And makes the nations prove*
> *The glories of His righteousness*
> *And wonders of His love . . .*

During the singing, one in a dark cape, hooded, came forward from the crowd, and knelt, and placed something in each of the trays. Another came, in velvet cloak and silken muffler, and did the same. The third, in academic gown, knelt between them.

As the singing died away, they rose and disappeared into the crowd. Then others surged forward, each kneeling as he left bill or coin. It was like a flood. The trays ran over.

When everyone was still again, another voice spoke out of the dark.

"May the Lord bless and keep us and make His face to shine upon us . . ."

As he was speaking, Joyce saw that the baby was asleep.

She rose and gathered him into her arms. She looked doubtfully at the lantern.

Ellen put her hand through the window and touched Joyce. Joyce turned quickly, startled. Ellen smiled at her and turned down the wick of the lantern. The light went out. Ellen crawled quickly through the window and stood in the dark with Joyce, her arm around her, her cheek against Joyce's cheek.

Ellen heard the others singing and sang with them.

O little town of Bethlehem, how still we see thee lie!
Above thy deep and dreamless sleep, the silent stars
    go by . . .
How silently, how silently, the wondrous gift is
    given!
So God imparts to human hearts the blessings of
    His heaven.
No ear may hear His coming, but in this world of sin,
Where meek souls will receive Him still, the dear
    Christ enters in . . .
We hear the Christmas angels the great glad tidings
    tell;
O come to us, abide with us, Our Lord Immanuel
    . . . Amen.

As she sang, Ellen heard the church bells ringing again, and the soft shuffle of the people as they turned from looking out over the town and moved down the hill toward the bells, a steady procession, a pilgrimage.

No one knew what Joyce was hearing.

When Ellen turned on her tiny flashlight, and the girls went out of the little house to tuck the baby into his stroller, only the trees were there, and the stars. Ellen waved her light toward the lights of the town. Joyce looked, and nodded and smiled. They went down the hill together, their four hands holding back on the stroller.

At the church at the foot of the hill, Ellen stopped. Joyce understood. She braked the stroller and took the

baby out. They went into the church together. Prayer
meeting usually was in the vestry. Tonight it was in the
auditorium, and the auditorium was filled.

They squeezed into a seat beside Emily and Sheila.

"How did you get downtown?" Ellen whispered.

"Sheila's father brought us," Emily whispered back.
"All of them and all of us, too. We were out on the hill in
their field to watch, like you said. He was standing in the
barn door. We saw the star. Sheila called, 'That's the
sign, Daddy. That's the sign of the miracle.' As soon as it
went out, he said, 'What on earth was that? Let's go
down and see what's going on.' He wouldn't let any of us
stop to change our clothes. We ran up McAllister's hill.
We got there just when the Wise Men — what made that
star, Ellen?"

"I don't know. Mr. Harwood — the Fire Chief —
made it. We asked him to make a Christmas Star that
you could see. He said he'd try. And he did."

"It was wonderful. All the way downtown we sang,
'While shepherds watched their flocks by night . . . the
angel of the Lord came down, and glory shone around,'
and that verse about 'Good will henceforth from heaven
to men, begin and never cease.' Our mothers and fathers
sang too . . ."

The organ stopped playing, and Mr. Paige said the
meeting was open for prayers.

About nine o'clock the people who passed the Town
Office on their way home saw that it was brightly lit and
full of people. They glanced with uneasiness at the faces
inside and were instantly reassured. Everyone in the office
looked as if a weight had been lifted from his shoulders.
Those who were talking looked eager. Those who were
listening looked pleased.

The passersby thought, Maybe things are going to turn
out all right.

Inside Charlie Dyer was saying, "Father Renaud gave
the trays to me and what had spilled over tied up in his

handkerchief. I told him I wasn't the one to take it, but he said somebody should take it. He said the kids meant for it to go toward the gym, so I said I'd give it to you, Ray. You're chairman of the building committee. You'll probably want to say something about it at town meeting."

"I will. Count it, Charlie," Ray Smith said.

"We'll both count it."

They emptied the trays and Father Renaud's handkerchief onto the desk.

While they counted, a woman said, "The children have shown us how. There are other ways to finish the gymnasium beside appropriating more money from taxes. We can make what we have go as far as it will, and we can earn the rest. If the gym is what we need most now, we can put that first, ahead of other projects that we're always working to earn money for. We can't expect to have everything at once."

A man said, "Funny nobody realized that before. We must have all been too mad."

"We felt under such pressure —"

Charlie Dyer asked, "How much do you make it, Ray?"

"Two hundred thirty-three dollars and fifty-seven cents."

"So did I. Beside the slip. Read the slip to the folks, Ray."

Ray Smith read aloud, slowly, "I give and bequeath to the Cambrook gymnasium fund the $10,000 my Nana left me, and which I did not need. Laurel."

The name was printed as a child prints.

"Mr. McAllister was one of the Wise Men," said Charlie Dyer. "That was the slip he left on this little tray." He turned the tray over in his hands. He cleared his throat. "Those kids have my stable full of old paper. I'm going to buy it of them. I guess it'll bring around fifty dollars."

"Ten thousand five hundred dollars will close in the

building as specified," said Ray Smith. "I'll move the acceptance of this gift and no further appropriation at the Special Meeting."

"We'll earn the rest," a woman said. "You'll see. In time. The churches and the schools and the granges and the scouts. Because we all want to do it, we can do it. The children have shown us how — Laurel, and Joyce and little Barry, and the girls who sang —"

People walked home slowly through the silent streets. One by one the lights of the town went out.

> *For Christ is born of Mary, and gathered all*
>   *above,*
> *While mortals sleep the angels keep*
> *Their watch of wondering love . . .*
> *Yet in thy dark streets shineth the everlasting*
>   *light . . .*
> *Praises sing to God our King, and Peace to men*
>   *on earth.*

christmas 1957

In a short novel called *While the Angels Sing* I once wrote: "Julie had promised that it would be the best Christmas ever, and it was. I realized suddenly why it always is. Christmas is cumulative. Whatever else it has lost, every year which has passed since the birth of Christ has retained and added to the magic of light and color against a dark background, to the human capacity for appreciation of chords and bells and melodies, to the sweetness of children's voices, the brightness of children's eyes, the delight of giving, the comfort of receiving, and the ecstasy of renewed hope and faith."

That story was written in a happier time than this, in one of the brief periods of our century when over every nation not actually at peace with others a flag of truce waved. The world was quiet enough so that all who would listen could easily hear the angels sing. This year there is an ominous roar in the air like that of a tremendous waterfall and there are strange new lights in the sky, alien travelers sent into outer space by men who have never heard the angels sing and who do not believe in them or in man's need of and responsibility to God and His son.

So, as we approach Christmas of the year of Our Lord 1957, we face a new challenge. May we meet it with a great surge of strength, of indomitable courage, of the keenest ecstasy of renewed hope and faith that humanity has yet experienced! When the word reached England that Czechoslovakia had been sacrificed to Hitler's insatiable appetite, Winston Churchill said: "It is a terrible thing. The future looks very dark. And I feel ten years younger."

With all the vitality and power that free men and women have at their command, we must labor to prepare for God this season the gift, humbly offered, of serene faith in the goodness of His ultimate purpose for the universe, of our mighty, united effort to serve Him selflessly, of our readiness to recognize and to develop, with His guidance, the best in the human spirit.

Having this gift to offer, and knowing that we can continue to offer it, despite opposition by the power of evil, at Christmastime the magic of light and color will glow more brightly than ever against the dark backdrop of the iron curtain, and even penetrate it; and we shall not only appreciate chords, bells, and melodies and hear the song of angels but also raise our own voices to swell the chorus soaring to heights no manmade projectile will reach until God has found mankind worthy of a place closer to Himself.

hristmas 1968

I heard the bells on Christmas day
Their old familiar carols play,
And wild and sweet the words repeat
Of peace on earth, good will to men.

Man is prone to periods of grave doubt. What native of a coastal area has never had the premonition that the sea is about to sweep in and take away all that is most precious to him on earth? What American midwesterner has not looked upon a funnel cloud? What New Englander has not received hurricane warnings, suspected that the sap would not rise again in his old dooryard maple tree and bring it to leaf, harbored the strange fear that he has seen his last bluebird, heard his last whippoorwill, that the hummingbirds may not recross the Gulf of Mexico this year or next year or ever?

We must have courage to overcome doubt. We must have stamina. We must have determination. We must have the capacity for sound thinking. Above all we must have faith that mankind is on this planet for a purpose and will remain here until that purpose — whatever it is, however obscure it may be to us — has been served. We must believe in Christmas, for as long as we are here it will surely return to every one who has ever known it. It follows the struggle, the agony, the problems, the doubts of the year as daybreak the night. It lifts our tired hands, dries the tears which have blinded us, fills us with new hope and new strength, and gives us a lamp for our feet.

We hear the bells, though the sound may seem to come from a great distance. Their music is wild and sweet like the voices of angels whose language we cannot entirely understand. We know they sing of God's good will for men and of the peace on earth — so desirable, so beautiful — which can only come with every man's good will toward every other man. We are aware, even at Christmas, that this condition of the world is very far away; but we are also aware at Christmas that it is possible, that we have been shown the way toward it, and that this is the way we must follow, however long and arduous the route. We must be capable of self-respect, worthy of the respect of others, respectful of all that is respectable in them; on this basis of respect we can achieve a love worth giving and deserve a love worth having.

The root and branch of Christmas is pure love. The love Wise Men in splendid robes and shepherds in their smocks brought to the Infant Jesus and by which they found His face transfigured as, lying in the manger, He returned it a thousandfold. Infant though He was, His knowledge of God was that many times a multiple of theirs.

> *Star of wonder, star of night,*
> *Star with royal beauty bright,*
> *Westward leading, still proceeding,*
> *Guide us to the perfect light.*

HOL WN